Justified License to Kill

Eddie Dee Williams

Contents

• • • • • • • • • • • • • • • • • •

Inspired by President Obama.

A True Story

Prologue

• •

Sabotage

My grandfather, Bishop H.B, Daniels, Sr., was the pastor of the Greater Mount Calvary Pentecostal Church (COGIC), otherwise commonly known as the hand-clapping, foot-stomping, praise-singing, instrumental playing, shouting-for-joy Holy Rollers located at 1234 N.E. 13th and Killingsworth Street. It happened to be in one of the most beautiful neighborhoods in Portland, Oregon. Known as the City of Roses, Portland, Oregon, is the third largest city in the Pacific Northwest. Oregon is bordered by four states: California and Nevada border the south and southeast, while Washington and Idaho are on the north and northeast.

This earthy red brick edifice was built in 1949. Bordered with a white trim, the building had landscaped flower beds and evergreen-colored, manicured, edged grass. The high, pitched ceiling provided great acoustics. It amplified sound, causing a small number of people singing to have a rich, full sound, like a mass choir. So, when I lead songs, the acoustics enhanced my powerful tenor instrument. Nestled on one corner of the intersection of two busy streets in the heart of Portland, this ten thousand-square foot dual-leveled edifice had a sound booth and a balcony overlooking the sanctuary. These spectacularly huge, hand-crafted, double-sided stained glass windows complemented the interior. The sanctuary's off-white walls clearly coordinated with the burgundy carpet and the extravagant, beautifully bright chandeliers with gold shades, equally spaced out across the high-pitched ceiling of the sanctuary, which also coordinated with the tan-trimmed, burgundy cloth-padded pews. A Hammond organ flanked the left side of the pulpit, while a shiny black grand piano flanked the lower right side at a ninety-degree angle.

Grandpa's exceptional wife—my grandmother, Jessie Daniels—was a God-fearing church lady: slender, tall, beautiful chocolate complexion, with the sweetest smile you will ever see. But don't let that fool ya—she could drop some discipline quicker than you can drop a wet dish rag. She was the elegant equation of the glue enforcer in my family and the one who kept us close together. Both of my grandparents were college educated, established, lived way out in the exclusive so-called white neighborhood suburbs, owned both of their homes, side-by-side, on a large corner lot, located in the southeast part of town. With an outstanding opera-quality soprano, any given Sunday at church Grandma frequently sang solos. My favorite was "How Great Thou Art." She made sure every last one of us grandkids sang in the choir, just as our parents had to sing and learn to play the piano at a very young age. You see, my ancestors had a no-choice scenario in which to relocate. They were slaves who were freed by the President of the United States, Abraham Lincoln.

"Not so fast, boy," Great-grandfather Thomas's furious former slave master informed Thomas as he attempted to leave with his wife and four little children. "I don't know where the hell you think you going, boy! You're still my property, nigger!" Then the slave master pulled out his rifle, warning my ancestor, "Boy, if you try to leave like you some kind of free nigger, you and your family will all leave this world dead-ass niggers!" He threatened to aim his rifle to kill the newly freed ex-slave. The newly freed, Hershey-complexion African-American man had no other alternative; in the blink of an eye he had to choose between freedom, life, and liberty, or the doorway to death. Taking action defending his life, he turned the rifle onto his former master, pulling the trigger, killing his ex-slave master in Liberia, Missouri, where freedom was not yet a reality. Guilty of self-defense, he fled with his family 2,500 miles to Clackamas, Oregon.

My grandmother, Jessie Marie Pierce, was originally from Eufaula, Oklahoma. Raised on a family-owned, self-sufficient farm,

Grandmother, her one brother, and five sisters present an interesting side of my genealogy. This side of my ancestry was adopted out of slavery by Native Americans of the Blackfoot Nation.

Grandmother was also cousin to the recording artist, Charles Brown, who was famous for recording the vinyl smash hit, "Merry Christmas, Baby," which radio stations played over the airways around the holiday season by request in the thousands. My Christian maternal grandparents were first introduced to each other at Mt. Scott Park in Southeast Portland at a Church outing wiener roast. I thought that was Christian Cool!

After our parents separated, our loving Christian grandparents made it a priority to attempt to reconcile them. Our parents finally divorced, and our mother worked on Sunday. Early mornings they would drive all the way across town, clear out to North Portland in their metallic-brown Cadillac Brougham just to retrieve us siblings, Mike and Nuffy and Keith. Mike's name is actually Hugh Junior. Denise (Nuffy) is my sister's real name. Keith, my baby brother, was named after an actor on the sixties prime time television show, *Family Affair*. You could say we siblings were somewhat close. I suppose our loving grandparents felt we needed to know the holy story. We needed it more so, since our parents were now and forever divorced.

My grandfather was Grandpa. He had a soft voice, wore prescription glasses, had a peanut butter complexion, 5'8", medium built to fluffy, and reminded me of a shorter version of James Earl Jones. My grandfather, Bishop Harry B. Daniels, Sr., was the original owner of Linoleum City, located on Hawthorne Street in the Laurelhurst district. Grandpa was known for walking up to practically anybody and speaking to them, helping out anybody, no matter who they were or what they looked like. Grandfather's relatives, Donald and Michael Hepburn created the Portland-based band, Pleasure, which is perhaps best known for the 1979 hit, "Glide."

One day, as I exited the Dart, shut the car door, and walked across the green grass up to the church, Grandpa was standing there on the sidewalk at the end of the stairs leading to the side entrance of the church. He was wearing a dark brown suit with his brown Stetson hat on his head and a Bach trench coat. As I approached, he looked at me like I had lost my ever-loving mind.

"Hi, Grandpa, what's up?" I asked, sort of indifferently.

"You going to sneak off and get married by the Justice of the Peace?" Grandpa asked me, giving me the third degree with extreme conviction. I must have looked vaguely bewildered at that airhead moment.

"Mother doesn't want me to get married," I replied, putting my hands together, holding my arms outstretched, pleading my case and searching for some understanding of sorts. "That's why I avoided telling you, Grandpa. I apologize if I offended you," I said sincerely, while my face melted, feeling very solemn at hurting my grandpa, since he knew I loved him.

"Grandson, as long as I am your grandfather," he said seriously, as if I suffered from some kind of mental illness, "I will marry you and I will bury you! Understand, Number One Grandson?" Grandpa said sternly to my face, igniting my ignorance while at the same time, showing me love by his act of forgiveness.

"Yes, sir!" I replied, solemnly respectful, embarrassed, and lowering my head to avoid my grandfather's disappointed look.

"How is my great-grandson doing?" Grandpa asked, changing the subject while going through his key ring to open to the brownish-orange side door of the church.

"He is fine, Grandpa. He's getting big and is trying to stand up and walk," I replied.

"Now, when are you leaving for Germany?" Grandpa asked in a casual tone of voice.

"Monday morning, Grandpa." I replied swiftly, fidgeting with my key ring with my right hand, trying my best not to feel any worse than I was already feeling.

"When do you want to get married, Grandson?" Grandpa asked, glancing at his silver watch, appearing to be running a tad late in tending to some pastoral affairs.

"This Friday, Grandpa," I replied, feeling a weight being lifted off my conscience, tremendously relieved that my Grandfather was going to perform the ceremony.

"Come back here to the church at six o'clock p.m., Friday (September 30th, 1977), Grandson, with your fiancée and your marriage license, and I will be more than happy to perform the ceremony," Grandpa said happily, with a pleasant smile.

Just that fast, Grandpa Daniels and I solved a family misunderstanding. He walked up the red steps to the side door of the church. Not forgetting his daughter, he said in a commanding but gentle voice, "Go and talk to your mother, Number One Grandson!"

As I finally found the ignition key to my car, I replied, "I will, Grandpa." I walked swiftly back to the car, somewhat relieved, somewhat bewildered.

I returned to Lisa's parents' house, but everybody had retired for the night. Lisa's parents, Mr. and Mrs. Earl Bowles, seemed to be quite nice people. Earl was a short, stocky, mocha-brown foundry worker; clean-shaven, a man of few words, and a decent family man. His wife, Rosalie—short, attractive, petite, cocoa-complexioned, and very vocal—worked at JCPenney's in the Lloyd Mall. They were the proud parents of four grown children, three daughters, and one son, Lisa being the youngest. Their home was a spacious three-bedroom, mint-green, split-level, ranch-style dwelling with a fully furnished basement: billiards table, bar, and a spare bedroom. There was a fireplace on each level. The house was on a corner lot in the northeast side of town, adjacent to an unpaved gravel alleyway. It seemed to me like I was getting along just fine with Lisa's parents, but I was dead, damn wrong.

The day after Lisa informed me she was pregnant and that I was the biological father, we both agreed that I should tell her parents about this unexpected development.

The following day at her parents' house, Mr. and Mrs. Bowles, Lisa, and myself assembled in the overly long but roomy breakfast nook in a kitchen like no other I have ever seen. The Bowles were originally from Tuscaloosa, Alabama, where this kind of decor originated, and it looked exactly like a magazine miniature restaurant: unique, upgraded style, carpeted interior with flowered wallpaper, an L-shaped brown leather booth of sorts, all modern appliances, and a large picture window with an excellent view of Mt. Hood on clear, sunny days.

Mr. Bowles stood in the kitchen with his arms folded, puzzled but not upset. Lisa's mother was sitting on the booth-like leather couch with Lisa and me. I was just about to inform them that I was responsible for Lisa's pregnancy and I planned on doing the right thing by asking Mr. Bowles for his daughter's hand in marriage.

Without any warning, Lisa took it upon herself, heinously blurting out like a snitch in a Witness Protection Program, or better yet a weasel for Wicked Witches of the Pacific Northwest, "Mom and Dad, I'm pregnant! Eddie's the father of my baby!" Earl, extremely pissed off, unfolded his arms and left the kitchen in a hurry. Mrs. Bowles tapped the small white table with her fingers and rose to her feet, disgusted. "Eddie, you should have told Earl the news man-to-man. You shouldn't have had Lisa speak up for you. Eddie, you've got to learn to be a man and do what is right," Rosalie laid into me with her hands on her hips, and she too left the kitchen without listening to anything I had to say, which was very rude and not very adult of either one of them.

"Why did you tell them?" I asked, bewildered. "We agreed that I would make the announcement, Lisa! Why? Why would you do a thing like this to me?" I asked again, standing quickly, ashamed and embarrassed, as if I had just fully shit my pants.

"I thought you might not want to tell them the good news!" Lisa said, pleading.

"What Martian in your mind told you that I would be scared to tell your parents the truth?" I asked, frustrated and irritated to the almighty max!

"Honey, I'm so very sorry. I don't know why I did that to you, Eddie Dee," Lisa said, standing and attempting to embrace me, insulting my intelligence, like that was really going to make every damn thing all right.

"I really need to get the hell out of your parents' house right now—like yesterday! I don't care where we go, just get me the hell out of this house now!" I replied.

Be all that as it may, pissed off Prissy—Prissy is what my Grandma Daniels nicknamed my loving mother, who firmly stood her ground—was one thousand percent against me marrying Lisa in this lifetime.

The eve of my nineteenth birthday, Mother wanted to talk to me, so after playing with little Eddie and changing his magnificent poopy diaper, I kept a respectful distance from Lisa's backwoods-thinking parents. I lovingly kissed Lisa and my son goodbye and drove our dookey-brown 1967 Plymouth Dart with a slant-six, three-speed transmission from Lisa's parents' Northeast 26th Street and Wygant house, which was one-and-a-half blocks from Alberta Street. Now proceeding west over to my middle-class neighborhood in North Portland, I was not at all lottery-excited about having this discussion with Mother Prissy.

The decision I've finally made with my life is final! I was convincing myself of this, driving up to my mother's house, noticing the reddish-brown, leaves falling . This particular mini-park of a yard on a nice-sized corner lot where I grew up had L shaped, manicured green hedges enclosing the west side and the entire backyard, which boasted four fifteen-foot maple trees, two full-grown transparent apple trees, one young Bing cherry tree, and seven other assorted trees that flawlessly bordered the rest of my mother's ranch-style home, which sat on a high incline. I had a thought that has never crossed my mind until then. My inner voice said to me, on a good note, *I won't be around to rake all of those leaves,* which usually takes about twenty full-sized lawn bags to complete the task.

I stopped the car on a partially cloudy day, stopping in front of the dwelling I was raised up in, harnessing a slight dose of attitude. However, this autumn September day, the day before my nineteenth birthday, I felt almost like I had stayed out all night without permission. I put the car in park, turned the engine off, held the keys in my hand, wondered how long this was going to take, and glared out the windshield as the sunset's bright light blinded me from looking at it.

I could have gone straight to heaven just then. *You could avoid all of this,* my inner voice said to me. I slowly trudged up the walkway, heart beating out of my chest, like I had committed treason against the Five Gangster Families. I briefly took in the landscape, admiring the blooming, soft pink roses that Grandpa Daniels and I planted last year, three on each side of the inclined walkway, evenly spread out in the flower beds. I was not at all ready to hear my mother's negative talk about how I was making the biggest mistake of my life. But it was way too late. I was there, under her roof, and Mother was going to let me have it. Rebellion is something that you have to work at in order to perfect it. I closed the door behind me, only to be greeted by General Georgia, ready to commence the attack.

"Hello, Mother," I said respectfully, shutting the front door behind me (walking the plank). My Mother was named Georgia; mother of four, black shoulder-length hair, very beautiful Hershey's chocolate complexion. She was wearing a brand new Bach blouse, coordinated with her dark-brown slacks and her one-and-a-half-inch-heeled dark brown leather boots. She had a slender build, never ever looked her age—which sent the wrong message to some younger men a lot of times; that she was not that old. But that was far from the truth! She was a surviving twin and the second-eldest daughter of five, employed as a police records clerk for the Multnomah County Sheriff's Office.

My mother was a private person. Her personal business was one thousand percent none of your damn business. Period! Mother's twin brother, George De Narval, passed away shortly after their birth. It was a strange coincidence that all but one of Mother's siblings lived in a two-block radius from one another in North Portland. Uncle Harry and his wife, Aunt Virginia, lived on Peninsula Avenue. My Aunt Marie and Uncle Mac lived on Curtis Avenue, right behind Uncle Harry. We first cousins all attended Peninsula Elementary School, just four blocks away. Mother's sister, Aunt Marie, who was 21 months younger, was practically an identical twin of my mother. They looked and sounded alike, except Aunt Marie was peanut butter-brown like her father, while my mother was Hershey's chocolate-complexioned like their mother. They were very close; however, their personalities allowed them to be nothing alike. They were night and day.

Uh-oh! Here we go, my inner voice said to me.

"Eddie!" my mother said, walking into the living room and sitting down at the white, circular dining table with its hip-swivel dining chairs. She put a cigarette case with a pack of Newports slightly sticking out by the ashtray on the table, alongside her medium-sized glass of gin and grapefruit on ice. She said in a very commanding voice, looking directly into my face, "You are my eldest child. I wouldn't waste my breath if this were not true." She said it very passionately, in a low-toned, decisively calm, unaware Scorpio-attitude. Out of nowhere, my mother blurted, "Don't marry that damn girl!" I stood there nervously, accepting the "too-young" sermon from the individual who unselfishly brought me into the universe. Yeah! Other scholars call it constructive criticism. I call it the angered-nerve-of-a-mother-in-law syndrome. However, in basic training, it's just physiological shock treatment.

"Why, Mother? Why do you hate Lisa so much?" I asked her respectfully.

"Eddie, son," my mother said, standing up, her left hand on her hip and her right index finger pointed directly at me like I was a hard-headed stepchild, trying to convince me as much as a mother possibly could that this was nothing but a baby trap while I stared at the black-and-gold antique clock hanging on the gray wall paneling. "Son, please go to Germany by your lonesome," Mother said, softening her tone. "All I ever wanted was for all of you kids to be law-abiding, enjoy your life, see the world, not be tied down, and don't depend on nobody at a young age, like me," Mother preached. Being the eldest, you can easily blame yourself after hearing that statement. "Lisa is nothing but a snake!" Mother fumed, flaring her nostrils. "I am just warning you. Only a caring mother would," my mother said proudly.

"Your own mother and father don't have a problem with me marrying Lisa, Mother!" I said in my defense. My mother stood up, highly pissed off, walked to the kitchen, got ice out of the freezer, placed it in her glass, and returned immediately.

"That is my mother and father, not yours. I am your mother. I gave birth to you, not my mother," she reminded me loudly, making her point crystal clear. "I am a woman. I know a no-good-for-nothing-ass snake of a woman when I see one, Eddie De Narval.

"On top of that, one day out of the blue, I remember it like it was yesterday, your Aunt Marie and I were sitting at the dining table, unwinding from one of those days at work, having a cocktail, catching a glimpse of the Dart through the large picture window, saw it park in front of the house, couldn't tell who it was, figured it was you until you did not open the door," Mother said. "Then there's a knock at the door, and me telling your Aunt Marie, 'That's strange,', as I walked to open the door. Snake-ass Lisa shows up without you in that Dart saying hello, standing on the porch looking crazy, handing me a note. 'What is this?' I asked her, not bothering at all to read whatever document she had the nerve to share. 'I have proof that I am pregnant,' Lisa says as I look at her like she is truly crazy. 'That doesn't mean Eddie is the biological father of your so-called pregnancy,' I pointed out, responding without hesitation. 'And you came over here without Eddie. That's really suspicious, Lisa, and I will make sure that I tell him so. Have a nice day,' I replied, closing the door, leaving Lisa with a blank expression on her guilty face. Just the thought that she was trying to trap you made me sick to my stomach.

"The nerve of her, Eddie! Nobody gets a doctor's slip saying that they are pregnant," my mother preached, walking away from me once she had made her point. She sat back down, picked up her glass, then set it back down, picked up the cigarette case, and grabbed a cigarette at the dining table. "Am I going to see you tomorrow on your nineteenth birthday?" my mother enquired, changing her tone of voice from preaching to soft, lighting her cig.

"Yes, Mother, I will make sure I stop by," I replied as I moved toward the front door, ready to slide out of her home. My mother completely refused to be supportive of or happy for Lisa and me. I never thought in a million years I could ever actually do something so outlandish to piss off my Prissy Mother that much! This was a very special person to me, especially considering that my mom and dad did pretty much the same.

My father, the eldest son and fourth child of eleven, married the preacher's daughter. On top of that, she was only—WHOA!—seventeen years old. Imagine that dilemma! My loving mother now all of a sudden believed for some strange reason—was cosmic certain—she was 99.9 percent sure that Eddie, Jr. was not my biological child. My Aunt Anna, Aunt Maxine, and my father's six other sisters also agreed with my mother, hands down. "He does not look like a Williams to me, Eddie," my Aunt Anna would sternly say to my face. And it just so happened that she was my favorite aunt who would never ever intentionally hurt me. She was my father's closest sister, 5'8", slender, caramel-complexioned, a very good woman who told it like it was, didn't bite her tongue, and treated everyone equally.

Father's gambling addiction proved to be lethal, losing us our apartment. Seeing my first eviction notice, I was instantly evil-enraged, sabotaged, feeling savagely rejected. My Aunt Anna unselfishly let me stay with her, treating me like I was her own child. Aunt Anna and her husband, Uncle Anderson Loving, had four cool children. Andy, Randy, Delores, and Tamara welcomed me with loving, open arms, in spite of my dysfunctional situation. They showed no jealousy or envy, treating me like loving family. I worked a summer job making trails at Forest Park and helped my Aunt Anna around her house. Then my other aunt, Sally Mae and Uncle ZJ took me in as well, treating me like one of their own, never ever making me feel less-than. They made sure I was not left out, but nothing can replace your family. Since my aunts lived a mile-and-a-half from one another on the northeast side of town, my paternal grandparents who loved me lots conveniently lived on NE Grand Avenue off of Union Avenue, which is now named Martin Luther King Avenue. I could always go there and camp out since I was their favorite grandchild.

My mother's, as well as my father's parents were convinced I was the biological father. By this time my dad worked in Downtown Portland as a correctional officer at the Multnomah County Jail Facility. People constantly walked up to me and told me how my father helped them out while they were incarcerated. He didn't have too much to say about my situation. He favored his future step-monster son and just said that it was my business.

Now, the Williams and Meadors side of my family was exceptionally huge all over America. My grandmother was biracial, bright brown enough to easily pass for white. My father's maternal grandfather, Thomas Meadors, of Summerville, Louisiana, was a biracial man, intelligent and handsome. He fathered 36 children! It was my understanding that he took care of every last one of them. That's how I am second cousin to Cheryl Ford of the WNBA, Demetrius Bell NFL free agent, and Sway "In the Morning" Calloway. My dad's younger brother, Clyde D. Williams, was a Guinness Book of World

Records three-time welterweight championship belt holder in the Pacific Northwest Division. Uncle Clyde passed away at the young age of twenty-seven. I was so sad. He was so much fun, always wore flashy clothes, always joked about getting knocked out on television. I was only thirteen years old when he passed away and his was my first funeral.

Big Mama, which everybody respectfully calls her, was my Dad's mother. Her husband, Hundley Williams, my grandfather, was the eldest child. Six-foot-six, slender, muscular, and believed in never taking food out of another man's pocket. He was wise, good, mocha-chocolate, cross-eyed, big-nosed and big-handed; an ox-strong, exceptional man, raising his own brothers and providing for his wife and ten children as a sharecropper in Warren, Arkansas. However, the man he worked for constantly took advantage of him since he could not read or write. He was not allowed to go to school in those days because of the color of his skin.

Amazingly, a European-American man taught my grandfather to mathematically dissolve an unequal verbal contract, making him aware of the landowner's abusive racial business tactics of knowingly taking advantage of the unfortunate and ignorant, and controlling people by any means necessary.

My grandparents migrated from segregation by purchasing a home in Oregon in 1952. Big Dad worked at the foundry operated by Richmond Manufacturing on Columbia Boulevard. We called Grandpa Williams "Big Dad," a southern term of endearment. His nephew was Eddie Juan Williams, 1983 1st round draft pick by the New York Mets, playing positions first and third baseman. Also my second cousin NBA retired Karl Malone.

Flash! What if my mother was right and we were the ones who were wrong? Naïve-ass thinking nut, on the last day of September, did I dare say *I do*? I had done the unthinkable: things would never, ever be the same in my neck of the woods for the rest of my life! How young is dumb?

This all began early in the windy, sunny, bicentennial year of 1976 in beautiful Portland. There was a crisp, clear smell of roses. Evergreen trees swayed as birds chirped, greeting Tuesday morning in the number one environmentally friendly, greenest, and cleanest city in the whole wide world. We had our share of rain, snowcapped mountains, rivers, lakes, creeks, beautiful green scenery, exquisite vineyards, hiking wildlife reservations, waterfalls, beautiful state parks, fun amusement parks, skiing, breathtaking views of the Columbia Gorge, our manicured, landscaped yards, and colossal stands of different fir trees seen everywhere. Portland, Oregon, nicknamed the City of Roses, had the ideal climate to grow roses, which incidentally is where the International Rose Test Garden is located on the west hills in gorgeous Washington Park, overlooking the City of Roses. Historically, Portland, Oregon is where Lewis and Clark and Sacajawea journeyed over the Oregon Trail to the Pacific Ocean. It's also the home of the NBA's Portland Trailblazers.

Folks still seemed to manage to keep my birth town forever decisively weird; population 383,000. Twenty thousand African-Americans and a multitude of European-Americans. Diversity is somewhat bogus as discrimination is a constant, invisible racism evident in the projected yearly housing statistics.

For some strange reason, the day after Labor Day was always the first day of school, which started with showering, brushing my teeth, getting dressed, picking my four-and-a-half-inch high, soft ebony afro with my four-inch-long afro pick long before it was time to get up and get dressed for school. Father knew I was very happy staying there with him. It was my senior year, then on to college studying law or acting and music.

My mother's plate was full with my younger and more demanding siblings' needs to fill. I took the city bus to school and transfered from the number 8 to the number 75 to Jefferson High School, along with some very familiar students who also attended Adams High School, which was east, in the opposite direction. Nobody at all was in a hurry. We were all half asleep from lack of sleep, which stemmed from the anticipatory teenage excitement of a new high school year.

The bus came to our stop and we slowly rose, single-file in the aisle to exit the bus. As I stepped onto the sidewalk, immediately somebody tapped me, friendly and respectful, on the shoulder. From behind me someone said, "Eddie Dee! What is going on, my brother?"

I turned to see who it was. It was a good friend from church by the name of Ronnie White.

"Mr. Ronnie White. What's going on, my brother?" I replied.

"Are you going to graduate from Jefferson this year?" he asked.

"You better know that, my brother, can you dig it?" I said swiftly, then shook his hand.

"Right on, man!" Ronnie replied. "You want to walk to the store with me?"

"No, I better go and register, since I have not yet done that this year," I replied.

"Check you out later, Eddie Dee," Ronnie said, walking away from the school.

"Lunch time!" I yelled, still walking toward the high school on Commercial Street. My first day of my senior year at Jefferson high, I walked the sidewalk with other students, sunshine clearly smiling on my afro, and in the far distance toward the horizon, I saw a gorgeous snowcap resting on top of Mount Hood.

Living with my dad, having the upstairs of the three-bedroom house all to myself, what more could I ask for? Living with father temporarily was not a cool demonstration of love, which was last year's news. Three years now my parents had been divorced, and it still made me feel somewhat inadequate, being the first generational divorced children.

I blamed myself after all those hospital bills, stricken with rheumatic fever on my ninth birthday, hospitalized on the West Portland Hilltop in the County Hospital. I was not a happy camper; I had constant dizzy spells where the room wouldn't stop moving while seeing little flicker flying lights, scared for dear life, nurses ignoring me until the doctor realized the penicillin I was taking was trying to close my throat. But in 1967, I was just a so-called Negro to them. I couldn't walk for a whole year. That was a traumatic period in my life: learning to walk again, physical therapy, fear in a wheel chair, feeling somewhat responsible for all those medical bills.

That day, my father was enormously embarrassed, since he immediately assumed I was faking ill, the day right after my ninth birthday, thinking for some idiotic, in-his-wildest-dreams reason that

I did not want to attend school. On that note, I could truly say he really didn't know me. I loved to go to school, getting good grades, loved going to church, singing, clapping, shouting, being joyous yet grateful, to the glory of God, for he is worthy to be praised. I was thankful for all blessings, most especially freedom from my siblings. Ah, the great getaway from my preoccupied parents, from hearing the stress of how they were too young to have four children.

My overbearing father, incidentally, was told by his own mother that he was not good enough to be with my mother. I loved my father very deeply; he worked three jobs at once to care for us. However, he was tough on Mike and me, while he favored my sister Nuffy and baby brother Keith. Mike and I learned very quickly to stay out of his way. Our father would discipline Mike and me for leaving the yard by whipping us with his wide, green-colored belt.

My mother scolded my father about disciplining us like we were savage animals, which made things even worse. Easily angered, father started putting us in confinement by way of two closets in our hallway instead of the usual extreme whipping technique. One closet at the end of the hallway, next to our bedroom, was Mike's closet. The coat closet in the living room was where I was put, sitting in the absolute, complete darkness with the door closed. Abused and mentally confused, that nightmare of traumatic torture still haunts me.

"Dad, I can't get up! I got no feeling whatsoever in my legs, like they both died!" I said carefully and respectfully to the six-foot-two, overbearing, smooth-skinned, mocha-chocolate, muscular, handsome, wavy-processed black-haired man approaching me.

"There is nothing wrong with you, boy!" he scolded, standing next to the bunk bed by the window. "You are just being lazy, boy!" my father said anxiously, instantly upset, as if I were lying. He took off his belt to discipline me as I lay in the top bunk, scared, unable to feel my legs.

"Hugh! What the hell is you doing?" my mother asked very firmly as she entered our bedroom with her hands on her hips. "That boy lyin', talkin' bout him can't feel his legs," my father said, pointing at me with his green two-inch-wide-ass belt gripped in his hand. I always assumed a belt was made to hold up your pants, but I wasn't saying a word right then.

"He is being lazy, just doesn't want to go to school," father replied with that same-old post-slavery, stereotypical statement. He knew that after the slaves were freed, White America didn't want to pay African-American people to work for money, they wanted them to work only for food. The fear of equality and an addiction to free labor only led to uncontrolled greed!

"Hugh, has the thought ever entered your mind that he might be telling the truth?" my mother logically, tactfully asked in my defense, now standing between Dad and the wooden bunk beds, challenging his authority, his cross-eyed manhood visually insulted.

"How is that, Georgia?" brainwashed Dad smartly asked.

"Because, Hugh,"—her hand feeling my forehead—"these are the same, identical symptoms I had when I was stricken with rheumatic fever as a little girl, silly! Now pick him up out of that bed and let's take him to the doctor," my mother commanded my father, with not another word said between them.

Still not totally convinced, he grabbed me, put me in the red 1965 Chevrolet Impala, and the three of us went to Dr. Marshall's office. Upon examination, I was diagnosed with rheumatic fever and a heart murmur. I was immediately admitted to the Children's Hospital on the Great Hill in Southwest Portland, thinking, *I am going to die!*

I felt very helpless and very scared in that hospital. It was a lonely tunnel; all I saw were needles, nurses taking vitals, probing, and more needles. Once, I thought my parents were putting me up for adoption. That was the night they didn't show up because the steep hill road was shut down due to hazardous weather conditions. Then, one frightening night, my breathing problems started, all because of my being allergic to penicillin. That was a scary encounter.

My childhood was far from picture perfect. Even after I was released from the hospital, it was an uphill battle; dizzy spells all the time, restricted to a wheelchair, nightmares in daylight, frightened of the bad nurses coming to kill me. It wasn't quite my interpretation of a normal childhood. The very next year my teacher at Peninsular Elementary School, Mrs. Tilden, made the mistake of informing my dad that I was a smart student. So now, out of the blue, Dad wanted me to go to law school. Me, I want to be a multi-talented entertainer.

Father had nothing but negative comments about this. We always butted heads, like two rams on meth. He never came to see me perform in my eighth grade talent show. I received a standing ovation for singing "Darling Dear" by the Jackson Five. My father was not able to be present.

Once I had recovered from rheumatic fever, I sang and performed yearly in the talent show.

Mr. Dietz, my music teacher, taught me to play cornet and recommended me to play cornet with the Oregon Symphony Orchestra, which was definitely on my life to-do list.

I had been singing in church for as long as I could remember. Sure, I would have loved to be a singer-songwriter, comedian, author, actor, and musician. It was definitely branded into my DNA. I always knew deep down in my soul that I was built that way. Misunderstanding his son, my father-of-little-faith was most certainly against "do what you are good at" and "love what you do" as opposed to, "no one really takes you seriously," his obvious avoidance of supporting my dreams.

Sophomore year, staying with my maternal grandparents, I won first place in the state speech tournament in the comedy category at Franklin High. First place. I nailed it. I performed Bill Cosby's *The Water Boy* and had the audience and judges laughing, clapping, and they finally gave me a standing ovation. Sadly, my grandmother as well as my multitalented Aunt Wendy seemed not the least bit interested in my comical, musically talented endeavors, always commanding me to get off the family piano or guitar that I did not need to learn how to play. It was like modern psychological slavery. I am aware of an ugly reminder that's kept quiet: as the eldest of four—three boys and one girl—I am the runt, quite smaller than my siblings. Being called scrawny and told that you eat too damn much can cause you to feel not very well psychologically, like being prejudged and found guilty of a sort of wimpy-ness, leaving you scarred and with a temperament that screams, "Bullies shall never ever prosper!" But I suppose my dad's insecurities, which are the embedded residuals of slavery within his walls of resentment, mixed with being told by his very own mother— who did not in any way try to hurt her own son on purpose—that he was not good enough to be with my mother, became the ultimate conditioning axe in the back. No therapy whatsoever could address the systematic residual atrocities of slavery, which I correctly figured contributed to my father's out-of-control gambling addiction.

As I arrived at the top of the cement stairs to enter the high school, there she stood: sexy, four-foot-nine, medium afro, peanut butter complexion, with those thick-ass, show-you-right-ass thighs. Smiling at the silhouette of my five-foot-two-inch lily frame, Lisa had on sexy, tight white Wrangler jean shorts with a kind of see-through short-sleeved white blouse, tan open-toed sandals, and an afro, looking like an innocent, underaged, sexy-ass secretary.

Disguising her beautiful brown eyes, innocently looking for lust in all the wrong places, were lavender-framed bifocals. She was undressing me with her eyes, obviously gesturing that she was not shy. Consequently, neither was I, check and mate, let's make paste!

"Hello, Eddie Dee. How are you?" Lisa asked with the quickness.

"Hi, Lisa. How are you doing?" I replied, smiling, checking her out closely, smoking a cigarette, posing with my black, silky smooth shiny shirt, huge butterfly collar, gold, double-knit polyester bell-bottom disco dancing pants, a funky black belt, and black-and-reddish-brown Flag Brothers two-inch platform shoes, my soft, four-inch-high Afro, with a big peace medallion around my neck and a black leather short Dog jacket. I frequently admired my reflection in the windows of the reddish-brown double doors at the east side entrance into the high school, looking like a blast from the past 1976 version of the Undercover Brother.

Lisa, smiling flirtatiously, beckoning with her index finger, said, "Want to go and have fun at late lunch?" She stepped to me, up close and personal, like she wanted to have her way with me. My heat-seeking loins detected her extremely hot undercarriage, menacing my sexual man.

Then, bam! Just like that, racing up the stairs were my maniac-crazy first cousins, my dad's Sister, Aunt Sally Mae's kids, Ronald and Donald Purifoy, fraternal twins like day and night: Ronnie fair-skinned, husky clown of a guy, very happy-natured, and Donny, mocha chocolate-complexion, medium build, and sensitively special.

"There he is! Eddie! Cousin, what is going on?" Ronald said, clowning, playing a security guard jumping into action like a superhero between Lisa and me, as if he were protecting me from the clutches of a man-eating woman who wanted to devour me, mentally and sexually.

"Hey, lady, he just got here. You slow down right now, little Miss Lisa! You can wait until lunchtime for some afternoon delight, in-between-time woman!" Ronnie loudly proclaimed, pointing his index finger up to her face jokingly, while he held her arm as if Lisa were under arrest and Ronnie was taking her into custody and escorting her to class.

"What is going on, cousins?" I said very excitedly.

"Hi, Ronnie," Lisa said, giggly, going along with Ronnie's antics.

"Eddie, are you staying with Uncle Hugh?" Donny asked.

"Yes," I replied, giving him an Afro-American handshake and hug. "Now tell my cousin, 'See you at lunchtime, baby,'", Ronnie commanded.

"Bye, baby, I will definitely see you at lunchtime," Lisa said, smiling, winking her right eye at me as they walked into the school building.

Dad's girlfriend, she was so cool! She was sweet, fair, and easy to get along with. Cousin Dorothy and I lived on Northeast 13th and Fremont on the East side of the street: three-bedroom, one-and-a-half bath, and I have the entire upstairs to myself. And I got a weekly allowance!

"First gray-and-white house from the corner!" I told Donny boastfully.

My Aunt Sally Mae, my father's older sister, and Uncle ZJ, her husband, had eight kids—four boys and four girls. In age, I am right in the middle of them all.

"Where is your car, Eddie?" Donny asked as we walked down the freshly waxed floor. "At Mama's. The brakes went out and I don't have the money to fix it yet," I replied. I was smiling, checking out the female students walking the opposite direction.

"I need to see about getting an after school job," I broadcasted comically as my other cousin, Selena, stopped me in the middle of the main hallway. Selena was five-foot-six, butterscotch complexioned, smart, petite, bright eyes, spoke her mind, happy to be seen, quickly hugging me like a big sister.

Selena said to me, "How are you doing, cousin?"

"Hello, Selena, can I get a hug too?" Donny instigated while admiring Selena's yellow dress.

"No, Donny," Selena said jokingly, smiling. "Are you still messing around with that Lisa girl?" Selena asked me curiously.

"You know what cousin Renee said last year: need to watch out for these fast-ass freaks up in here, Eddie. Selena, how does Renee say it? 'You better be careful, Church Boy!'" Donny said, laughing loudly. "You are too late, Selena. Lisa made her move on Eddie already," Donny snitched. "Eddie has a lunch date with that Hot Pocket Lisa today," Donny confessed, laughing, attempting to score buddy points with my cousin.

"Cousin needs to slow down! I will talk to you later. Love you," Selena said, walking away.

"I love you too!" Donny said, still being flirtatious. "I'll see you later, Eddie," Donny said, running down the freshly-waxed, squeaky-clean hallway of the school.

There I stood in the main hallway, adjacent to the front doors which led to the front porch, with a view of the grassy green football field, marked in white chalk. Directly behind me were the two wide staircases leading to the upper floors, where most of my classes were located on both sides of the enormous hallway. Jefferson High school, built in 1908 and still in excellent condition.

In spite of my relative's warnings, I meet Lisa for lunch on the west side of the school. Soon, and very often, we were racing over to Lisa's cousin's house two blocks away, like as it was part of science social study subjects for our active sex education class. Sex Ed afternoon delight. Lisa and I became lovers, agreeing to stop seeing other people. I gained part-time employment at Albertson's grocery store on Killingsworth, next door to the liquor store, four blocks down the street and minutes away from school. I was cleaning up the bakery for four hours, four to five nights a week. Seeing a lot of Lisa, roller skating at the imperial rink, dancing at the Disco Lady, going to the 104th St. drive-in movie.

But nothing was quite as crazy as when we were parked in a semi-alleyway located in North Portland, just yards from Columbia Park where I used to swim as a kid. High and buzzed off Thunderbird and 7up, Lisa and I passed out buck naked in her 1960 two-tone, blue-and-white Comet after having mega sex all night long. Passing morning light speaks, startled owners of the home called the police saying there were two blacks dead in a car in the alleyway where they pulled their automobiles out to access the main road. Needless to say, when the police arrived we were still comatose as to what was going on, the police banging on the windows for a half an hour or so before calling the coroner.

When the coroner showed up, he knocked on the door, alerting Lisa and me, causing us to awaken, fiercely frightened, instantly panicky, jumping up buck naked. The coroner jumped directly into the police officer's arms, like he had seen real live ghosts!

"What the hell are you kids doing?" the police officers yelled, as we were surrounded by a half-dozen police cars. "Let me see some ID and get dressed!" Handing us back our IDs, realizing we were just kids, the officer got more furious and told us, "Get the hell out of here! You scared the hell out of us, now you just get out of here! We thought you were dead!"

We were getting along, enjoying each other's company, just being friends with benefits. But without warning, this was the least of my worries, as I no longer wanted to go to school anymore. Not even two damn months into my senior year, my father sat me down to inform me that I could no longer stay with him. Once again rejection, time's resentment, left a sour taste in my mouth because he was moving out of the house, not because he loved me and wanted to do the right thing.

No. *He really does not give a damn about me*, my inner voice said to me, as the demons tried, horrifically, to get me to hate him. My dad would rather live with this ready-made stepfamily, who he thought I didn't know anything about. But I had seen his white 1969 two-door

Bach vinyl-topped El Dorado with Bach interior parked right in front of her house.

We four siblings love our Father so unconditionally that it shall never, ever fade away. With that said, how in hell could he do this to his biological kids? Mr. Rebellion was now my friend. I was so tired of being rejected, let down, and made to feel like some defective boomerang whose only purpose in life is to just keep coming back for more pain. My wall of resentment was so high it was hard to tear it down. It was bad enough that we were the first to divorce in our family. Now we had become the misfits. Why?

Lisa and I went to our senior prom even though I was expelled from school due to cutting classes and other mischief. I needed just a few credits to graduate. I didn't care. Self-sabotage was my friend now. Lisa informed me that she was pregnant with my child after having a miscarriage a few months previously, which is why I signed up for the Army National Guard in the first place.

June 13, 1976, I flew out of PDX to basic training at Fort Sill, Oklahoma, only to be greeted in the scariest, most attention-getting formula shock treatment of my life! Drill instructors stayed on our asses for twelve long weeks; strict discipline, front-leaning rest position, extra duty, rigorous physical training, running, pull-ups, latrine duty, kitchen duty, repetitive marching, and the PT test from hell in 100-degree weather to graduate from boot camp.

And I am so glad I did. I left a boy, and I returned home in September a somewhat disciplined man.

To a very pregnant girlfriend! I needed a full-time job before Lisa had the baby. She gave birth to a healthy, beautiful boy the tenth of February, naming him after yours truly. I quickly came to the realization that my National Guard check couldn't and wouldn't support a child. Consulting with my fellow guardsman, Sergeant Whitmore, he informed me how to go army via Germany.

Soon, I was activated to serve with the branch of the army headed to good old Germany, on the continent of Europe, which is exactly where I wanted to go. I was so excited to receive my active duty orders.

Then, to my surprise, out of the blue Bill Walton and the Portland Trailblazers beat the Philadelphia 76ers, 109-107, 80 degrees in the shade on June 5th, winning the NBA Championship, during an all-time record low of zero crime in the Rip City! The best summer Portland Oregon has ever seen. We just partied, everybody was happy, cool, and nonviolent!

The City shut down, partied, and extended the Rose Festival Carnival an extra week.

We were gathered there, my Grandmother Jessie, my grandfather, and my uncle Harry at my church on a sunny September Friday, Lisa and yours truly becoming man and wife in holy matrimony while my mother and stepfather Robert stand still in utter silence.

Robert was mocha, six-foot-five, slender, muscular; a cool, funny-ass character, very easygoing, life of the party, an army veteran from Bayonne, New Jersey, who met my mother while stationed at Fort Lewis, Washington.

Lisa and I stood facing Grandfather at the altar of the sanctuary. I was in my three-piece, bell-bottom white suit, an ice baby-blue silk shirt with a white tie. Lisa had sewn a white two-piece outfit, the skirt with a sexy slit on the side, and a white jacket to complement her blouse.

Lisa even made me a few jumpsuits with matching apple hats to wear to the disco club. She was quite the seamstress and attended cosmetology school while in high school. That made a great impression on me, which made it much easier to fall in love with her. A talented human being, she was gifted in so many ways I couldn't help but love her for that, especially being the mother of my son.

My sister Denise, Mother's favorite and the all-American snitch, who always conspired to trap me about every time I had Lisa over. Nuffy was her nickname and she could do no wrong in my mother's and father's eyes. Prissy was very visibly pissed off but held her tongue because her mother, my grandmother, would have never let her intervene. There was no way she was going to make some kind of scene in her father's own church.

"I now pronounce you husband and wife," my grandfather, Bishop Daniels said, smiling.

I saluted my loving bride for the first time as Mrs. Eddie Dee Williams, placing my mocha-chocolate lips on her butterscotch mouth, my long, skinny arms around her frame as if I were to never let her go. However, Lisa, dressed in white, wasn't all that overwhelmed.

Something was already wrong and we had just said "I do"! I looked around to see that her parents never did bother to show up due to the fact that I did not ask her father for Lisa's hand in marriage. It was also no surprise my father did not show up either. He had another family to see about, and I needed to get it through my thick skull that this was the way it was going to be for the rest of my life. I expected that I had not heard the end of this—not by a long shot!

As we all left the church, my mother suggested that we stop by the 7-Eleven to pick up cases of party favor libations. After leaving the store, we shortly arrived at our destination: Aunt Marie's house. Lisa rode cemetery-quiet, giving me the wandering willies with the eight-track stereo playing. She looked like there was no reason at all to be celebrating, almost acting as if it was just another day.

"Are you going to be like this the rest of the night?" I asked quickly, not being harsh, smiling into her big, dark brown eyes.

"Eddie Dee, baby, it's not you, it's just me. I will be all right," Lisa reassured me.

That my mother was taking my marriage to Lisa so very well put me in a complete state of shock! We were having a decent time at my Aunt Marie's warmly decorated, three-bedroom home. Had my mother had a lasting change of heart?

About a half hour after our arrival, a spark from Hell broke loose in every way possible, like an out-of-control Fourth of July party gone very bad, one of those crazy days in life. Bam! Only in America!

My sixteen-year-old cousin David T Duke, six-foot-four, slender, mocha-complexion, Marie's eldest son and Grandma's favorite, rushed into the living room where I was minding my damn business, sitting relaxed and happy on the comfy gold-trimmed white easy couch, glancing at the nice piano, having a drink, getting advice, listening to my stepfather Robert about what to expect in the army and Germany. He had been stationed there himself and completed his tour honorably.

"Eddie! Come quick!" David said to me. "Aunt Georgia and my mother got Lisa in there hemmed up in the corner crying, cussing her ass out! Seriously! Come on, Eddie!" David commanded loudly.

I rushed into the dining room where Lisa was crying, my drunken mother standing over her, not at all at a loss for words, as she proceeded to tell Lisa off, cussing her out loudly and viciously while Lisa covered her face with both hands. "You aren't good enough for my son!" my mother said loudly.

"You know damn well that is not Eddie's baby, bitch!" my Aunt Marie said rudely.

"Nobody gets a slip from a doctor to say they're pregnant," my mother started preaching. "That's why your own parents didn't even show up!" my Aunt Marie stated boldly. "Even they know that is not Eddie's baby, bitch!" my mother replied stubbornly.

"You guys quit talking to my wife like that! Shame on you!" I said, offensively loud.

I immediately got Lisa out of the house and into the car while Cousin David and my baby brother Keith restrain our pissed off parents who were releasing their complete hatred on Lisa.

No longer caring about out attire, I took one last look at my aunts before I drove off and headed east for Interstate Avenue to the Oregon motel, which was only five minutes away and where we were going to stay the weekend.

I pulled up to the motel, parked, and entered the front office, paying the attendant in cash for the room for the entire weekend. I returned to the car, taking off of my white suit coat as Lisa got out of the passenger side. As I walked to the room and opened the door, she hesitated, sat down outside on the steps of the motel room in her white two-piece ensemble that she personally made for our wedding day.

"There is something that has been bothering me, Eddie Dee," Lisa said to me very tearfully, with that almost kind of apologizing, drunken look on her face. "Eddie, does you promise you won't get mad or anything like that?" Lisa asked crying.

"I promise I will not hurt you or abandon you," I replied to her question calmly. "So now, tell me what is your main function in life?" I asked.

"You remember when your father was over your mother's house one evening we were all there? Your father gave me a ride home. Do you remember that?" Lisa asked. I said nothing, just standing there, staring down at her, paranoid and puzzled, exactly no idea what she was talking about, making no sense to guess.

"Before he took me home, I had sex with him," Lisa replied, looking sickly and ashamed.

"What the hell? Are you crazy?" I asked, agitated to the mighty max, getting even more so, pacing quickly back and forth in the motel's driveway, then away from her presence, trying to suck down rather than swallow this revelation in my dammed life.

I don't know what the hell to do now! My damn wedding night is cursed, my inside voice screamed at me. I lit up a cigarette like that was going to solve something. I still had a son to consider. I didn't want him to wind up confused like a straight-stupid sucker dressed in a white three-piece bell-bottom suit with a baby-blue, butterfly-collared, shiny silk shirt, Flag Brother's black leather and suede platform shoes, trying hard not to produce a shitty attitude. I couldn't even begin to look at Lisa.

Flip-flopping, now she was saying, "Eddie, I did not mean it," crying, getting up, trying to make eye contact with me.

Finally, Lisa stepped into the motel room, kicked off her white high-heeled shoes, flopped down, sitting directly facing me on the double bed, petite feet dangling just above the floor.

Disgusting-ass smell in this room, like a decomposed old folk's home engulfing whatever decent, free air that wasn't already tainted by the extreme odor, causing me to leave the off-white door wide open, in extreme need of fresh oxygen to alleviate that funkiest stench.

Lisa, crying unstoppably, lying flat on her backside, gamming, matrimonial lovemaking lower extremities spread apart, now sniffling umpteen times, hypnotizing my non-member, revealing her beautiful peanut butter thighs, nostalgic hot pubic undercarriage, staring away from the doorway, making the best of a bad situation. I swallowed my pride, walked into the room to finally join my bride.

Mother and Aunt Marie cursed Lisa out. Her own parents did not show up. Pain we sustain makes us say things we don't generally mean to say. Being in love is that way, I guess? So I calmly retrieved the champagne, beer, cigarettes, and cannabis from the car. I would never, ever be the same.

I stayed drunk like my drill instructor taught me. "Get drunk, suck it up, take the pain and be a man" kept on playing in my head, which allowed me to block out my new bride, unready to consummate our marriage until I was intoxicated. After consuming two of the four Colt 45 six-packs about ninety minutes later, like a slap to the back of my head demon logic started showing his shiftless face, sinking in, urging my stupid thinking, sleeping with my insecurities and foremost ignoring the plan necessary to be successfully career-minded.

Family man realizing I was married, that fine naked woman in my naked lap was my wife and this was our honeymoon. Hands down I could make it the last time we saw each other before I left the country. Needless to say we loved each other, but how much?

I had said goodbyes to my family, focused on the path of my life: retiring at age thirty-seven from the army, twenty years of service in the year 1995. Monday morning, contemplating in what parts of the world I could be stationed after Germany. The Philippines would be a nice place to be stationed, or Hawaii, or Japan, or Guam.

I was dressed and ready to leave Portland, Oregon for who knows how long. Time for a change. Lisa was very sad, unsure of what I was going to do. Clearly, I was not sad in the least. I drove the dart excitedly down Colombia Boulevard all the way to the airport exit. I was so excited. The day had finally arrived; I was having a military mind meltdown. I parked in the short-term lot, grabbed my luggage. Planes were landing and taking off loudly. Carrying Little Eddie and my one and only suitcase, I reached the gate long before Lisa. She was crying heavily as I handed Eddie over to her, kissing him then Lisa goodbye as I boarded Continental Airlines. Lisa sadly waved back as I waved goodbye, sad plus excited to be all that I could be in a foreign land, making positive progress, in my life.

Years later!

1

· · · · · · · · · · · · · · · · · · ·

Time-Out Knocked Out

I t's copasetic not to check my watch, body perspiring. My, how time
flies when you exercise and the very last order of fish and chips is
in the window, no more tickets on the waitress's order wheel, have
totaled up all their books, unwinding, sitting facing the bar, relaxing
on black spiral stools while inhaling their nicotine of choice, enjoying
the complimentary post-shift drinks. Ignoring their girlish laughter, I
look to make sure that the dining area is officially closed and allow the
kitchen door that leads to the restaurant to swing shut. Now it's time to
systematically break down and prep the lunch line, as well as replenish
it with fresh condiments. With a knowing eye, Boss Kathy commences
her timely inspection of the entire anatomy of the kitchen before
relinquishing my check, plus three days' hiatus pay. Once I step out
of here, it's Eagle-Flying Friday. I'm a sweaty mammal sporting
a white cook's uniform and a stained apron, with the aromas of
chopped onions and diced raw bell peppers rising deliciously out
of the pores of my mocha skin. I'm presently employed as a lunch
shift line cook at the Prime Rib Restaurant on Sandy Boulevard in
Northeast Portland. Originally, I was working a full-time job for
my stepfather, Robert when I was performing janitorial services
here, sanitizing the restaurant lounge and restrooms during closing.
Then one rainy day the owners, Rick and Kathy, said they needed
a dishwasher desperately, and I grabbed the opportunity. I've been
promoted from dishwasher to prep cook to line cook since I started

here, and I feel I'm here for the duration because of the friendly atmosphere, and because nobody's lazy.

I ignorantly blew a real opportunity to be a full-time firefighter. I attended Fire Science classes at Portland Community College for a year, racking up a hundred credit hours of on-the-job training while employed as a fire cadet at Engine House Number Seven, beneath the Hawthorne Bridge on the East side of the Willamette River. I flunked by scoring ridiculously low on the curve for the firefighter's exam, effectively screwing up an obvious opportunity to be hired by the Portland Fire Bureau, even though I was considerably respected as a hardworking, upstanding, perfect fit for the job. However, my lack of attention to detail, dysfunctional study habits, and daughter in the oven from my new relationship with Angela—who dumped me like I was rat poison for an illegal immigrant Cuban drug dealer—all conspired to torpedo that opportunity. Full-time employment is as essential as breathing when you have child support to pay. You don't pay, you're just a deadbeat, dumb, dysfunctional dad, and I am not going to go there.

Hindsight being 20/20, I regretfully realize that leaving the army was not a logical decision. Lisa's infidelity tilted my foolish pride to the point where I couldn't stomach reenlisting; fellow barracks buddies I knew smiling in my face, pretending to be anything but good-for-nothing-ass friends while we're out in the bush, taking turns knocking the lining out of the wife's boots. Things don't always come out the way you plan, and you don't always get what you want. That's just life, I suppose. I was under the impression that Lisa gave birth to my biological son, which was not the case, unfortunately. She deliberately missed five scheduled appointments to do the paternity test. What can be learned from all this? Mirror, mirror on the wall, which sex can manipulate the greatest lie of all? Exhibiting unnerving genius, upon my return to America from Germany, she purposely got pregnant by yours truly. Gloating cheerfully when Deon was born, Lisa bragged, "You cannot say he's not your son," admitting to my face while she was lying in Emanuel Hospital, resting in an elevated bed—eye to eye, short, sweet, and to the point—that I am not Eddie Dee's biological father.

Here comes Boss Kathy strutting toward me, inspecting everything in sight, as expected. She's Caucasian, five foot six—slender, sensuous silhouette with nice athletic legs, an attractive, sexy, seasoned brunette with a nice aura about her when she's intoxicated; sassy, yet pleasingly bossy. Kathy's companion Rick—last name Go, who couldn't slow down even if you cited him with a speeding ticket—is the restaurant's very versatile chef, cook, dishwasher, bartender, manager, and waiter combined. He's also Caucasian, five foot ten, medium build, straight black hair, looks Italian. Other than coke falling out his nose at will, Rick's an all right human being when he's not geeking. One way or another, we humans all have our addictions.

I finish up the kitchen by bleaching the prep table. Everything's complete and double-checked: sanitation cans, freezer, dish tank. Let the inspection begin! I love a good challenge. "Hello, Eddie," Kathy says as she walks around, inspecting the kitchen in a navy-blue dress, walking toward me in black high heels, lady scented like a tropical, perfumed flower. "How was lunch? Everything go okay, Eddie?" she asks, checking the soup.

"Yes Kathy," I reply. "We had a nice little push at the end. Everything is replenished, all the prep is done, and the line is ready to go." I put my hands behind my back because I know they're sweating.

"Well, Eddie, here's your check. You can take off," she says as she walks down the line, checking and inspecting each wall and every container in every section thoroughly, one by one, like she's a health inspector for the State of Oregon. I'm smelling sweet victory. Apparently, I've got the green light. "Good job, Eddie. Enjoy your days off," Kathy says, nodding and handing me my check. "Stop by the bar and have a drink on me after you're off the clock," she adds.

Officially off the clock, grabbing my gray cowboy hat, my blue, white, and gray Dallas Cowboys jacket, I head out the door, blazing through the ghost-quiet, maroon-carpeted restaurant, past the quaint wooden dining tables, where I take a seat at the end of the bar far away from the few customers drinking socially, unwinding. I just want to cash my check, not jumpstart happy hour. Today's protocol: pay bills right away. Tammy and I have been invited over to my folks later on for some state-of-the-art, five-star collard greens, neck bones, potato salad, chicken, lemon cake, and bomb-ass barbecue ribs.

I'm looking at the television but not watching it, impatiently trying to get noticed by Rick, who is tending bar. I grab a book of matches, pull a cigarette out of the pack in my shirt pocket, light it, blow out the match, toss the match in the ashtray, reach over the bar and get Rick's attention. The broadcasters on the news are discussing the Trailblazer's most recent ridiculousness in the NBA Playoffs, employing the well-known media phrase, "the no good news cycle."

"Eddie!" Rick says loudly, as he approaches quickly. "Yukon Jack, right?"

"Yes indeed," I reply, flicking my ashes in the ashtray.

"Coming right up, Eddie, but I can't cash your check."

"That's okay," I say as I pick up the shot glass and swallow in one gulp, as if it were cough medicine. Setting the glass down as I retrieve my cigarette from the clear glass ashtray on the bar, "See you in a few days," I say, inhaling, exhaling, putting my cigarette out, spiraling off the bar stool, walking toward the exit.

Out on the street, my eyes take a while to readjust to the bright sunlight. Wow. No rain. As I'm putting on my jacket and hat, my ears instantly detect the engine noise of the approaching bus. Without delay, I zoom across the pavement as if I were some kind of bionic man. The driver notices me running across the street for the bus stop and slows the gray-and-orange bus down, indicating he is definitely going to stop. The door opens and as I step aboard, I flash my bus pass, thanking him. He nods and I try to brace myself as the bus abruptly takes off downhill on Sandy Boulevard, forcing me to grab the silver pole, swivel, and slide into one of the front seats. There are only a few other riders, which means this will be a fast trip. I'm standing less than a mile later, alerting the driver I want the next stop. The sweaty aroma from prepping all those vegetables engulfs the front of the bus like a dirty aerosol salsa blast has just exploded, clearing out everyone's plugged-up nasal passages.

Exiting the bus, I walk around the corner to 39th Street, just a few yards from the stop where I need to transfer. Eyeing my watch,

I see I have time to cash my check. The next bus arrives in twenty minutes, so I'd rather get it done sooner rather than later. I fast-walk to the bank, cash my check, and then sprint two and a half blocks to the Hollywood liquor store, which is a huge-looking warehouse of a building at 41st and Sandy Blvd. Inside, there is an easy-on-the-eyes, short, fluffy, well-rounded, redheaded lady, standing behind the counter in a long multicolored blouse with black slacks. Uh-oh, and here we go, I'm touching my rear—bingo!— discovering my wallet, relieved. I'm awaiting a compliment—ah, yes! My intelligence informs me that this will definitely be Fun Friday as I open the door, that glass door of opportunities, with a mid-evil smirk. Already, she casually assumes I'm a minor who thinks that he is slicker than a snotty-nosed child in the middle of an oil spill.

"Hello, how are you?" I inquire. She says nothing, just stares with her hands on her hips, like I slept with her last night and didn't call the next day. "May I have a fifth of Seagram's Gin, please?" I ask politely.

"May I see your ID?" she demands, being seriously sarcastic.

"Well…thank you for the compliment," I say happily, grinning as I reach into my wallet and hand the lady my Oregon ID card. Her eyes get really wide, which is normal, since I am 31, not 21. "You black people don't look your age at all," she says as she turns to get the fifth of alcohol off the display shelf just behind her. I hand her a twenty-dollar bill and she gladly hands me back my change. Not having enough time to explain that I am not black, I just let it go this one time. "Now, you have a nice evening, sir," she says with a big smile.

"You do the same," I reply, smiling as I push the door open to leave. I have just five minutes to spare before my bus comes. I love it when a plan comes together. Simply marvelous!

Now all I have to do is hand Tammy the money for the bills, take a shower, and we are off to the Friday night barbecue. The bus is practically full, but I manage to get a seat just as I was looking for a one. Being in the right place at the right time makes for a wonderful day. I'll probably arrive home in less than a half an hour or so. Tammy, who is my lady and nine years younger, and with whom I have been in a relationship over a year now, has a handsome son named Devinare, and things are going all right, I suppose. We met at the Tamarack apartment complex one sunny July summer day. I was gallivanting around my old neighborhood, headed nowhere in particular, when I happened to catch a glimpse of her sexy smile as she stood there wearing sporty black stretch pants and a white tank top, staring out the doorway of her apartment at me. She is five foot eight, biracial, light butterscotch complexion, freckle-faced, sexy eyes, beautiful shoulder-length brown hair, voluptuous breasts, long sexy legs, and also has somewhat of an atomic temper.

This was during a very depressing time in my life. That day, I set out to get into mischief. As far as I'm concerned, I bit off more than I could chew.

My cousin Ronnie, one of my favorite, had his brake lines tampered with after working on an oil rig in Kansas, goes over a seventy-five-foot cliff, killing him instantly, twenty-seven years old, same age as my Uncle Clyde. Then, ten days later, my maternal grandmother passed away from cancer. I did not know what to think, because a few weeks later, my Aunt Anna also passed away from cancer. I was feeling abandoned, losing my mind, in a chronic state of grief, constantly being a pallbearer. The same day I met Tammy at the complex, I decided to get intoxicated, drinking Night Train and Mad Dog 20/20 wine with some degenerates who lived in the housing development a couple of blocks west of Tammy. As the night stood still, this dude named Archie Williams got my tipsy ass all riled up out of my comfort zone and dared me to steal some liquor with him. We both entered the double doors of the brown-bricked neighborhood store, and as we immediately split up, the cash register opened. A short man with black hair was handing a customer his change when I spun into action, saying, "Don't move!" I took the money out of the till and ran out of the store to the escape vehicle parked one block away in the pure, dark shadow of a huge oak tree. I was safely in the car, Archie jumped into the driver's seat, turned the ignition as the police sped by to the scene of the apparent crime. He hesitated in taking off as a police officer driving by took notice of us. Archie panicked and gave himself up. Then he snitched on me while I was hidden in the dark, curled up like a brown ball. The cop handcuffed and arrested me and escorted me to jail, where I was charged with robbery.

My family and friends were in utter shock because they knew I was no criminal. At my trial, the district attorney attempted to have me sentenced to five years in jail, but the furious and logical Judge Abraham stated, "I am not going to send this young man to prison. He took 28 years to commit his first crime, has a very long, steady work history, and he's an army veteran. I'm sentencing Mr. Williams to five years' probation. Now, Mr. Williams, get your act together!" and smacked the desk with his mallet. For the first time in my life I was a certified felon, checking in with my probation officer promptly every month, paying my fees on time, everything going just fine, as long as I stay away from that hideous-ass wine.

Tammy can be quite the sweetheart, in spite of a genuine lack of trust and all her various accusations. Among the many splendorous reasons, mainly it's her uncanny disposition that makes me love her so. Can you really love crazy? I've pretty much tried to make her feel special, but the more I try, the more she suspects something. In the final analysis, after she repeatedly conducts her bogus investigations, time after time, she finds I'm not a cheating man. Sure, my ex-relationships' luggage is a thing of the past, but not so easy to overcome, and often trying to break your spirit, not allowing you to rise above your insecurities.

Finally, the next stop is where I get off. With the bus being so full, I reach carefully over the elderly man's head with my left hand to ring the bell. After I get off the bus, it's impossible not to notice how badly I reek of onions, garlic, and other dastardly, unnamable smells. I feel like a walking health hazard, a totally unfamiliar inferno of uncontested funk. As a precaution against having to smell myself, I quickly pull out a cigarette, ignite the nicotine, and take a long drag, exhausted while welcoming my second wind, right here, right about now.

I approach the castle, making my way up the stairway ever so carefully, holding the bag containing booze, fantasizing about the day I can comfortably afford to purchase a home of my very own and pay the mortgage instead of shacking. I notice that I've done an excellent job of trimming the four evenly spaced shrubs in the yard, while at the same time letting a huge, wild-growing holly tree in the backyard go crazy. This funky green two-bedroom house with the finished full basement, mid-sized kitchen with dining room and standard-sized bathroom is more than likely in desperate need of a tree maintenance facelift. But it's home.

Standing on the porch, finally no longer perspiring like a petrified pig, I fish out my keys, peering through the glass window door that's camouflaged with a white fleece privacy curtain. I enter the quiet, petite, very clean and orderly dwelling, close the door, set the bag down on the stained pine, smoked-glass coffee table in the living room, take off my hat, place it smoothly on the six foot tall, dark gray antique coat and hat rack behind the front door, along with my Dallas Cowboy's jacket. I grab my cigarettes out of my cook's uniform, finally sit down on my comfy burgundy couch. I try to slip off my left black, food-ridden, low-quarter work boot with my opposite foot while leaning on the coffee table, ultimately convincing myself I must physically untie my shoes, like my father's unconventional wisdom once taught me. Tammy's scuffling walks from the master bedroom just down the hallway on the left hand side breaks the silence. She cruises slowly, slippers singing against the stained hardwood floors, slides into the living room with a gorgeous smile on her face, wearing deliciously tight jeans, a cute white tank top, fuzzy pink slippers, and a cigarette between the skinny, lengthy index and middle fingers of her right hand. She walks up between the coffee table and cozy couch, leans over, matter-of-factly opens the brown bag and then flicks her cigarette ash in a large gold, glass ashtray on the coffee table. Then shifting, still bent over, Tammy sweetly lays a welcome-home kiss on my mouth. I instinctively return it, French-tonguing her back, being a little overzealous, wanting to joke by sliding my tongue up her nose, which she is definitely not expecting every time I do it.

"Hi, baby," Tammy says, backpedaling from our embrace.

"Hi, baby," I respond passionately, in an upbeat tone. "You know, baby, I could have easily slipped my tongue right up your nose," I say, grinning as I sit there, wet yet somewhat dry, stuck on the couch, looking at the mahogany, nineteen-inch console color television, situated at eleven o' clock to the often-used fireplace with gold-trimmed spark shield, which is flanked by an upright floor lamp. The pictures along the entire wall straddle the exquisite built-in cabinets with glass doors.

"Baby, that is so gross!" she says as she darts away, headed toward the bedroom. Seconds later, returning slippers squeaking their orchestra music to my ears, she re-enters the living room, drags on her cigarette, and finally crushes it out hurriedly in the large ashtray. "You smell like a stinky-ass onion factory! You do know that, don't you, baby?" Tammy says with a taste of attitude, walking toward me but still keeping her distance.

"Yes, thank you, dear. I know I stink, baby," I reply, hardly looking up. "That's why I'm getting in the shower right about now." I reach into my back pocket and pull out my wallet, which annexes her attention, and relinquish my putrid money for household expenses to Tammy, completing ninety percent of my tasks for the day, leaving only a thorough bathing of the body to assassinate my bio-labor of funk.

"Thank you, baby," she says as she kisses me lightly on the left check with no hesitation. I stand up, quickly strip down to my birthday suit, unaware my member is now hanging proudly, free of the white trousers, arousing Tammy's Na Nu.

Now, more than ever, the very ripe stench is violating my own air space. I bend down, forcefully snatching up my rancid white cook's uniform off the freshly polished hardwood floor. As I walk nakedly down the hallway on my way to the bathroom, I shoot my work clothes, scoring a three-pointer in one of those white wickerwork hampers, entering the facility proper, running the shower till hot, then step into that wonderful warm. Our shower has an acoustically excellent sound and serves as a spectacular auditorium where I am free to unleash my soapy symphony:

Ain't no sunshine when she's gone, only darkness every day. Ain't no sunshine when she gone, and she's always gone too long, anytime she goes away.

I shave and brush my teeth, reassuring myself after smelling both armpits, again one by one, just to make double sure it's not embedded in my skin. No more onion smell on me.

After cleaning whatever mess I may have made in the bathroom, I make my way to the bedroom, trailing slightly wet footprints in the hallway. Opening the upright reddish-mahogany dresser, I scrape up fresh new socks, underwear, a new pair of jeans, and a shirt from the closet on the opposite side of the bedroom. I triumphantly finish getting dressed, grab my wallet, glance in the mirror attached to the wooden dresser, inspection complete, load my pockets with Vick's Cough Drops, a blue lighter, and wait for Tammy to make her powder move so we can enjoy a nice Friday night. I steal a moment to relax, sitting down on the warm waterbed, collecting my thoughts as my pant leg rubs against the king-sized, stained-wood frame. Tammy thoughtfully enters the bedroom, two tall chimney glasses of a chilling mixture of gin and grapefruit juice in her hands, sporting this obvious, puzzled look of dismay written all over her attractive, freckly face. "Here you go, baby," she says, handing me one of her exclusive concoctions.

"Thank you, sweetheart," I politely reply, overlooking the very apparent warning signs, unaware of how intoxicated Tammy is, staring me up north and down south, as if I was casually overdressed for a barbecue.

"Where do you think you are going?" Tammy asks, visibly agitated. I swallow the liquor, consuming almost the entire strong chimney drink.

"Excuse me? It's Friday. What is wrong with you, honey?" I ask, setting my drink down on the mahogany nightstand. I tell her, "We're going over to my parents' house. Robert is barbecuing some ribs. You knew that, sweetheart."

"No, I don't remember!" Tammy says, with an attitude straight out of Hell.

"Well, are you coming with me or not?" I ask, wondering why it always comes to this.

"I was not invited. Besides, it's your family," Tammy replies, looking at me with that *I'm not going anywhere. I have more important things to do* look.

"Okay, Tammy. Then I am going to go ahead and walk on down there. You change your mind, come on down, then. Okay? All right?" I say, attempting to establish some kind of understanding. Ninety-five percent of what I said I was going to accomplish today manifested into an absolute positive only to be ruined by the insecurities running our lives. In no hurry at all and stopping just long enough to finish my drink, I walk the glass into the long, clean, yellow kitchen with tan paneling on the walls, black-and-white large-checkered floor, where a white middle-aged refrigerator sits on one corner, and directly across the room, a matching white oven sits in the other. I wash the glass in the old school double sink, dry it, and put it on a shelf in the overhead wall cabinet. I walk back through the white swinging doors that separate the kitchen from the living room. Tammy sets her drink down abruptly on the coffee table, lights a cigarette and places her hands on her hips. I kiss Tammy gently on the lips, grab my black Members Only windbreaker and Dallas Cowboys' hat off the rack while Tammy is standing right behind me, as if she is just going to lock the door, since her son is spending the night with grandmother. As I placed my hand on the doorknob, opening the door to exit— POW! Technical knockout! Consequently, everything in this galaxy goes completely blank, stuck in utter unconscious limbo, Sir Blackout, that you just don't see coming. When I finally regain consciousness, not at all sure who I was on the planet that's spun me around for a neon second, a recollection kicks in. I did not know, nor did I remember how I ended up laid out—very well, I must say—on this ice-cold concrete porch, glaring up at the porch light, while a lump is perturbing, rapidly throbbing out of the top of my cranium. Tammy is no longer a lady; this primitive bitch is CRAZY! She has lost her ever-loving crazy mind! Turns out that *POW!* was Tammy hitting me in the head with a black-and-red telephone receiver made of super hard plastic. You know, the ones that were given out as gifts with a yearly Time Magazine subscription. Unfortunately, I supported that ideal subscription, knocking me unconsciously the hell out, leaving me traveling in the valley of danger, switch off a deep blank.

My legs will not respond to the emergency red alert system command to run away. Truthfully, I've technically been knocked the hell out. And, not to be a sexist, but being knocked out by a woman does nothing for a man's ego. The ability to flee in case of an emergency is a highly underrated gift. Rarely, in times like these, do you want to take it for granted. "Tammy! What in the name of all hell you do that for?" I shout, attempting to drag myself down the first flight of gray-painted concrete steps. "What the hell did I do to you?" I ask her, dizzy, everything quite hazy, not blinking or taking my eyes off of her, scared like she's the Witch Doctor of Pain. I realize I am in no position to sustain another assault, which could be deadly. Hell, I'm barely surviving the first attack. Tammy could have easily killed me. "You are going to see some white bitch!" Tammy yells loudly while walking down the porch steps with one hand on her hip and the other behind her back. I'm hoping that phone is not still in her possession, because my motor skills have all but left the building. In other words, she is in close proximity to assaulting me once again, leaving me exceptionally helpless in the company of Psycho Woman, who is straight out of Beat Down, USA. "You are not going over to your mother's house, Eddie! And if you dare leave, I'm burning up all your clothes in the fireplace, including the ones you've never ever wore before!" Tammy promises, still standing closely, her adrenalin pumping. I'm anticipating her striking again as I attempt to stand, still somewhat scatterbrained from the amount of pain I've sustained, but I'm on my feet. Tammy instinctively steps back.

"You are crazy as Hell," I say, walking away, grabbing the black railing, going down the final steps, head throbbing. "We are *done*, you dysfunctional idiot!" I shout at her very loudly. "I have never, ever cheated on you, or anybody else, sucker!" I proudly state, as Tammy turns and walks back into the house, revealing the phone receiver she's still carrying in her hand, which tells me she considered assaulting me again. I gently touch the lump on my head. Ouch!

"Don't plan on getting your clothes back! They are as good as burned up, punk!" Tammy shouts, slamming the door horribly loud, causing the big picture window in the front of the house to tremble, almost causing the three-eighths-inch-thick glass to shatter. My new, throbbing lump weighs heavy on my head as I semi-stumble down the avenue toward my parents' house to get first aid and barbeque. It's definitely over, and I got knocked the hell out! For an imagined sex crime I did not commit! Man, I sure can pick those grapefruits. They are so much more likely to knock you the bizarre hell out!

2

• • • • • • • • • • • • • • • • • •

One Booty Two?

Tragically dazed, stumbling north on Peninsula Avenue as the evening swallow's daylight, every step I take echoes in my lump, throbbing to the point where it's really nerve-wracking, attempting to make it to my folks' house without blacking out again, when out of nowhere there's music to my ears. I hear a sexy female voice yell, "Hey, cutie!" at me, as if she knows me like a long-lost friend from way back when. Another time, another place, not really concerned, ignoring the greeting, thinking she's not talking to me anyway. Out of curiosity I turn slowly, staring in the direction where the voice is coming from, noticing an attractive, free-thinking young Caucasian lady sitting on the front porch of this light-grayish little cottage of a house almost directly across the street from my Uncle Harry and Aunt Virginia's house. "Yes, I am definitely talking to you, baby," she says forcefully. "What up?"

As I carefully cross the street, I get a better view because of the light from the setting sun Wow! She's a cutie: heavy-breasted woman with long brown hair, solid athletic body, obviously looking quite like a comfortable, relaxed soul in her short jean pants and a white T-shirt. Now this is more like it! Tammy said I was going to meet a white bitch! *Now, I don't want to make Tammy a liar*, thinking crazy to myself as I move up the walkway, saying to the owner of the voice, "I was in a hurry because I need to sit down. I am very unsteady. I'm not well!"

I confessed. "I just broke up with this crazy girl who just knocked me the hell out!"

The lady starts smiling, trying hard not to laugh at me, putting her hand over her mouth, trying to stop herself from looking at the top of my traumatized cranium. "Well, sweetie, come here and sit down with me. I won't bite you. Unless you want me to," she replies, friendly, smiling very boldly with no shame in her game whatsoever. As I slowly sit down next to the lady whose look says, *Damn! That's a huge lump!* written all over her youthful face, she says, "My name is Dawn," putting her hand out to shake mine, staring into my eyes.

"My name is Eddie Dee Williams. Nice to make your acquaintance," I say, shaking her hand, smiling into her eyes as well, holding her soft hand and hoping she's not jailbait. Dawn's flirtatious brown eyes inspect me from my inseam all the way up to the lump on my head as I retrieve my hand slowly, a million scenarios invading my mind. "You must have just moved here. Correct?" I ask, knowing what the answer would be.

"Yes, we just moved here," Dawn replies. "And just exactly how did you know that?" she asks. I explain to her that I grew up in this neighborhood just two blocks around the corner.

"My aunt and uncle live right across the street in that OD, green house directly in front of us. Your neighbor Top is my stepfather's drinking and domino playing friend. His wife Wanda and I attended Jefferson High School together. Also, two houses down on this side of the street in that blue ranch-style house is where my Cousin Junior and his wife Joyce and their two sons live. But enough about me and my family. You are fine as wine and just as intelligent. But the question still remains: before I can get to know you better, I need to know something very personal about you, and I don't want to anger you in any sense of the word."

"And what might that be?" Dawn asks, looking as if I have lost my mind.

"Can you vote?" I ask, sincerely serious, while Dawn gives me this look like I am mentally detached and should seek medical attention quick, fast, and in a hurry.

"Let me get this straight," Dawn says. "You are actually asking me if I can vote? Are you fucking crazy?" she asks me, slightly pissed off and no longer being sexy hot.

"No. I am just not well, that's all!" I respond with a smirk on my face.

"Well, nobody has ever asked me a question like that," Dawn replies.

"That's because there is nobody quite like me," I commented.

"If this is your way of saying you want nothing to do with me, then just say so!" She instantly assumes the worst with an attitude.

"No, I am just asking a simple question," I state nicely. Turns out Dawn didn't register to vote when she was 18, just three years ago. But I didn't really care; I just wanted to find out if she was legal.

"Why didn't you just ask me my age?" she says.

"I was trying to give you a compliment, actually," I say, reaching in my pocket, pulling out my cigarettes and giving one to her.

"Please, baby, call me Dee," she says, now that we are friends.

"Now tell me, Dee, where are you from? You are way too damn cool and too laid back to be from around here," I ask.

"Well, actually I'm from the coast. Have you heard of Seaside?" Dee asks.

I nod yes. "So why did you move up here?" I ask.

"Well, my roommate just split up with her husband and now she's renting this house," Dawns says. She tells me that I would get along well with her roommate, Sherri, and that she'll be back from Seaside the next day. "I would love to live at the beach," I voluntarily confess.

"No, you wouldn't. For a while maybe, depending on how they treat you," Dawn responds.

"Oh, you mean me being mocha chocolate?" I say as I flick my cigarette.

"Yes, just you being black," she says.

"I have always been someone who gets along well with practically anybody. To me racism is an ignorant, fundamental fear-mongering tool. It infiltrates the human race causing divisiveness, destroying trust, and perpetuating cultural stereotypes," I tell her.

"I like the way you think. So, what's up? What do you plan on doing tonight?" Dawn asks, appearing shameless bold, flirting as if she is the ultimate Friday Night Delight.

"Well, I'm going over to my parents to visit, get something to eat, and put some ice on my head. But I also wanted to know what's on your mind for tonight," I ask.

"Come back over later and find out. Besides, you've got to meet Sherri," Dawn says, short and sweet.

"What's with this Sherri? What exactly is she like?" I ask.

"Just come back over after you leave your folks'. We can keep each other company until Sherri gets here," she says. I tell her I'll be back in an hour with beer and cigarettes. "It doesn't matter how late, baby!" she yells to me as I cross the street, headed to my parents' house.

It's quite dark now, so I'm pretty sure Pops is done barbecuing the ribs, or close to it. But I'm concerned about my suits, ties, jeans, sweaters, underwear, shirts, shoes, tuxedo, and leather leisure suits, not to mention my cook's uniforms that I had purchased not very long ago. I'm sure Tammy has carried out her promise by now. I'm not looking forward to Pops and his friends talking to me about how I'm messing with crazy-ass women. I enter the beautiful, manicured green yard and walk up the incline to the backyard, floodlights illuminating the entire area, smoke still coming fuming from the grill. I can also hear people talking over the music and playing dominoes. This is my family on a Friday evening. They work hard, and believe me, they play hard. I see Popeye, Bub, and Mr. Slim from next door, sitting at the picnic table, drinking and playing dominos. Pops is at the grill in a plaid shirt and jeans with his back to me, a fork in one hand and a drink in the other. Like me, my stepfather loves people, a real Libra who has comical mannerisms, loves to drink, loves to barbecue, loves my mother, loves to socialize, and loves loud-ass music, whether it is day or night. "Hey! Look who finally decided to show up! Robert, your son is here!" says Popeye.

"What's going on Mr. Slim? Popeye, Pops?" I say, walking up to the table, shaking hands with the fellas. "Bub, good to see you," I say. Bub just smiles with his hands together as if he were praying to his drink. As I walk over to my stepdad at the grill, he turns toward me, frowning from the smoke in his eyes. "Hey, son, I was getting a little worried about you. I figured you were going to be here a long time ago and give me a hand," Pops says.

"I know Pops, but Tammy hit me in the head and knocked me the hell out," I explain. Bub, Slim, and Popeye immediately start laughing. But my stepfather doesn't find it amusing. At all.

"Did you just say that girl, that redbone you live with, knocked you the hell out, son?" he asks, excitedly. "Is that what you are telling me?" Pops asks, finding it hard to swallow. And that's when my mother walks out of the back door from the kitchen ready to add her commentary to the table.

"What did you do to make her do something like that to you?" my mother asks, standing on the porch with her hands on her hips. She steps down off the porch and walks toward me, ready to hear my explanation about what happened.

"You need to bring your ass home, son, save some money, and stay away from crazy-ass women before one of them kill you son," Pops says. "If you don't believe me about crazy-ass women, go ask them old-school veterans over there and see if I'm lying," Pops says proudly, sipping his drink while continuing his barbecuing.

"Say, Eddie, you want a drink? Get you a glass and get me glass with some ice, please," Slim requests. Mr. Evans—Slim, we call him— is our next-door neighbor: six feet tall, butterscotch complexioned senior citizen, set in his ways, lives with his wife Eva, and has known my family for years. My sister Nuffy calls him Dumbo because he has the largest ears we've ever seen.

"Let me see your lump, lumpy," Popeye says, grinning from ear to ear. After my stepfather's partner examines the lump on my head, the jokes continue. "She knocked the hell out of you, boy! She was trying to take you out!" Popeye says. Popeye is my stepfather's friend. His real name is Charles. He's five foot eight, medium build, mocha-chocolate, big bright eyes, quite the practical joker. His daughter Charlene and my brother Keith have two children together. And then there's Bub, whose name is also Robert Sr., my best friend's father. Bub is a five-foot-seven, mocha-chocolate, big fat nosed, short afro, medium-built, very sensitive dispositioned, non-violent machinist who wears jean overalls all the time, never raises his voice unless he's laughing and crying simultaneously—one of my stepdad's dedicated, closest drinking and fishing buddies. "Well, Eddie, we have all messed with a crazy woman at one time or another, but none of us got knocked the hell out with a damn phone!" Popeye says. The guys started laughing all over again.

"But, Eddie, answer me this, why did she say she hit you?" Bub asks, holding his drink, eyes getting very big from hearing the outrage of a beat down by the opposite sex.

"Tammy swore up and down I was going to see some white girl," I reply.

"What white girl? I've never seen you with a white girl," Popeye asks, curiously excited.

"Neither have I, come to think about it," Bub says.

"Eddie, you messing around with some white girl?" Slim asks. Feeling like I am on trial, I tell them I have never cheated, especially after what Lisa did to me while I was stationed in Germany. "Ironically, on my way walking down here, I met this Caucasian girl named Dawn. That is where I have been for the last hour or so," I say calmly.

"See?" Popeye yells. "She knew that you were going to meet this so-called white girl today!" Everybody in the yard starts laughing. Even my Pops started laughing.

"Now, son," my stepfather says, "are you talking about them white girls that stay next door to Top?"

"Yes, Pop, those be the ones, and I am going back over there tonight," I tell him.

"Son, you should move back home," he advises me.

"No thanks, Pops, I will be just fine," I reply, ignoring the constant throbbing of my bump.

"Well, at least take a plate with you," Pops replies.

Before I leave, I do take a plate with me, and some beer. I head into the house to say goodbye to my mother, but I grab the phone off the wall and dial Tammy's number. The phone rings and before I can say anything, she starts yelling insanely at the top of her lungs, "I burned up all of your clothes in the fireplace! You have no more clothes here!" Then click. I just sit down in the living room with my head down, frustrated, trying hard not to get mad, and thinking how to get even. Then I finally realize: I'm single, it's Friday, I'm not broke, and I have a date down the street. Also, I get to meet this girl Sherri tomorrow. I go outside to the backyard and announce to everyone that I am leaving. Even though I got knocked the hell out, even though Tammy burned up all my clothes, and even though I have a lump on the top of my head from a dysfunctional relationship, life will go on. But now I have another dilemma. I am not, and never will be, a player in any sense of the word, but I have some choices in front of me. So, should I take my time and wait to meet this Sherri tomorrow? Or should I just go ahead and have stress-releasing mega-sex with Dawn tonight? As I walk up the steps to Sherri and Dawn's house, I come to the conclusion that after what has ironically occurred today, I should just go with the flow while no longer roleplaying the victim of these atomically shitty circumstances. I knock on the door, glancing back at my shadow, waiting for an answer.

"Who is it?" Dawn asks.

"Who do you want it to be?" I ask back, ignoring the shooting pain in the center of my head. She opens the door smiling. Her large breasts are practically falling out of her tight lingerie. I walk into this very small house with a very small kitchen, dining room, and living room.

Dawn immediately closes the door and offers me a seat. "Make yourself comfortable," she says to me.

"I wish I could, but I just met you," I say, sitting down on the grayish couch.

"You can really get as comfortable as you want to," Dawn says.

"You don't want me to really get comfortable, because comfortable to me is being naked," I say proudly.

"I dare you to do it!" Dawn challenges me. Setting the brown bag down on the end table, I voluntary strip down, being careful not to hit my lump with my shirt. I sit back down on the couch and Dawn starts to giggle when I open the brown bag to pull out the food and beer.

"What is so funny?" I ask.

"It looks like you have a little penis sticking out of your head," she says humorously, as I open my beer, taking a good swig while she continues to laugh.

"Go right ahead. That's it, get it out of your system," I say as I set my beer down on the coffee table. "She also burned up all of my clothes!" I confess.

"Are you serious?" Dawn asks, in shock.

"With the money I have left from my paycheck, I will have to start all over and purchase some more clothes," I tell her.

I guess anybody can get more clothes. However, another brain is priceless, and that's a different story. I pull two cigarettes out of the pack, light them both with a flick of my Bic, and, gentleman-like, hand over one to Dawn. "You have nice, big, chocolate full lips," Dawn says in a sexy voice. "I'm sure you have heard that line before, haven't you?" Now she's rubbing her hand against my chocolate, skinny leg, and I'm anticipating how long before she grabs me.

"Yes, I have heard that expression a few times," I reply.

"But the question still remains: Do you know what to do with them?" Dawn asks, as she moves her hand toward the south of me.

"So, let me get this straight. You are going to allow me go up in you, and then you are going to hook me up with your roommate tomorrow?" I ask.

"Yes. That is absolutely right," she says, flicking white ashes in the ashtray. Apparently, Dawn is going to find out if I'm a good lay so she can let Sherri know.

"What makes you think she would even want somebody like me?" I ask.

"Simple. You are exactly what she is looking for." Then Dawn goes down my list of desirable attributes. "You are cute, funny, intelligent, you work, and you are not some kind of pimp or player."

"By the way, Dee, how old is Sherri?" I ask. It turns out Sherri is also twenty and went to high school with Dawn in Seaside. I then break the news that I am more than ten years older than the both of them. Of course, Dawn doesn't believe me, so I show her my Oregon ID to prove it. "Listen up really good, sweetie. I really like you, but we will never be," Dee says. "Not because of you. It's simply because I'm gay. I am very much into women. Okay?"

"That just makes two of us now, don't it?" I say humorously as she stands up, bends over to put out her cigarette. Then she starts to walk away from me. "So, are you coming to bed?" Dee asks softly. This has been quite the day; I paid the rent where I am not welcome. I was assaulted by a phone and knocked the hell out, and on top of all that, my entire wardrobe went up in smoke. Fun Fridays always seem to bring out the best in me, for some strange reason. Hours later, after Dee and I have had sex, as she lies next to me half asleep, she informs that she plans to share me with Sherri. So much for the so-called test drive.

The next morning, I wake up in the bedroom to the sound of two women and a little child. I glance out of the only window in the room. There's typical Portland weather, an overcast of clouds, minus the rain. I look up at the ceiling with its white-spackled accents and notice that the light hanging there is looking old, out of style, and about to detach. I move my hand to the top of my head gently to feel if the lump is shrinking. But it's not, and it still hurts quite a bit. I know I am going to have to wear a hat for a while. I lay in bed, trying very hard to eavesdrop on their conversation. I am convinced they are talking about me, however I can't quite hear exactly what they are saying.

First things first. I get up and have Dawn bring me my clothes out of the living room to officially meet this new Special Somebody. Rubbing sleep from out of my eyes, calling to Dawn in a sort of loud tone, her opening the door, barely peeking she catches me off guard, and realizes I'm freezing in my nakedness. "Good morning, Chocolate Fantastic," Dawn says with an awkward smile.

"Could you grab my clothes, please?" I say, planting both feet on the cold, hardwood floor.

"Since you are so comfy, why don't get them yourself, Mr. Man? I dare you!" she says enticingly, as if I don't have the buck naked nerve to do it once again. Opening the door wider, Dawn eggs me on to make this wild first impression. I quickly stand to my feet, walk out of the room into the hallway, turn to my immediate left, and there she stands in the hallway, not at all happy to see me. "Good morning," I say—skinny, proud, and naked. Immediately my eyes latch onto this unfamiliar woman. She has long, dark-brown hair, green cat-eyes, thick eyebrows, cute nose, medium brick house build with a T-shirt on, thin waist, perfect chest, nice, round, deluxe ass fitting excellently in her black spandex pants, barefooted with painted pretty ruby-red toes. In other words, a triumph of gorgeous packaging. She's holding a little boy on her hip who looks like he could be her son. She just stares at me like I had just let out some bad flatulence and consumed all the oxygen in the room.

"Eddie, this is Sherri and her son, Jeremy. Sherri, this is Eddie," Dawn says.

"So, you are the one who kept us awake all night," Sherri says disapprovingly. "What do you plan on doing with that little thing?" Sherri says, glaring at my penis, then going into the next room, slamming the door, acting out some major attitude. Moving through the very chilly air, I glide over to my clothes, waste no time in putting them on as Dawn enters the bedroom, closes the door as I finished getting dressed, not at all embarrassed about what took place, not even the lump on the top of my head!

Minutes later, Dawn, followed by Sherri and her young son on her hip, exit the bedroom as if they had had a come-to-church conversation that just resulted in a consensus. With Sherri's eyes glaring seriously, but her body language saying something entirely different, Jeremy smiles eagerly at me, so I give him my full attention by stepping up closer, face-to-face near Sherri. Then I bend slightly forward and oblige Jeremy with my Donald Duck impersonation, which instantly tickles Jeremy all the way to Giggle City. "He likes you, Eddie," Dawn mentions, hooking up me up with double bonus points.

"Where is your bathroom?" I ask, looking down the hallway, really having to urinate; all of that beer just can't wait. My bladder's screaming, "Release the Liquids!"

"The second door on the right hand side," Sherri replies. As I walk away, smiling, Jeremy doesn't take his eyes off of me. I walk down a very short hallway into the bathroom, shutting the door anxiously. I lift the toilet seat and handle my business while scanning the entire bathroom for toothpaste. After wiping my hands on the towel hanging on the rack, I curiously open the medicine cabinet hoping for toothpaste and behold a tube that has been squeezed to the limit, which I manage to get just enough out of to kill my Devil's Breath. I return from the restroom relieved as I tippy-toe down the hall where Jeremy is watching me, giggling, ready to be entertained. Sherri smiles along with Jeremy as I sing "Under The Sea" from Disney's animated classic, *The Little Mermaid.*

"You are full of surprises. aren't you?" Dawn says, pouring it on real thick.

"You haven't seen anything yet," I answer, daring her to give the wrong response.

"What is that supposed to mean?" Sherri asks, staring into my eyes as I start singing the one song she would never expect me to sing right out of the blue:

My Cherie amour. lovely as a summer day. My Cherie amour, distant as the Milky Way. My Cherie amour, pretty little one that I adore, you're the only girl my heart beats for, how I wish that you were mine.

"What is your name again?" Sherri asks, smiling at me sensually. Now that she's no longer being standoffish, she's someone I want to get to know better.

"It's Eddie Dee Williams," I respond, making faces at Jeremy while he giggles.

"Well, Eddie Dee, what's the story with that big-ass old lump on your head? It looks like a hard cock sticking out of it!" Sherri comments, while staring at it. Dawn busts out laughing. This'll be the third time I tell that story in just a matter of hours. "After he paid all the bills, he was knocked the fuck out by his woman because she insecurely assumed he was going to see a white bitch and burned up all his clothes! How damn insecure is that?" Dawn says, making a relevant point.

"But right now, I have got to go and do some shopping, and figure out exactly what my next move is," I say smoothly.

"Would you like something to eat?" Dawn asks.

"No. Thank you, though," I reply.

"What are you doing later?" Sherri asks with a smile.

"I'm not sure yet. But I was hoping that we will get to know each other better, if that is a possibility," I say, while making faces as Jeremy laughs.

"You really like kids, don't you?" Dawn asks.

"Yes, I do. I seem to recall I used to be one, once upon a time," I answer, waiting for a reply that doesn't come. "So, Sherri, when would you like to get together?" I ask very abruptly.

"Well, how about tomorrow morning, say around nine?" Sherri replies.

3

· · · · · · · · · · · · · · · · · · ·

Kinfolks

"Sounds good!" I reply, grinning. So, just before I open the door to leave, I wave bye to Jeremy and hug Dawn goodbye. I close the door, thinking, wondering if Dawn is right about me and Sherri. Once outside, I realize I need some clothes and toiletries. I have maybe a hundred dollars left out of my check, if that much. I change my mind about wanting to count it once I realize it's only about ninety-six bucks! Now, my cousin Junior, who lives only two houses down, works graveyard at Boeing and I'm pretty sure he's at home, being that it is almost noon. As I walk down the steps from the house onto the sidewalk, I can't help but notice a car in their driveway on the left side of the house; a dookey-brown, could-use-a-wash Datsun B210 with Washington plates, in good shape, meat on the tires, with a shiny object hanging on the rearview mirror. Now I am walking by Top's house, but it doesn't seem like anybody is at home. His truck is gone, but his blue Cadillac Coupe Deville with the two-inch white walls on the chrome wheels is definitely in his driveway. This means he's probably out scraping metal. Now, Junior's light-blue, late-model, ranch-style house with the really nice white trim sits up high on a hill, so walking up the inclined driveway is a workout in itself. His car is here. Now, the question is, is he up yet?

I walk up the steps onto the porch and ring the doorbell with one finger. Cousin Joyce, Junior's wife, opens the door. She's five foot five, peanut butter complexioned, wearing glasses, a comfortable gray sweatshirt, jeans, and white slippers. Very attractive and nice! "Hey, cousin, is Junior home?" I ask.

"Hi, Eddie, he's here, come on in," says Joyce. I walk in and ease the screen door shut, making sure it does not slam. I don't bother to shut the front door and I stop just inside and stand there, admiring all the photographs of my family on the walls. Joyce immediately walks into the dining area and alerts Junior. "Junior, your cousin Eddie is here! How are you doing, Eddie?" Joyce asks, and I answer, "I will tell both of you at the same time." Seconds later, Junior walks into the living room. Junior is two years older than me, five foot nine, mocha chocolate complexioned, medium afro, medium build, good-looking— we could very easily pass for brothers!

"What up?" Junior says. As we shake hands, Junior blurts out, "Eddie! What the hell happen to your damn head?"

I lean over and show it to Joyce. "Tammy knocked me out," I reply. Junior immediately starts laughing.

"That is not funny, Junior!" Joyce insists.

"Yes the hell it is!" Junior replies, continuing to laugh.

"It is kind of big, Eddie," Joyce says sadly. Junior starts laughing even harder as he walks back over to sit on the couch. "Eddie," Joyce says, "I know it's early, but would you like a drink?"

"Yes, thank you," I answer as I take a seat on the couch. Joyce exits the living room. Junior is in tears laughing, sitting on the other end of the L-shaped couch.

"Go ahead, that's right, get it out of your system!" I say, since Junior cannot stop laughing. Joyce enters the living room holding large glasses of mixed drinks with both hands. She hands me one of the drinks, I tell her "Thank you" as she walks around the coffee table and hands the other drink to Junior, who is still laughing so hard he can't hold the glass, so she sits it down on the coffee table right in front of him. He can't stop laughing.

"How did you do that?" she asks, looking directly at her husband, who's laughing like he's crazy.

"Tammy burned up all my clothes in her fireplace!" I reply loudly. Instantly, Junior snaps out of it. Joyce takes a seat next to Junior with a dismayed, unhappy look on her face. "She did what?" Junior asks, looking concerned. He is finally able to pick up his drink and takes a good swallow. "I just gave you a leather coat!" Junior says.

"She burned that up, too," I reply.

"We just went shopping two weeks ago and you bought some more clothes!" Junior says.

"Gone," I reply, waving bye-bye with my hand. I quickly explain the entire situation. "Damn! That's messed up!" Junior says, shaking his head.

"And now for the good news," I say, followed by a sip of my gin and juice before setting it on a coaster on the coffee table. "I will most likely be your neighbor, cousin!" I tell him.

"Yeah, right! How you going to pull that off?" Junior asks.

"You know those two white girls who just moved in a couple of houses down the street on the same side as you?" I ask.

"Yeah, I know!" he says, surprised, "We met them."

Joyce immediately turns her head, looking directly at Junior. "What do you mean 'we'?" Joyce asks, looking puzzled.

"Well, I meant I met them. Top introduced them to me. Joyce has seen them," Junior says, looking guilty.

"Yeah. And I better not see *you* messing with them, Mr. Russell!" Cousin Joyce intones with an air of finality. "

Well, anyway, I got the cute one with the thick ass," I state boastfully. "The other one, the tomboy-looking one, she is not interested in men," I add truthfully.

Just then, my two very active little cousins, Alvin Jr. and Anthony, run through the living room. I say hi as they run back out of the living room, giggling and playing. Joyce gets up and goes after them. "So, what are you going to do about Tammy?" Junior asks, smiling, ready to begin laughing again.

"Stay the hell away from her!" I quickly reply. "And that is exactly what I am going to do! Bam! I am done with her," I add. "By the way, did you know the new neighbors are from Seaside, Oregon?" I ask, somewhat boastfully.

"I did not know that," Junior says. "Why? Is you thinking of moving to the beach?", he asks jokingly.

"No, but I always wanted to live at the beach!" I add. "Say, Junior, I need to go buy some more clothes, Cousin. Perhaps you could take me up to the swap meet," I ask, "or, just maybe take me to Freddie's?"

"Sure, Eddie, not a problem," Junior replies. Cousin Joyce enters the room and lets us know that breakfast is on the table in the dining room. I guzzle my drink, gasping for air as I swallow the very sour, very strong drink, and put the glass down. I stand up and announce to Junior that I'm going to wash my hands. Junior nods his head as he attempts to guzzle his drink as well. I proceed to the bathroom, which is the first door down the hallway. The bathroom is open, but I knock first anyway, ensuring that nobody is occupying the facilities. As I enter, I'm trying to remember which wall the light switch is on. Lucky for me it's on the first wall I decide to check. I close the door, handle my business, put the seat back down, flush the toilet, wash my hands with soap and water, and dry my hands with a towel. I open the door and turn the light off as I exit the restroom. A beautiful baby chandelier hangs directly above the middle of the table, while Junior is sitting at the head of the table drinking orange juice. To Junior's immediate right is a complete place setting and a large glass of orange juice with my name all over it! I quickly sit down, close my eyes, and say this blessing: "Lord, bless this food which we are about to receive, for the nourishment of our bodies. These things we ask in Jesus's name," and we both finish by saying, "Amen!" Then Junior and I partake and devour a scrumptious breakfast fit for a king.

"This is exactly what I needed," I announce. With a glass of orange juice in one hand and a piece of bacon in the other, I say, "Thank you, Cousin Joyce," loudly, so she will hear me in the kitchen. "You welcome, Eddie," Joyce replies.

"Did you watch the Blazer game?" Junior asks me.

"No," I reply. "Did they win?"

"Yes, they won," Junior replies.

"We should be winning!" I exclaim. "We traded that Sam no-playing-ass Bowie for Buck Williams, which was a very good move. I mean, we are already sick in the noggin for trading Michael Jordan to Chicago! Who in their right mind would do such a thing? Joyce enters the room and collects the plates. "Get enough to eat?" she asks.

"Yes, I did, thank you very much," I say again. "Now I need to get some clothes and some toiletries," I gracefully hint in front of Joyce, so Junior will have no problem taking me, even though we have been known to stay out a long time when we two get together. Junior lights a cigarette, stands up, and says, "C'mon, let's ride." I rise from my seat without hesitation.

I reach in my pocket for my cigarettes, pull one out, and light it as I walk through the living room and out the front doorway, making sure it's lit before going out in the open air. Then I put my cigarettes and lighter back in my pocket as I open the screen door and exit the house, blowing nicotine into the atmosphere. I walk down the porch steps toward Junior's car in the driveway. As I walk toward the black car, it just so happens I can see Jeremy on a bike two houses down, and Sherri bent over, pushing him. Even at a distance, I can observe that ripe behind of hers in front of me, looking like she's doing it on purpose, in her tight, black-ass spandexes, bending over. Then she looks over at me, waves, and does it again as I wave back, watching her as I smoke my cigarette. By this time, Junior has walked up beside me and sees the same thing. I have just now come to the conclusion that I am smitten. "You been with that?" Junior asks, referring to Sherri bending over.

"That is the future!" I say, smiling at her eagerly. Junior takes out his keys, unlocks the black car door, grabs the handle, and opens the door while smoking his cigarette with no hands. I walk around to the passenger side and wave once more to her, and smile. I turn around, open the car door, and sit down in the passenger seat. Meanwhile, Junior is getting his eyes full of Sherri's rear and starts to laugh. "Eddie, how old is she?" Junior asks while he's getting in the driver's seat.

"She's just twenty," I answer proudly.

"She is going to wear your little ass out," Junior says, shutting the driver side door. Both of us are looking in her direction, admiring her sexy silhouette as she proudly bends over again, clearly loving the attention her rear is getting.

"Yeah. She just might do that," I happily confess.

Junior starts the car. I push the electric window button on the door panel to make the window come down smoothly so I can flick my cigarette ashes out the window and to let fresh air push out the stale. I can't help but stare at Sherri. Junior puts the car in reverse and twists around in his seat to look out the rear window. We back down the steeply inclined driveway into the street and proceed north like we are headed to Vancouver, Washington.

"Yeah. She likes you," Junior insists.

"I hope so," I say. "When I first met her, she looked at me like I pissed on her cat!"

"So, what did you do?" asks Junior.

"Let's just say I made a long, lasting impression on her. I was just being me, that's all," I say. Now we're headed down the hill to Columbia Boulevard. Junior stops at a traffic light, flips on his turn signal, makes a right, then, finally, he turns on some music. We go approximately two miles, turn left on Vancouver Avenue, and we wind up at the swap meet. We park in the lot directly in front of the huge building.

"Well, isn't that special?" I say, being sarcastic and slightly pissed off. "Junior, weren't we here just a couple of weeks ago?" I ask.

"Yes, we were," answers Junior. I butt out my smoke in the ashtray, grab the car door handle, open it, and exit the car. Junior gets out after leaving his still-burning cigarette in the ashtray. "There is hardly anybody here," I say, looking over the empty parking lot, "But that's a good thing! This won't take long," I tell Junior.

"I don't doubt that," he answers. I pull one of the double doors open. Junior enters, and I follow. It is a big, warehouse kind of store with a nice selection of tennis shoes, socks, jeans, shirts, sweatshirts, and all that type of thing. I go directly to the shelf where they stock my size and pick up practically the same jeans I bought two weeks ago but never got the chance to wear. I quickly round up a couple of shirts, some underwear, and socks, then head straight for the cashier. I put all the items on the counter, ready to pay before Junior can find anything he might like. The cashier bags the clothing, totals up my bill, and it reads eighty-six dollars and no cents on the register screen. I reach for my wallet in my back pocket, pull out four twenties, a ten, and pay my bill. The cashier gives me back four singles, the receipt, and hands me my bag. I alert Junior, who is looking at the fancy sweat suits over in the corner on the right side of the store. I start walking slowly to the door, waiting for Junior to finish looking at all the different hats hanging along the wall. "I know you are pissed, buying the same things twice in one month," he reminds me. "That means we should get a drink."

And, as I usually tell him, "Junior, you are the driver and I am just the passenger," I say with a smile on my face. "I still need some toothpaste, a toothbrush, and deodorant. Then I am done," I say. Junior opens the door and I exit first with him following behind.

"Yeah, somebody was going to get with them girls. They have been asking for it," Junior says, opening the driver side door and unlocking the passenger door. I open it, put my bag in the back, and slide into the bucket seat.

"Of course somebody was going to get with them," I declare. "Two young vanilla ladies with no man? In North Portland? Maybe in the fifties, but here in the late eighties? Three letters, Cuz: N-F-L!"

"What that stand for?" Junior asks.

"Simply put, it stands for Not For Long," I reply, and both of us laugh.

"But did you know that Top goes over there?" Junior asks, starting up the car before putting on his seat belt.

"Really? Well, I can use the competition. Plus, Wanda is his lady, *and* she always liked you-know-who!" I tell him.

"No?" Junior says, as he starts driving out of the parking lot.

"Oh yeah! We went to school together at Jefferson. Hell, she grew up down the street from our cousin Donny," I say, eager to fill him in.

"Is that right?" Junior asks.

"Yes, that's right," I say with confidence.

"So…you are not worried about Top?" Junior asks me as we head south.

"In all actual reality, no, I'm not. You see, Sherri, she has a cold, and the doctor knows exactly what she needs. She deserves it. She's going to have no choice but to want more! And everything will be kosher. Pay attention," I instruct Junior.

"What if she wants to move back to the beach? Would you go?" Junior asks. "I am single. That is the furthest thing from my mind," I say. "But! I know what *you* are up to!" I add quickly.

"What's that?" Junior asks, smiling wide. "You are hoping we get together and move to the beach, then you can come down there and play, so Joyce can come down there and kill you!", I tell him. Junior starts laughing.

"Are you going to tell her I asked?" Junior wants to know.

"Of course not," I say, "because I'm not moving to the beach!"

"I thought you said, 'Never say never,'" Junior replies.

"That is my motto," I say.

"Eddie, the only reason I say you would probably move to the beach, because that's just the way you are! Don't you want to go back to Germany?" Junior asks.

"Yes, I do. But that's not going to happen without a DNA test," I reply.

"But that's my point, Eddie. You have no problem leaving!" Junior states.

"That's only because I believe Eddie D can make it anywhere!" I say proudly, smiling. "So, where are we going first? To Cleo's or the liquor store?" I ask.

"How about we go over to the liquor store on MLK first, and then let's go to the bar. Sound like a plan?" Junior suggests.

"Ain't nothing to it but to do it!" I say, smiling. We come to an intersection, light is green, Junior makes a left on Freemont. heading east toward MLK Avenue.

"You never cheated on Tammy, did you?" Junior asks.

"No! I don't cheat. Period!" I say quickly, "I just got the shit knocked out of me for what? Nothing," answering my own question. Junior starts laughing again. "But, no! Little Miss Insecure decides in her brainwashed-ass of a mind that I am going to see somebody else! Something I would never, ever do! She's straight psycho! She is worse than a crackhead on the first of the month," I declare, feeling ticked off. "Just because you are female does not give you the right to just knock the shit out of anybody! That is just straight up sexist. That is some real ignorant shit! I had just handed over eighty-five percent of my paycheck to her before she knocked the shit out of me! And Pops personally invited her *and* her mother over!" I say, still pissed and in pain.

The traffic light is red, Junior slows down, slides into the left turn lane with his blinker on, and comes to a stop at the intersection. "Where is Cousin Keith at?" Junior asks as he makes the left on MLK, moves into the far right lane to make his turn into the driveway of the state-controlled liquor store's parking lot.

"Keith? My brother, he's around," I say, flatly. As Junior pulls into a parking space, I tell him, "It's hard to say where he is, or *who* he's with, this week," I reply. Junior kills the engine and we both get out, close the car doors, and proceed to the liquor store. As we walk through the parking lot, the clouds seem like they're moving while the sun tries to poke its way through. Once out of the lot, we both make a right onto the sidewalk heading north. Ten yards away, on our right, is a brick building with two businesses operating inside. One is a small grocery store at the far end, and at the other is the state-controlled liquor store. I pull the door open, allowing Junior to enter first. We both walk over to the shelves that cover the entire wall. "Junior, do you know there is enough alcohol here to turn any size AA meeting into an all-out orgy?" I say very loudly. Junior starts to laugh, and so does one of the cashiers. As I look at him and smile, the cashier gives me the thumbs up about the joke. I turn back around, and just then a couple of blonde-haired ladies walk into the store. Junior and I try to get their attention, but they act like we do not exist.

"What do you want to drink?" Junior asks. "Well, how about some 151, or some gin?" I answer.

"Oh? That's right," Junior points out. "You are getting ready to get pussy-whipped tonight!"

"Yes. I believe something strong *would* be appropriate for the task at hand, if you know what I mean, Vern," I say. So Junior grabs a fifth of gin for me and a fifth of Seagram's Seven for himself. Junior approaches the counter with wallet in hand and pays for the alcohol. The cashier bags up the liquor, takes Junior's money, and hands him his change. I grab the large bag off the counter, and as we're heading out the door, Junior says, "Yeah, that girl's going to put some white lightning on you!" He opens the door and holds it open for me to exit, then he follows out onto the sidewalk.

"Number one: all pussy is pink. It's not black, white, or any of that bull," I tell him.

"You can call it what you want. But. You are *still* going to get pussy-whipped!" Junior exclaims, laughing.

"Now, Junior, you know I have a saying. Don't be pussy-whipped! Whip that pussy!" I say, very loudly. At the same time, a carload of ladies drives by, honking and yelling, 'Yeah!' and going in the opposite direction. "See? I told you!" I say, smiling.

"Yeah, right," replies Junior. "It's going to happen!" he assures me. "All I want you to do is tell me I was right about you moving to the beach," Junior says, taking his keys out and opening the driver side door. I walk over to the passenger side with the bag of bottled libations in hand, holding it firmly while I open the door. I lift the seat back forward and move my bag of clothes over so I can safely put the bag of alcohol in the back seat as well. Once I get everything situated, I put the seat back, sit down, shut the door, adjust myself, and I am good to go. As Junior starts the Grand Prix, he announces, "Next stop, Cleo's bar! Are you ready for some lessons?" Junior asks. He puts the car in reverse and looks behind us as he's backing up.

"You are going to give me lessons? Doing what?" I ask.

"Pool," Junior says, laughing,

I tell him, "Wait a minute!" as I start looking up, down, and all around the car.

"What are you doing?" Junior asks, as he puts the car in drive and proceeds to leave the parking lot.

"I'm trying to find out who the hell you are talking to about giving out some lessons in pool! You should not even be driving, talking like that. You know it's the other way around!" I say, smiling. Junior starts laughing again. "You know, people have daydreams and nightmares every single day," I say.

"What exactly are you trying to say?" he asks, lighting a cigarette, grinning.

"Simple. I am not going to cut you any slack whatsoever. No mercy! Understand? And it's going to *hurt*," I say calmly, with a slight touch of mock menace.

Junior merges onto the main drag, proceeds south on MLK until he can move over into the right lane, makes his turn on Northeast Graham and heads west to Cleo's Bar. Now we get to stop and go at every intersection, four to be exact. Our final stop and go is around the corner and then we turn onto Williams Avenue where Cleo's Bar is located. Junior makes a right turn and parks at the curb of the two-lane, one-way street, right behind a red 1988 Mustang GT. There are long lines of parked cars on both sides of the street. Cleo's, on the left side of the street, is a powder-pink old shack of a building right on the corner, about forty-five-hundred square feet in area, with a small neon sign directly above the door, announcing in not so big letters that this is Cleo and Lillian's Social club. They serve hard alcohol, beer, fried chicken baskets, and offer gambling, music from a juke box, and four pool tables. I reach in my pocket to get my cigarettes and lighter as a couple of people exit the club across the street, then three, and then four more people enter the club in a matter of seconds. I light up and put my cigs and lighter back in my pocket. Junior turns off the engine once he is satisfied with where he parked. The sun is now actually hiding behind this gray overcast, darkening the light from the sky, as if it is going to rain. "It looks like it's going to rain," Junior comments.

"No way. Not in Portland, Oregon," I say sarcastically as I open the car door. Junior checks his rearview mirror to make sure it's safe to open the door without getting it torn off by the passing traffic. I exit the car and flick the cigarette that I did not really want on the ground next to the curb, grind it out, and shut the door. There's no oncoming traffic, so Junior quickly exits the car. We both wait patiently to cross the street since traffic is a little bit heavier this time of day. After ten cars or so fly down the one-way street, we take our time crossing since there's no immediate traffic in sight. We walk between two parked cars to get to the sidewalk that leads up to this pink building sitting on the corner. We eagerly approach the door, which is closed, but you can still hear music and people talking, having a good time. The front door of the establishment is a dark, maroon color where hangs a very unique sign that says No Minors Allowed in big black letters. Under the left-hand side of the sign is a doorbell, and beneath that is a doorknob. I reach to turn the doorknob, but it will not turn. "They must be starting that membership drive again," I mention to Junior. I push the doorbell, which sounds just like a buzzer. A few seconds later, a man my height with a short afro, slim build, mocha chocolate, and a black goatee opens the door. He looks at me and asks, "Do you have your membership card, sir?"

"Hell no!" I answer.

"Well, brings your black ass in here anyway, Eddie! What's up, my brother?" he asks.

"Ain't nothin' to it but to do it!" I reply happily. James and I embrace, then shake hands. Junior and I walk in as James shuts the door behind us. I look over to my left where the kitchen station is to see if my daughter's aunt Pearly Mae is cooking, and there she is. The kitchen station, as I call it, has five little stools which sit very low to match the level of the low counter, which is about eight feet long, two and a half feet wide, and has a white Formica countertop. I quickly say hi, she says hello back, and I assure her that I will eat something in a little while. There are quite a few people in the club this late in the afternoon. Junior is waiting patiently as I begin to work my way up to the bar, which is directly next to the kitchen. I see Christmas lights just below the ceiling, strung above the bar, which is built in the shape of a horseshoe. It goes from one side of the place all the way around to the other where the pool tables are located. There are chrome-and-black accented stools lined up around the entire bar. Midway around the bar against the far wall is the juke box, which is currently playing Johnny Guitar Watson's "Ain't That a Bitch"! There is a very small, four-by-six-foot tile dance floor in front of the juke box. You go beyond that to get to the restrooms over in the corner. Then come the pool tables and the rest of the bar. The poker room where they gamble is in the back, and where my biological father usually hangs out. Junior and I walk to the side of the bar where the pool tables are, and he orders drinks from the bartender. Then, Junior just has to go there. Turning toward me, he asks, "Eddie, do you think Uncle Hugh is back there?"

"I didn't see Daddy's car out there," I reply. "He could have easily parked on another street where we could not see his car. Besides I don't want to hear it from him either!" I say, seriously.

Junior walks up to the bar and asks me, "What do you want to drink?"

"Gin and juice. I started out with gin today and I am going to finish with gin tonight," I reply with a smile as I look over the pool tables, checking out everybody's game. I'm also checking to see how many quarters are lined up on the green felt trim of the tables so I'll know how many people are waiting to play. "I see a lot of people are waiting to play, but I'm not going to sweat it," I comment. "Once I get a real buzz going on, it will be pretty much a done deal. And, Junior, you know this," I say with confidence.

"No, I don't know. What's alcohol got to do with it?" Junior asks, smiling.

"Not a damn thing! It relaxes me just enough to whip that ass!", I say.

"You got a lot of asses to whip, because there is a lot of people in here feel the same way you do!" Junior says, laughing.

"I feel with my hands, but I kick ass with my brain! There is a difference, you know," I reply. The bartender brings our drinks and Junior pays for them. I take a seat on the barstool directly in front of the drinks, looking at the other side of the bar. The drinks are so strong the fumes have engulfed my airspace, which leaves me no choice but to take a drink. I grab the strong concoction in the chimney glass off the bar and proceed to unload it down my throat. "Oooo-weee!" I gasp, exhaling the alcohol fumes from my anatomy, placing the glass abruptly back down on the bar. Then I spin my stool around away from my drink and proceed to watch the pool games. "Now that's what I call a drink," I say, looking very exasperated.

"You all right?" Junior asks laughingly.

"Yeah, it's just the sour-ass grapefruit juice, that's all," I reply in a whisper. Then, through the door of the gambling section in the back of the club, comes a large, six-foot-two, wide-chested, huge-armed, mocha-chocolate handsome man with a mustache and long wavy black hair tied in a ponytail. He looks directly at me, and then at Junior. I quickly alert Junior, "Here comes your Uncle Hugh."

The large man walks up to us and speaks, "Hey, what's going on?"

"Hello, Daddy, how are you?" I reply.

"Uncle Hugh! How are you doing?" Junior asks.

"Well, I'm wondering why my eldest son has a lump on the top of his head," Dad asks. Junior starts laughing. "Eddie, what happened?" my dad asks in a concerned voice.

I start explaining. "Okay, I'll tell you. I got off work, cashed my check, bought a fifth, went home, and gave Tammy money to pay bills. Then I took a shower and got dressed because Mom and Rob had invited us over for barbecue, but Tammy swears they didn't invite her. So, since she wants to play games, I told to come on down if she changed her mind. As I'm going out the door, she just hits me in the back of the head with the telephone and knocked me the hell out!"

"You have got to be kidding," my dad says, bewildered.

"And she burned all of my clothes because I was going to meet some fictional white girl," I tell him.

"Son, I did not know you mess with white girls! I never seen you with one," my father states.

"That's because I didn't. But I do now," I exclaimed.

"That girlfriend of yours, what's-her-name, is just highly insecure, and there is nothing you can do to fix it, son," my dad interjects. "How is your Mother?"

"She's fine," I answer.

"Tell her I said hello. Have you heard from your sister?" Dad asks.

"Yes, she's fine," I reply.

"How are your kids?" he asks.

"They are all right, too," I inform him.

He throws a glance at the door to the back room and says, "Well, they got all my money, so I'm going to get out of here, son. Junior, you talked to your mother?" asks Dad.

"Yes, she's doing all right," Junior answers.

"That's good. I need to get by there and see my big sister. Son?" Dad asks.

"Yes, sir?" I reply.

"You take care of yourself and watch out for those crazy women. You will be just fine. I will see you later," my dad says.

"Later, Dad," I reply as he starts to walk away.

"Later, nephew," Daddy says to Junior.

"Later on, Uncle Hugh," Junior replies, while reaching in his pocket for his cigarettes. He pulls one out, sets the pack on the bar, puts the cig in his mouth and pats his pants pockets for a light. I grab the pack on the bar and fish one out for myself, set it back down and bend forward slightly to get a light from Junior, who's lighting his cigarette. "Uncle Hugh was in a hurry to get out of here, wasn't he?" asks Junior.

"Well, I suspect he's been here all day and stood up my future step-monster-mother. Oh well, not my business!" I say, dragging the ashtray closer toward us. Just then, a few people who finally got tired of waiting to play pick up their quarters and proceed to leave the area. I know the people running the tables were getting sloppy and buzzed, and pretty much barely winning each game. I spin the stool halfway toward the bar and flick my ashes in the ashtray, then turn back around facing all the pool tables. The brother on the pool table directly in front of me scratches on the eight ball. Game over. There are only two quarters on the table, so I butt out my cigarette and stand up quickly, fish a quarter out of my pocket and walk to the pool table, place the quarter on the table, make eye contact with everybody, and say, "What's up?" Then I return to the stool and sit down next to Junior. "I have just two people in front of me. Then it's time for Shut Up and Get Down!" I say eagerly. I reach for my drink, take a good sip, and then grab my cigarette out of the ashtray and begin smoking it. Junior flicks his ashes in the ashtray and orders two more drinks from the bartender. "Yeah, I'm up next! The brother just scratched the eight ball!" I proclaim.

"You can handle another drink, can't you, Eddie?" Junior asks me.

"Yeah, one more, sure," I reply.

"Have you talked to Cousin Gordy lately?" Junior asks.

"Yeah, he stayed with me for about a week a while back. I'm pretty sure he's staying with Aunt Maxine over at the house on Grand Avenue," I tell him. Now it's finally my turn to play. I grab my glass and proceed to swallow all of it. Then I stand up, exhaling the fumes, walk to the side of the pool table and grab the quarter I had put there previously. Then I put the coin in the slot, which is just below where the rest of the quarters are sitting. I push the mechanism in and let it snap back out so the balls flow into position down at the opposite end of the table. Then I retrieve the rack located just above the opening where the balls are accessible. Placing the rack on the black break spot, I begin racking up the balls in their proper positions. After finding a straight cue, I take my seat while watching my opponent break. "This won't take long," I tell Junior.

"You sure are confident today. Or you got a good-ass buzz going on there," Junior replies, smiling. Two hours later I am still running the table. I'm on a ten-zero streak. Junior is talking to some people at the bar while down-home blues is playing on the jukebox. "Eight ball cross-side," I call, letting my opponent know how I am going to win. The eight ball goes in, but the cue ball goes in the opposite corner pocket as well. I lose. Everybody who saw the shot goes, "Oh!" The agony of defeat sets in immediately. I shake my opponent's hand and tell him, "Good game," which he says back to me. I walk back to my seat only to find Bonnie, who I went to high school with, sitting there next to Junior. "Hey, Bonnie Baby!" I say happily.

"Hey, Eddie Baby, what's going on?" she asks as she spins the stool around to face me, stands up, gives me a hug, and then a kiss on the mouth in front of Junior. Then Bonnie sits back down on the stool, spins around, and grabs her drink.

"Where do you guys know each other from?" Junior asks curiously.

"We go to the same church. And we both went to Jefferson High School," Bonnie says.

"Eddie, he said that he is your first cousin. So he must be on your father's side. Right?" she asks.

"Yeah, that's right," I answer.

"Now, Bishop Daniels is not your grandfather?" Bonnie asks Junior.

"No, he is not. That's Eddie's grandfather," answers Junior.

"So Big Hugh, Eddie's Dad, is your uncle. Right?" Bonnie asks.

"Yes," Junior replies, looking at her back side. "I've known Eddie a long time and I know his family pretty good, I must say."

Bonnie is a five-foot-five, Hershey-chocolate, short black hair, pearly white teeth, lovely shaped sweetheart of friend. "What the hell?" Bonnie says, looking at my head. Junior starts laughing real hard. "Eddie, what happen to your head? It looks like somebody knocked the hell out of you," Bonnie says as she retrieves her cigarette from the ashtray, grabs her brandy glass, and turning back towards me, exhales her last drag. "It's a long story," I reply.

"Okay, cool. Eddie, where's your cousin Donny?" she asks.

"Oh, he's around. He's doing alright," I answer.

"Donny is crazy. You know my cousin Donny too?" Junior asks.

"Yes, I do. Eddie has a big family and I know a lot of them," replies Bonnie.

"Man, I am so hungry," I say.

"Way ahead of you. I already ordered it," Junior replies.

"It's just about that time, too!" I suggest.

"You got somewhere to be tonight, Eddie D?" Bonnie asks me.

"Yes, but it was very good to see you again,", I say, giving her another kiss on the lips.

"It was good to see you too, Eddie," she says as she stands up and walks away, with cigarette and drink in hand.

"Hey, man! Why you turn her down?" Junior asks.

"I did not turn her down. I told her the truth. That's what she likes best about me," I say as I sit down on the stool. "Besides, I am going to be your neighbor, Junior. One thing is for sure: I need a lady who does not resort to violence, or one that hasn't got substantial, irreversible mental brain-block," I add. The bartender brings us two chicken baskets to go. Junior has already paid the tab. "Thanks, Junior," I tell him.

"Not a problem,", he replies. Then, we down our drinks. Junior says, "You ready?" I stand up and say, "Born that way!" We collect our grub and head out the front door. We get outside the club and its already nightfall. And it's raining. But not really raining. Just that nagging sort of rain, the kind we get here most of the time, but not necessarily all of it. We walk south to about midway down the block and cross the street between two parked cars before any traffic is visible. We both have a good buzz on so the rain's not bothering us. Junior hurries to open his car door because there are a lot of trucks coming up the street and he wants to avoid getting splashed. And there's plenty of it on the street to get soaked with. He gets in, shuts the door, unlocks my door. I get in, shut the door, and the car all of a sudden smells of fried chicken. Junior starts the car, puts it in drive, carefully pulls out, and we take off down the road.

Twenty minutes later, junior pulls up into his driveway and parks. I exit the car and pull the seat forward, grabbing the alcohol and my new clothes that were in the back seat. I close the door using my hip, Junior grabs the chicken dinner, exits the car, and locks it. "You are coming in, aren't you?" Junior asks.

"Yes! I am hungry as a three-legged pig. Besides I got to get myself together and prepare for the manila in her villa!" I reply, smiling.

As we walk up to the front door, Junior is laughing, feeling no pain, and with his free hand finds the right key to open his door. He unlocks the door, swings it wide open, allowing me to go in first. I take only a couple of steps into the darkened living room, letting Junior go ahead to turn the damn light on so we can see what's really going on. He turns the light on and I continue on to the dining table. I set the bag of alcohol down on the table, set the bag of clothes on the floor next to a dining table chair. I hustle to the restroom and wash my hands, then return to the dining room, ready to get busy on some chicken, fries, and toast. Junior and I sit down to eat, not saying a word to each other. Once we finish, we both light up smokes and relax for a minute. "Well, I think it's time for me to ease on down the road, if you know what I mean, Vern!" I say, intoxicated, putting my cigarette out in the ashtray.

"Yeah, cousin. You go on ahead and get turned out by that young thing! Have a good time for me," Junior replies.

"I will do my best," I say, standing up and fishing the fifth of gin out of the bag and reaching down to retrieve the plastic bag that contains my new clothes. "I will talk to you tomorrow, all right?" I add as I walk to the door, putting the bottle under my arm so I can open the door by oneself. I leave the house and shut the door behind me, all excited, like it's my birthday.

4

· · · · · · · · · · · · · · · · · · · ·

Eddie and Sherri

The next morning, head throbbing sore as hell, I wake up on the full-sized blue velvet couch in my parents' TV room. I glance out the double windows through the white plastic venetian blinds, past the cloudy gray skies north toward Vancouver, Washington, the Evergreen State, far off in the distance. However, the good news is, no precipitation yet. The eight-by-ten photo of me in my class A uniform, my military portrait, is prominently displayed on a mahogany stand with accented glass doors next to the nineteen-inch color television, which sits against the wall next to a narrow, carefully designed closet with tall, sliding doors set in an eggshell-colored room. In my highly excited state of anticipation, my testosterone level is maxed to the outer limits of imagination. I speed-dress in no time flat, put on my new t-shirt, jeans, the same shoes, and new black windbreaker, and inform Pops, "I am out of here!"

His response is merely, "Have fun, and don't take any wooden nickels." I exit the house, thinking about wearing a hat but realize that's not a good idea as the cold air reminds me of the temperature of my lump. I light a cigarette as I stroll up the walkway over to Sherri's house, carrying the brown paper bag of liquor Junior brought me—strictly for medicinal purposes, of course. Just as I'm about to knock on the peeling, weather-beaten door to Sherri's house, I notice a brown, late model Datsun B210 with Washington plates parked in the driveway on the side of the cottage, which I assume is Sherri's transportation.

Someone inside is coughing heavily, like a dude. I rhythmically knock on the door with the knuckles of both hands, pre-celebrating Eddie's ready-to-make-sweet-spaghetti with Sherri, since my lump and she have been on my mind all night long. I listen carefully but hear no movement from inside the gray cottage. I glance up at the old-school outside porch light, which is still on, and I hear this unfamiliar, crabby-sounding voice booming, "Come on in, the door's open!" from within the dwelling, and it sounds nothing like the nice-looking, twenty-year-old, green-eyed country girl I met yesterday. Or is my mind playing tricks on me? So I turn the worn, brass-plated doorknob, open the door and enter the silent abode, close the door behind me, then pick my way carefully across the hardwood floor, which is strewn with toys, looking all around as if I'm in the wrong place, feeling a little bit out of my comfort zone because that voice did not quite sound like Sherri. However, at the same time I'm thinking, *Who else could it be?* Dawn doesn't sound like that, so maybe I am mishearing?

"I'm in here!" the voice announces in a very hoarse, unladylike tone.

"Where is in here, and who are you?" I ask, unsure who I am talking to as I follow the sound. The voice gets louder the closer I get to the bedroom entryway.

"Just come to the first bedroom," the voice intones very harshly. I move slowly toward the first bedroom, truly wondering what's behind door number one, and I am then instantly relieved to see Sherri lying on the cast-iron bed, wearing only a T-shirt, with no blankets or sheets covering her, just a box of Kleenex at her side, legs semi-open, as if her entire flaming inferno's mission is to make her sweat. She's dripping wet, which speaks to the germ's resistance to Sherri's attempts at drowning it in a concoction of gin and grapefruit juice, a rather erotic combination designed for anti-bacterial doom.

"Hello, somebody I am here to heal!" I announce, smiling. Sherrie replies by sneezing, coughing, and trying hard not to laugh, even though she finds my introductory statement amusing.

"I really don't feel good. I just feel awful," she says, closing her eyes while blowing her reddish nose into a Kleenex. I put the bottle down on the dresser, take off my windbreaker, and sit very close to her on the bed while avoiding the wastepaper basket right next to it. Sympathetic to her present condition, I gently take her temperature, carefully placing my hand on her forehead. She's so soft, so fresh to me, I have to remind myself what I'm doing, because it's very evident she has an extraordinary effect on me in a way that's different from anything I've ever experienced before. Hot and yet clammy to the touch at the same time, she definitely has something of a fever. I retrieve my hand slowly from her Bach-smooth face. I can sense she is not shy and very proud of her beautiful body: her breasts are full, the light-brown nipples showing through the fabric of her soaked T-shirt, and her unshaved vagina is absolutely smiling at me in all its natural human beauty, saying hello without saying anything. Body language never lies, so I've got to pitch my prognosis quick because the doctor's more than ready to operate on this patient. I lean in a little closer wanting to kiss her, hoping it would somehow heal her, a remedy that would make her believe in me, to truly see me with those sexy green eyes under thick black eyebrows, allowing me to do all the things Dawn whispered in my ear yesterday while she was hugging me as I was leaving: "Sherri wants to get with you." I should therefore heal her, even if she doesn't want to admit her own secret desires as she plays coy, yet far from innocent, consciously or unconsciously sending obviously unmistakable signals, driving my inner nature crazy, setting her hot hand on the thigh of my brown denim jeans, just short of where my anatomical creator wants to get busy. I'm still eager to kiss her but wrestling with an overwhelming fear of her sneezing in my mouth; that's a sick thought.

"Now, I know this might sound crazy, but I can help you get rid of your cold," I say as I'm appreciating her curvy silhouette.

"And how you plan on doing that?" she asks with a doubtful look on her face, yet game to hear my solution as she wipes her sniffing, reddish nose.

"I can show you better than I can tell you," I reply, smiling, gazing straight into her green eyes. And she makes a special effort to smile back at me. "Are we all alone?" I ask, curious since things are going so smoothly and hearing only the empty acoustics of the rest of the house.

"Yes, we're alone. Dawn went down to her mother's and Jeremy is with my sister, Kelly," Sherri says as she tosses another sodden Kleenex in the wastepaper basket.

"Your sister lives in Seaside as well?" I ask, attempting to get her mind off her lousy yet healable condition.

"Yes, she does. Now, how do you plan on healing me? I really want to hear this," Sherri says, retrieving her hand from my leg. Better make my move. I shift my weight and the bedsprings connected to the old-school cast iron headboard squeak lightly; the screws could use some adjusting since it slams the wall under a lot of vigorous movement.

"Now, Sweetheart, all I want you to do is close your eyes and don't open them, no matter how good it feels. Promise me, okay?" I instruct her as she gives me her full attention, very much interested in what I have to say, which is scoring points big time.

"Why, what are you going to do to me?" she asks, smiling almost daring me to take my best shot right here, right now.

"I am going to do what you wished for," I tell her.

"And what would that be?" Sherri asks modestly.

"Didn't you wish for a man who would put his hands on you the right way? And treat you and your son right? And who would never, ever lie to you?" I ask her.

"Yes, I did. But that was just a dream!" she adds hurriedly, without considering that sometimes reality is not always far from make-believe. I lean over, finally, gently kissing her on the lips, then slowly lean back from her.

"Well, I wished for a country girl who would never, ever knock the hell out of me, but just love me forever," I reply, looking her straight in the eyes, dead serious.

"That is so sweet, if you did really wish for that," she says, then blows her nose again, followed by a loud, shrieking sneeze.

"Bless you," I reply, solemnly tender. "I wished for you a split-second after I survived a blindside assault walking down this very street that left me with a contusion on the top of my dome. Thank God Dawn called me over to hook up with you. Now I'm right here, aren't I? Don't answer that. Just close your eyes and let me heal you,

Foxy Lady," I state as I stand up, confident, very boldly taking off all my clothes until I am chocolate-naked.

"What are you doing?" she asks, staring at my anatomy, licking her lips.

"Oh, I'm just getting comfortable, that's all," assuring her that I will be very gentle. After Sherri inspects my mocha-chocolate, buck-naked anatomy, ready-equipped with an erection, she closes her eyes, smiling with anticipation, and lays down flat on the bed like she's my very-willing-and-ready-to-participate patient. Then I start to sing "My Cherie Amour," kissing her on the neck, then down to her nipples, with my full lips easing down to kiss her bellybutton. Her body quivers. I then situate myself between her legs, facing her while she moves her hands upward well above her head into a submissive position. I proceed south down her belly, and she starts moaning once my tongue reaches the right spot.

"Uh-huh, yes, uh-huh, yes, uh-huh, yes, OH SHIT YES!" Sherri screams out. Her body is still convulsing as she attempts to take off her T-shirt. I lift my head. "Sweetheart, you are not going to get well if you take that shirt off," I tell her.

"But it's hot in here," she says. I step out of bed and grab the gin bottle off the dresser and walk into the kitchen. I find some glasses, fill them with ice, grab the orange juice, and make us a couple of drinks. "You and I are going to sweat and sweat all day and all night, as long as it takes!" I yell from the kitchen, "When your shirt is sweaty wet, then you can take it off and your cold will be gone," I say as I return to the bedroom while stirring the drinks alternately with my index finger.

"Okay, but don't you think you're a little overconfident?" Sherri asks.

"No. And let me tell you why," I say seriously as I take a seat next to her on the bed. "There is something about you that speaks to me, which allows you to let me have you all night long, and even into the next day, okay?" I say as I hand her a drink, holding her eyes with mine, being as serious as I know how.

"Oh? Is that right?" Sherri asks, then takes a heaping swallow of her drink, and immediately gasps from the strength of the gin within. I return to Sherri and kiss her, embracing her, guiding her back down onto the bed. Two hours into it, she can no longer handle the T-shirt. Sherri and I make spaghetti until the sun's rays filtered through the bedroom windows in the early morning, and then fell asleep in each other's arms.

Later on, into the afternoon, I awaken to the lovely aroma wafting down the hallway of breakfast being prepared in the kitchen. It smells terrifically good, and I am a very finicky eater. For instance, cantaloupe and watermelon make me very nauseous, tomatoes suck, and I'm not eating your grits or your groovy-ass coleslaw. I am a meat-and-potatoes man. I reach up to feel if the lump on my head has gone down, and it seems to be smaller. Sherri walks into the room looking refreshed, bright eyed, showered, and sweet, carrying a plate brimming with a well-balanced breakfast: two fried eggs, six link sausages, hash browns, three buttermilk pancakes, and a big glass of orange juice.

"Well, good afternoon, Baby," she says, as she walks over to give me a kiss.

"How are you?" I ask curiously.

"I am just fine! You were right. My cold is completely gone. And yes, you healed me, okay? I admit that it was really good," she adds. She gives me a prolonged smooch, and smiling, leaves the room on cloud nine. She's got me daydreaming, thinking that maybe, *I'm supposed to be with only her.* What is wrong with me? Hearing the rain spattering against the window, I realize I have just been abusively dump-trucked, with a missile-lump on my head and no clothes to prove it. I just need to chill slowly the hell down for once in my life.

One evening two weeks later, my stepfather comes over to Sherri's house to inform me that he has quit the Prime Rib because Rick accused him of stealing liquor from the bar, and that I would probably be the next employee to get axed. A couple of days later after the lunch rush at work on the kitchen line, Rick's constantly shaking a leg back and forth with his hands on his hips, not being really social, white powder visible under his nose. He turns abruptly to me while I wait for the dishwashing cycle to finish, then says in a hyper-uncanny attitude, "Get your thumb out of your black ass or punch out on your timecard!" in a very loud and very crystal-clearly annoying voice.

I question the owner by saying, "Excuse me? What did you just say?" I'm already way past the level of not taking any shit off this whacked-out jerk.

"You're fired! Now get the hell out of here! You can pick up your check tomorrow!" he says loudly, in a threatening and accusing tone of voice. Realizing I don't have any legal ground from which to launch a counterattack, I exit the premises before my aggressive, temperamental demons get the better of me.

Eventually, after I start receiving unemployment compensation, I finally come clean with my lady friends and explain how, on one ignorant night of self-pity and tired of being held a virtual prisoner behind sky-high walls of resentment, yours truly made some horrifically bad decisions, and that I am also on probation for three more years, to which they reply, "Nobody's perfect."

Sherri and Dawn enter the living room while I am watching my favorite Bobby Brown video on MTV. I'm already dressed in my black, long-sleeved shirt, silver-gray slacks, and black dress shoes I bought yesterday at the Volume Shoe Store. Whoa! I can't believe what I'm seeing with my own optical lenses! Behold! These two double-damn-delicious ladies are dressed-to-kill: white, see-through blouses, identical naughty, black, mini-ass skirts, so short you could just about see their Val Gina's, banging' hair and makeup, sporting tasteful black pumps, looking like a couple of sexy dancers right out of Robert Palmer's "Simply Irresistible" video, or all prepped up like some very high-end call girls. This club where we are going is in the hood and people will undoubtedly assume I'm their pimp, and that's not me. Anyway, they are absolutely breathtaking as they take turns modeling for me, like I'm a judge in a beauty pageant who has to declare the all-time winner. Hands down, Sherri is seductively drop-dead gorgeous and she knows it. This twenty-one-year-old, young, wild, and free-times-two just didn't quite know what to expect. "What the shut-the-front-door do you ladies have on?" I pant out, admiring Sherri and Dawn's Playboy-style model show. "You want to go to the hood dressed like that?" I ask seriously, but inwardly not really caring.

We arrive at the Esquire Club around 10:00 p.m. in the warm-to-cool evening air and stroll to the upstairs entrance of the club where the six-foot-tall, mocha-chocolate-complexioned, clean-shaven, mouth-full-of-pearly-white-teeth doorman, who's happy as all get out to see yours truly, has a natural freaky fit, "Brother man! Brother man! What is your name?" he asks with a wide grin.

"Eddie Dee Williams. What's yours?" I reply, getting out my ID.

"Brother, my name is Calvin, my new friend, and which one these fine-ass women did you bring for me? Hello, ladies!" he bubbles out.

"Hello," Dawn replies, while Sherri's too busy for pleasantries as she's checking out the club's interior action over Calvin's shoulder until, "We are both with him," she says abruptly, setting him straight. The club is packed: balls-to-the-wall Chocolate City, and as we come through the doors, the eyes of the entire club are on us, as if we are celebrities. Mission accomplished, since both of my ladies are eager to strut their stuff. Sherri takes me by the hand before Dawn can even think about considering dancing with me first. The throbbing vibration of the club's sound system sends the powerful bass up our anatomies, prodding us to move our feet forward unconsciously, I'm already snapping my fingers as we start our descent to the dance floor, which is surrounded by an ocean of people seated around circular Kirkwood tables, furnished with multicolored, bumpy glass candleholders and crystal-like ashtrays in the center of each table. Dawn, not missing a beat, starts dancing with Sherri and me. A few songs, a few dances, and a few liberating drinks later, Sherri finally starts showing her true colors, keeping me on the dance floor. Sherri is plainly obvious in her attempts at trying to introduce Dawn to any man she can find, just as long as she can hook her up with one. Uh-oh, the telltale writing is definitely on the proverbial wall: it is a sure sign things are going sour.

When we get home, Sherri makes it very clear that she is no longer into sharing. Of course, this comes as no surprise, since she'd already stated she wanted me all to herself. Early on, I knew this cliffhanger of a *Three's Company* honeymoon of happy campers would eventually develop into a dysfunctional, head-on collision of obscenely ugly scenarios involving claws-and-fangs-out cat fighting. The tension is building like a bull suffering from extreme celibacy. Nobody's backing off, and it's only a matter of a very short time until the big showdown. And when it hits, it will be like a tidal wave moving up a river, Dawn being the tsunami, which I have seen coming as evidenced by the growing number of the ongoing, confrontational catty female attacks they launch on each other. However, when you are having fun, as I have been, well, you develop quite a convenient case of air-headedness!

Sherri and I return to the cottage from Columbia Park after having a lovely picnic lunch, just the two of us, talking for hours. We had a beautiful day of drinking in the sight of the gorgeous scenery, hiking up the mountain to watch the beautiful, six hundred and eleven feet of roaring, icy-wet Multnomah Falls, then back down again to finish off the outing with a supremely relaxing lunch in the shade. Unfortunately, Dawn returns from the coast right after we arrive. Bad timing. Its clear Dawn is still pissed off because, before she left, she commented that she needed to get away from us, and it's pretty obvious she's still not in the greatest of moods! She strides up to Sherri, who's sitting on the couch, apparently ignoring the approaching shit storm, but not really.

"So, you are trying to take my man?" she asks Sherri, who just sits there, not at all concerned about the situation.

"I don't need to take something that I obviously already have!" Sherri replies as she stands straight up, getting directly all up in Dawn's face. Then, out of the basement—POW! Dawn slugs Sherri in the jaw and Sherri goes down hard, a technical knockout. I instantly break it up, trying to restrain Dawn's aggressiveness. She replies, "Get your freaking hands off of me, you motherfucker!" I respond by turning my attention to Sherri, who's still lying on the ground. A few days later, Dawn, and her new, so-called man friend show up in a maroon Buick to retrieve her clothes, and she moves out.

Weeks pass quickly into months, and my feelings for any other ladies are slowly evicted from my thoughts. I finally accept the fact that Sherri and I have strong, genuine, deeply ingrained feelings for one another; our formula for love ignited just like a young man entering puberty. Crazy as happy glue, or happy as Crazy Glue, we just can't get enough of each other. Every day is an ultimate honeymoon-fun, sugar-sweet adventure. Our opposite persuasions guide our emotions to appreciate each other from the inner depths, rather than rely on our *Jungle Fever* stereotypical exteriors. Mornings, as well as nights, we always wind up soaking in the old-school cast iron bathtub, talking and laughing until our skins are prune-wrinkled. Sherri frequently, spontaneously, and aggressively asks me to sing "My Cherie Amour," whether in public, at the beautiful Rose Garden in Washington Park, or better yet, in private before some afternoon delight on top of Old Rocky Butte Scenic Lookout, with its panoramic view of Portland and Southwest Washington.

This particular time is an extra special, eighty-six-degrees-in-the-shade, and for a change, smog-free, beautifully sunny Sunday! Yet a nice, lazy, adventurous day at the Portland Zoo seemed even more appropriate. Jeremy, Sherri, and I, all dressed in T-shirts, shorts, and sandals, pack a picnic lunch and loaded up the brown, four-door, four-speed Datsun B210, and are cruising our way to Southwest Portland by way of Highway 26 South, the gateway to most Pacific Northwest Beaches. We arrive at the zoo and are lucky enough to find parking close to the main gate. As we exit the car, we can't help but appreciate the well-planned landscaping that integrates perfectly with the composition of the surrounding park. Jeremy is so 100 percent boy excited; he runs across the sunbaked pavement without a care in the world. Sherri and I make it a race to the main gate, leaving Jeremy in the dust, and stop in the shade under the green branches of the tall fir trees, swaying slowly in the fresh, cooling breeze as we wait for Jeremy to catch up. The zoo's souvenir store directly in front of us is painted gray and trimmed in a shade of weathered orange, flanked by the two main entrances. As we wait in line, I read over the statistical placards placed around the admission gate and am informed that the zoo provides humanely designed habitats for 2200 animals from 260 different species. Once our little trio has passed through the entryway into the park, the blended scents and aromas of different types of wildlife fill the air, and I whisper to Jeremy that I can talk to the animals since I speak Donald Duck. Astonishment overwhelms his boyish face, utterly surprised at the thought that I could really do such a thing. His eyes instantly lock onto the beautiful Indian blue peacocks; royal-blue bodies, with long, decorative, gold-accented tails with large, multi-colored eyes at their feathery tips, strutting right in front of us, casually going about their daily routine. We stroll along the cement-paved pathway to our left where a cyclone fence allows us to look down into manmade caves where the Siberian Tigers are kept. They are slumbering in the cool shade after having finished a hefty meal, king-of-their-jungle style, which reminds us of how hungry we are. Once we finish the delicious lunch Sherri prepared for us, and after resting a bit, Jeremy spots the Zoo Train in the distance heading our way: platinum-gray engine with a burgundy stripe running along both sides, with six passenger cars behind decorated in the same colors, gliding along on the steel railway tracks set into the concrete, pulling up to a stop. Sherri, Jeremy, and I quickly run to board the kiddy train. Somewhat out of breath after our dash across the pavement, we pay the fare and board the now-empty train, quickly finding seats on the hardwood benches. Minutes later, filled once again with parents and their children, the Zoo Train begins its mile-long loop around the animal enclosures in the park. Cruising at a moderate speed, we journey through stands of natural vegetation. One hundred-foot-tall fir trees are everywhere in the forest. We pass by a huge, still-intact, wooden, old-fashioned fifty-foot-tall water tower with a twenty-foot diameter water tank made in the early 1900s next to the railroad tracks. The tall trees shade us from the hot sun as we cruise by the brown-and-white, skyscraping giraffes, then the muscular rhinos, the lioness and her cubs, and the grizzly bears, without having to take a single step. After we complete the entire loop, the engineer brings the train safely to a stop at the station where we originally boarded the train. Sherri decides to become our tour guide and we change directions onto a different scenic pathway where we manage to come across my old nemesis. Not the gorgeous gorillas. I am so down and cool with them; it's those damned chimpanzees! After enduring two traumatic scenarios involving chimps, they have ever afterward had a weird physiological effect on me.

The first was when I was four-years-old, sleeping on the top bunk in my room. In my nightmare, chimpanzees would tie me up, spread-eagled between two tall Douglas Fir trees, buck-ass-naked, eight feet in the air. And then a dozen of those crazy apes would leap up from the ground, hovering in mid-air, tickling my armpits with their monkey hands, laughing their obscene monkey laugh, which made me laugh so hard my eyes would water in my sleep and I'd piss myself. I was stuck in that surreal dream, so comatose that I couldn't seem to snap out of it and wake up! Fun fact number two: when my siblings and I were really small, our babysitter was Sister Quinn, who lived just two blocks up the street from our house, and she had a chimpanzee named Sam, who did not like us, at all. Sam would take off his feces-laden diaper and twirl it while swinging from the chandelier over the dining room table when we were trying to eat, dropping dark-brown, pellet-shaped manure like a World War II B-27 bombardier into our cold cereal or hot vegetable soup, screech-laughing maniacally as he swung from the light to the corners of the ceiling, an insane trapeze artist on a permanent day-to-day mission to ambush us with his manure bombs, like we were some kind of infidels who had invaded his turf and needed to feel the sting of his punishing wrath.

Meanwhile, flash-forward back to reality, I'm studying cloud formations, the cracks in the sidewalk, anything but looking at the chimpanzees running freely about in their enclosure, letting off flatulent explosions as I conveniently forget to share this particular part of my story with Sherri. As far as I'm concerned, we depart gratefully from the presence of my nemesis, and we enter the huge aviary that houses the exotic talking birds. All around us there are birds flying, landing, taking off again, vibrant shades of red, blue, green, orange mixed with purple, all with curved yellow beaks as they fly, then land on your arm or shoulder, flying from one person to another without hesitation, sipping nectar from tiny, white paper containers visitors can buy to give them a drink. Quickly thinking outside-the-box, I decide to try to teach the Toys R Us kid's song to an African Gray Parrot. However, Jeremy is totally exhausted and ready for his nap, so we decide to call it a day. Both Sherri and I are somewhat dragging too, from all the excitement and fun of our pleasant, sunny Sunday adventure day spent with the always interesting animal kingdom, sharing, however briefly, their 400 acres of trees, gardens, and other interesting activities at the Washington Park/Portland Zoo. It wasn't just a four-year-old's day of delight.

Whenever Sherri and I get lucky enough to be alone, the most romantic means of expression, at least in her world, is for me to sing her favorite songs, "My Cherie Amour," and "Ain't No Sunshine," which I am beginning to understand. She loves a soulful romantic. However, when I play, it's hard to sing at the same time. But, if Sherri wants, Sherri gets, even if it takes bribes, flirtatious sexual advances, or the occasional therapeutic erotic proposition. Her prodding persistence overwhelms me, which I more than willingly submit to; the sight of her beautiful, green, cat-like eyes that sparkle, her very petite lips framing her perfect set of white teeth, smiling sensuously at me as she is captivated by the sound of me singing her name. Sherri is so taken with the fact I sing to her that she habitually calls me Baby, an uplifting erotic endearment of sorts, this to a man who never gets too old to hear it, and I love it! Now, on this particular happy-honeymoon, sunny day, on the spur of the moment, Sherri and I decide to go the movies and check out the action-packed film, "License to Kill," the latest James Bond movie. We arrive at the theater in the early evening, park on a side street next to the huge, historical St. John's Theatre on North Lombard Street, and walk to the box office, which is centered under the façade of the light-gray painted exterior, and trimmed in burgundy. We both gaze up to read the scheduled show times, letting go of each other's hand, letting them fall to our sides. After all, we're still in the Pacific Northwest. Us holding hands in public out of habit could easily be misinterpreted. Or worse. I eagerly pay the attendant for our tickets and we proceed cheerfully into the well-appointed lobby's interior, decorative walls flowing with layered silk curtains in red and black, accented by upright silver stanchions stretching a red velvet rope that leads to the main auditorium across a worn, antique brocade carpet. We glide to the snack bar to shop for some movie house groceries: buttered popcorn, Junior Mints, and a large fountain soda. Heading for the entryway into the auditorium, I find myself starting to think outside the box again. I can't help it. I purposely slow down, watching Sherri walking ahead of me, her beauty reflected in her perfectly moon-shaped booty, swaying in its skintight black spandex—that sexy yet quirky country walk that makes a man just have to wonder, *Mmm?* Sherri, realizing I am no longer right beside her, stops without a second thought, turns around with popcorn in her right hand, waits for me to catch up with her, then leans slightly against me, gives me a sly smile, and looks down approvingly at the white T-shirt she wanted to me wear, the one that has a picture of the both of us on the front of it. The shirt was made the day we went to the Portland Rose Festival's carnival photograph and print booth. As we're sidling down one of the empty rows of seats in the auditorium, me with a large Coke in my right hand and box of Junior Mints in my left, I have to smile as I watch other men in the theatre who can't help but drool over Sherri's captivating beauty, some even doing a double-take. One husband gets slapped in the back of his head by his wife for looking too long in Sherri's direction. Nature has a way of driving a man's loins crazy, which is called an authentic moment in time by some. This is the ultimate unexpected Kodak moment, and I am proud to be her man. She turns her head back, sees the look on my face and asks, "What are you doing?" Smiling, but slightly suspicious.

"Smokin! Come here, breakfast," I reply quickly.

"You are so crazy! That is why I love you," she says, smiling heavily, all eyes on her walking back to me with this sexy smirk, embracing me passionately in front of the now half-full auditorium, with the house lights up, almost forgetting she is holding the popcorn in her hand. "I love you too, Snooky Nooky Poo Poo!" I reply, smiling, attempting to get my concentrated manhood under control. "Let's sit somewhere in the middle?" I suggest smoothly. We take our seats in the middle rear of the theatre just as the house lights dim and the red neon exit lights materialize in the now-dark auditorium. The huge, silver-white screen brightens with colorful, attention-grabbing, soul-snatching, mind-boggling, overly-dramatic, and hilarious movie previews. We finally settle down into our seats, cuddle, and Sherri unselfishly begins to feed me popcorn while I feed her Junior Mints like we have been kidnapped and held captive in Cupid's castle of love. I start daydreaming in the dark, ignoring the previews, about how I first met My Sherri Amour: I was knocked out just to get hooked up. She carefully sets the popcorn box down on the empty seat next to her, lays her head on my shoulder, and my arm automatically responds by cuddling her closer still. It's so relaxing for a change to have someone who believes in you, and you believe in them. Someone who realizes I am multitalented, slightly mentally unwell, and knows I am a hilariously trusting, loving soul.

Technically, I was literally knocked into the arms of this green-eyed, thick eye-browed, dark-brown haired, intelligent, sugar-sweet twenty-one-year-old country girl with the damnedest, most voluptuous silhouette. Built like a brick shithouse from Seaside Oregon, who, more than most likely, had me the minute I smiled into her big, green eyes. How anyone like her could fall in love with a man who has a lump in the middle of his afro that resembles a penis is beyond me. If recollection serves me right, I distinctly remember praying for a country-loving woman, once upon my dizzy as I was walking down the street, minutes before I ran into her friend, Dawn. So my prayers have literally been answered. The rest is all of to me, I suppose. Here I go, thinking I'm in love again.

Sherri, Jeremy, and I are closer than ever, so we move to the northeast side of town, renting a two-bedroom, one-bath garage, three houses north of Alberta Street, which was close to Sherri's job at the convalescent home. A couple of weeks after we are pretty much settled into the new rental, Sherri decides to go out with some of her coworkers for a night of fun, leaving Jeremy with me. Of course, this calls for the ultimate popcorn party: chocolate-covered raisins, and root beer floats. Sherri leaves looking absolutely elegant, wearing a figure-hugging pantsuit and kitten heels. She leans over the couch and kisses Jeremy goodbye. He frowns as he wipes the smooch off his face, then she kisses me goodbye, heads out the door, and gets into her dookey-brown, four-speed Datsun B210 and takes off into the night. Jeremy and I watch movies until he falls asleep. I pick him up off the couch gently, carefully carry him to his bedroom, and lay him down in his bed. I cover him with the blankets, being careful not to step on any of his toys that are scattered all over the floor. I return to the living room, right foot limping from having stepped on a fire engine. Fighting sleep and boredom, I decide to watch one, maybe two more movies. But by now, the clock says it's almost four-thirty in the damned morning. I go into the kitchen, grab a tall forty-ounce beer and walk back to the living room where I sit on the edge of the brown couch, calling myself calm, cool, and collected. The lateness, or maybe the earliness, of the hour has me fist-fighting the thought of being put in a compromising position: women don't cheat on men, especially when said men are babysitting their four-year-old sons. Or do they? Well, I don't really want to know. Twenty long-ass minutes drag on by until I hear the Datsun pull up and the engine shut off. My mind is really going through some changes now; it's quite obvious from the fumbling noises coming from outside the front door that she's had way too much fun. I hear the sound of her key hitting and missing the keyhole as she attempts to unlock the door more than a couple of times. Sherri walks in staggering noticeably; her blouse is buttoned up wrong, and her lipstick and make up have completely vanished, as if she had never put any on at all. She slams the door and sways into the living room, her hair completely rattled up, like she had gone a few rounds upside-down in a haystack in some barn. I stand up slowly from the edge of the couch, somewhat bewildered. Then, the powerful, reeking stench of wild sex slowly engulfs the room, eating up all the available oxygen therein. She sets her purse down on the end table, tosses her keys where I was sitting on the couch, rolls her eyes, then stares at me with this whatever expression, knowing she's in a very peculiar position.

"Where have you been?" I ask respectfully, caringly. "I have been worried sick about you!" Though I can see very well I was just wasting my breath by asking. Sherri has been acting strange lately.

"What does it look like I've been doing?" she slurs out boldly, swaying drunk, daring me to do something. Then, in an instant, she's all up in my face, not holding back, as if I better recognize my place in this world. "It was all worth it, cheating on you! I had big fun!" she shouts boastfully, breathe smelling like a straight-up distillery-ass, up-close-and-personal. Then, with my demons aroused and my anger uncontrollable, I swing my right arm, hitting her in the face. She has taken me for a sucker, just like another woman I know. Her legs buckle under her and she goes down on the floor. *Shit! What am I doing?* I think to myself. I must be losing my crazy-ass mind. Look what I have been reduced to. That's right, I went there. I damned me, hook, line, and sinker. I sank down to her level of hell, exactly where she wanted me to go. Bamboozled once again by a booby-trapped relationship. "I am so sorry, Baby. I did not mean to do that," I say immediately, sincerely, trying to console her as I help her get up.

"Get your damn hands off of me!" Sherri commands, as she tries to push up off the floor with one hand, holding her face with the other.

"Why did you have to rub it in my face like that?" I ask loudly.

"You get the hell out of my house! Get your shit and leave! Get your ass out of my house!" she shouts seriously, the tears streaming down her face.

Pissed off at myself to the extreme max, I pack my few things in my blue suitcase. I'm kicked out again! I am tired of being in this situation. Six o'clock in the damn morning and evicted again for some damn shit! As I walk down to the bus stop on Alberta Street, I console myself with the solemn reassurance that the next place will be MY place, in MY name, and I'm not going to settle for anything less! What I'm I thinking: my cousin David T. Duke sabotaged my credit. I am so screwed!

5

. . . .

Starting All Over Again

Having survived the dysfunctional train wreck of my last relationship, I swallow my pride and abort my usual trajectory of living with someone I am involved with and move in with my mother, stepfather, and little sister, Nicole. However, before I can even entertain the thought of unpacking the few clothes I had managed to round up, I'm given a very harsh lecture on what I should and should not be doing. My mother literally lets me have it and own up to my mistakes, the psychological tongue-lashing of Tough Love. "Have you lost your damn mind, Eddie? You know I did not raise any of you to hit a woman. Unless she is trying to kill you! Now that is a different story altogether," she tells me, standing in the living room with her hands on her hips, then employing the pointing finger technique as she continues preaching to me. "She should not have done what she did, either! I am not excusing her."

"Yes ma'am," I reply, sitting down on the couch, very embarrassed, holding my head down out of shame, knowing I have been told time after time not to raise up on a female.

"I told you to let them crazy women alone, son," Pops says, sitting at the dining table with his legs crossed, nursing his shot of whiskey, cigarette burning in the ashtray. The smoke streaks the beam of sunlight through the double-pane window's white venetian blinds just behind Pops' head as he gently rubs his thick, black moustache. "See, Number One Son, you young. You just don't understand about life," Pops continues as he taps the table slightly with his fist. Pops always presents kind of a comical picture when he starts that speech. Mother and I both know Pops is quite tipsy, so we just listen and laugh as he just goes on and on. Then, somehow, he always winds up talking about Vietnam. My beautiful, weird little sister Nicole comes out of her room. She's about twelve years old, the fifth child, with long, curly black hair, and a butterscotch complexion. She's somewhat of an irritant, but she's still my little sister.

"Hey Lil' Mama, what are ya doing? That's a pretty dress you wearing there, Mama," Pops says to Nicole.

"What's up, Sis?" I say, looking bewildered while I sit on the couch.

"Are you moving back here, again?" Nicole asks me sarcastically, entering the living room, ready to get on my nerves like it's her main purpose in life.

"Yeah. Why? You got a problem with that?" I ask defensively, smiling, moving forward and sticking my tongue out at Nicole, which always triggers her snitching to Mother.

Then, about two weeks later, after I get home from spending the day rolling on the city bus, beating the concrete searching for employment and trying to maintain an upbeat attitude, my cousin Sally Ann, Donny and Ronny's little sister, gives me a call on the phone at the house. She says her buddy Tammy, my psychotic ex, has received her settlement and that I should spend some quality time with her to get my wardrobe replenished, as she has mentioned the situation to Sally Ann. Tammy stops by in person momentarily, riding copilot with my cousin Sally Ann, and offers a heartfelt apology in an attempt to persuade me to give her another chance. I remind her it is against the law to have burned my clothes and that it was an outright terrorist move on her part. I tell her, "I could only allow myself to be involved to a very minor extent, for my heart belongs to someone else." I'm in a slump and the only thing is to work my way out of it. So, after a couple of dates, I have only gotten one pair of jeans, a gray sweatshirt with my favorite NFL team's name across the front of it; Dallas Cowboys, a brand new black belt, and a very cheap, flimsy black sort of pullover jacket. I suddenly realize with my damaged cranium that she's just not going to keep her word. It's all just a dump truck full of bullshit. Finally, the next time she calls, I ask her exactly what her intentions are concerning the replacement of my clothes, which amounted to quite a large wardrobe. "I bought you some more clothes. If you acted right, I would let you have the rest!" she replies, stabbing my demons awake, the monsters that now have me hanging on a string.

"I will be up there to get the rest of the clothes you purchased for me, so please quit playing games. I will see you shortly, okay? Goodbye," I reply as she hangs up the phone in disgust. My blood begins to boil as I hang up. I'm tired of being stepped on. All because Tammy's mother told her a witch tale that if a so-called black man turns you down for sex, he is most likely cheating on you. Deadly dumb phrase!

Stepping out of the house into the backyard, I light a cigarette, plotting in my mind some kind of resolution to this ignorant dilemma so I can move on with my life and put this into the past where it rightfully belongs. I fish a can of beer out of the cooler sitting next to the freshly stained, burnt-red picnic table where Popeye, Bub, and Pops are sipping some afternoon delight from their white Styrofoam cups. Sitting on the table in front of a large, clear ashtray is a fifth of Seagram's Seven. I suddenly remember I'm tired of being stepped on. This is not over. I open my can of beer and take a vicious swallow of barley as I walk toward the sundried table where Pops and the seasoned man-gang are assembled. They're lounging with their drinks, comfortably discussing current events on this unbelievably beautiful sunny fall day, somewhere on the downside of four o'clock in the afternoon. I sit down just in time to be the butt end of a joke. "Hey, Eddie, there you are! I've been looking all over for you!" Popeye says. He's sitting next to Bud, smoking a cigarette, dressed like its summertime, inspecting the inside of his Styrofoam cup as if a fly had just made a fly-by. He's on the far side of the table looking like there is something really important he has to inform me of. I can just imagine what that may be.

"Yes, Popeye? What exactly is on your mind?" I ask, putting my foot in my mouth. I sit down next to Pops on the opposite side of the table where the shade blocks the unfamiliar light, set the almost-empty can of beer on the table, curious to hear these great words of esteemed wisdom Popeye has to bestow unto me and his middle-aged friends.

Popeye sets down his Styrofoam cup, pauses for a moment, then asks me, "How is your head?" Everybody at the picnic table starts laughing loudly.

"It's getting quite the attention it deserves. But the lump has disappeared. Maybe for the duration. My head is fine and I'm back too normal," I am pleased to report, defending my medical disposition. As Bud and Slim chime in laughing at my expense, Pops shakes his head with his legs crossed, sipping on his concoction. In an effort to inject some adrenalin into the situation, I decidedly go ahead and fix me a stiff shot of whiskey, pouring it into a Styrofoam cup also, and relax from the situation at hand because when Pops gets to talking, there's no telling when he is going to seize up. Somehow, after fixing my drink, my haunted mind has come to the conclusion that Tammy is constantly serving me a silver platter of bullshit.

"See, Son, you're young and you don't quite understand about life!" my stepfather, buzzing happily, starts his rendition of, "These crazy-ass young women out here be brainwashed and devious under the umbrella of Pacific Northwest cabin fever."

For some strange reason, as I absorb my drink and the criticism, the absolute nerve of the truth makes me realize that just thinking about Sherri makes me feel better. Maybe it's because she believes in my many talents and always encourages me to sing, entertain, or write. She pumps me up and makes me feel like a king. Sherri's influence is obvious as I find my thoughts turning back to one August day when everything we attempted to do went incredibly very wrong.

For the record, it started out just fine. Sherri and I were cruising at residential speed in the dookey-brown Datsun. She was driving, heading east down Killingworth Street. We arrived at 42nd Avenue and the car just stalled, halted, and broke down. Dead battery. Then the key broke in the ignition. Then the right-rear tire went flat. The final straw was when we learned we were also out of gas, just across the street from the gas station, which was being pounded with pouring showers of rain. We were all in route to picking up our checks at the same time, and all we could do was laugh and laugh about it. There was no other solution to this seemingly ongoing, unlimited series of progressively worsening events. Talk about drama. We both agreed that if we could make it through twenty-four hours of a "damned if I do, damned if I don't" dysfunctional day of our relationship, we could understand that our love for one another should be able to endure the hands of time. Forever. That was the day of the automotive intervention, mixed with constant showers which kept us cool and wet. Rather than argue, we literally laughed all the way to the bank. And it made no sense to be enraged about anything, now that the power in the area was out, also.

"Still trying to get your clothes replaced from that woman?" Bub asks seriously catching me off-guard, daydreaming. He starts to laugh, motioning faintly with both hands, cigarette protruding between the fingers of his right, sipping his cocktail from a Styrofoam container with his left, being real low-key for a change. However, there's no blues playing, either. What Bub had just asked me snapped me out of my exclusive daydream, but it has no effect on my advancing intoxicating buzz. I am now caught up in one of the lowest levels of frustration junction. Thinking weirdly to myself, I replied to Bub by saying yes, then standing up, secretly pissed, and wanting the rest of my damn clothes. Who in the hell does Tammy think she is? I find myself easing away without drawing attention to myself. Pops is busy telling his Vietnam War stories of how, back in the day, soldiers couldn't really tell who the enemy was. So , without an explanation of my destination, I take off. Fast. Striding across the green, freshly cut grass while the sun heats up the spot where my hair no longer grows. For some strange reason, every little step I take up Drummond Avenue causes my blood pressure to rise to the level of instantaneously experiencing a large dose of self-pity. So to combat it, I ignorantly speed walk, panting heavily like I had one cigarette too many, and the alcohol has me sweating through my black, short-sleeved, tight-fitting shirt while my legs stay heated up in my blue designer jeans, even though sunset was approaching gradually. The six blocks seem to take forever. I finally make it to the familiar abode where I once resided, until that insane Friday night months ago. I'm looking across the street from Tammy's at my favorite neighbors' place, Charlie and Sheila's.

Now, Charlie is Caucasian, pale, medium-build, five foot nine. He has blue eyes, mid-length blonde hair, and has a heart more precious than gold. He's the kind of person you can always count on and a very easygoing guy. He lives with his beloved Sheila—who is five feet, has green eyes, long sandy-blonde hair—and their three young blonde-haired daughters in a large, high-pitched yellow dwelling with four bedrooms, two baths, a basement, and an unattached double garage. There's a spacious wooden front porch with wide cement steps that lead to the walkway to the yard. I'm now having flashbacks of what is not going to occur ever again, so I jog up the stairs since I'm now feeling my second wind. I decide not to accept no for an answer. I knock on the wooden doorframe while looking through the window in the door, its white lace curtain slightly open, giving me a view into the living room. I get no immediate response. However, I see the shadows of two individuals, one finally coming to the door after I have made it very apparent by constantly knocking that I am not going away. Tammy approaches, talking through the door saying, "I don't have any of your clothes here!" like I'm some unwanted insane person. "That's just too bad what happen to your clothes!" she says proudly, walking away from the door, ignoring my request as if I was a lost puppy from the Humane Society. Annoyed and feeling disrespected, I grab and try to turn the crystal-like knob, hoping it is unlocked. Nope. I use my shoulder, hitting the door three times. On the third try, I miss the wooden frame, breaking the window glass out of the now-fragile door.

"Give me my damn clothes!" I shout. As I enter the dwelling I notice another man around my size with her.

"I don't have any of your damn clothes, Eddie!" she says, as I'm standing just barely inside the doorway, suddenly feeling very wet around my shoulder area. Tammy yells, "You are bleeding all over the floor!" as the blood has taken a fast trip in trickling down my arm to the point where I realize that I had better do something quick, even though it doesn't hurt quite as bad as I am bleeding. I back cautiously out of the doorway, grabbing my shoulder as I go down the stairs. What the hell to do is staring straight at me once I arrive at the bottom of the steps. And that would be to see if they have a First Aid kit, which would be appropriate, even though I assume it's not that bad, since it does not hurt as much as I thought a self-inflicted wound would. But not here at Tammy's. I rush over to Charlie and Sheila's in the dim twilight because Sheila is a nurse of sorts. Anyway, I'm knocking loudly on the basement door because they frequently use it when they want to seriously get away from their offspring. From inside, Charlie asks who it is, and I reply, "It's Eddie! I kind of have an emergency, Charlie!" through the worn yellow basement door, which seems to be barely hanging on by its rusty-looking hinges.

Charlie, naked as a jaybird, quickly opens the door, looks at me and says, "Get the hell in here! What happen to you?"

"I ran into Tammy's door window glass instead of hitting the frame," I explain.

Charlie takes a look at my bloody shirt and says, "Get the hell in here! You need to take your shirt off, Brother Eddie."

Sheila, coming to the rescue, takes one look at the blood covering my shoulder and says, "Charlie, get the cocaine so he won't go into shock." She's wearing a pink nighty robe with her long hair hanging down elegantly. As I step into the basement, I become aware of feeling a great pain that my buzz is doing nothing to deaden, but nowhere near as great as being technically knocked out with a hard plastic phone receiver by the opposite sex. There is just no comparison. Sheila, with her arm around me, leads me over to their bed and sits me down, then asks me if I'm slightly light-headed. "I don't think so," I reply, but I'm really not sure because I'm not at all well psychically, or feeling embarrassed at all about the entire situation. This whole thing is like it's a movie. I'm sitting on the comfy but worn mattress, trying not to get blood everywhere. Sheila helps me get the shirt over my head while Charlie slips into some jeans, then starts playing chemist with a razor, a playing card, and a ceramic plate whose surface contains a considerable amount of cocaine. The majority of the plate is covered in nice thick lines. Charlie rolls a dollar bill very tightly for me to snort my way to painlessness, courtesy of the drug called candy. Once my shirt is finally off, I feel like passing out. In a shocked voice, Sheila gasps, "I can see his shoulder bone! Quick! Put some cocaine in the wound!" Now they're holding my arm as if they are attempting to disconnect it from my anatomy while blood has trickled down my arm to my fingertips. Losing the precious, dark red fluid is now causing me some concern. I'm probably already in shock and don't know it.

"Hold still, Eddie, my friend!" Charlie says. "This is going to make it all better!" I am having second thoughts, since I've never experienced the white, chalky looking drug in this manner. Charlie administers the baking powder–looking substance with a slightly bent card, sprinkling it directly inside my fabulous laceration as if it were pepper on potatoes. Instead of the door, I managed to break myself against the glass. I certainly learned a lesson this time: I have the constitutional right to fuck myself up. Literally! Thirty-something year old's think they know it all! No choice in the matter but to move on.

All right. Describing spontaneous combustion would be the equivalent of the utter silence of the pain in my mocha shoulder. This shows up immediately when the cocaine is introduced into my wound, causing me to relax into the glow of the red lightbulb inside the off-white shade of a lamp sitting on the antique pine dresser in the basement. Then I realize the see-through pink robe reveals Sheila's sexy, beautiful anatomy as Charlie is slipping into his black boots, and then his T-shirt, which made the shameful situation all that much better. "I should be going," Sheila states, being a good caring friend. "But there is no one here to watch the girls." She also starts to get dressed, though she is not one bit ashamed of her precious body. She slips on some jeans and a sweatshirt while I manage to snort two huge lines up each nostril, which immediately stings the insides of my nose, squinting my face into an ugly mask of agony.

"Let's go, Eddie! We've got to get you to Emanuel Hospital emergency ASAP!" Charlie says, accepting the rolled up dollar bill from my hand, then snorting a couple of lines himself. Once Sheila is dressed, she brings me a sweatshirt to wear, partakes of two rails of the numbing candy, and we all head out of the basement and into their yellow two-door, beefed-up '78 Dodge Charger with fat, wide chrome wheels and air shocks jacking up the back. Charlie starts up the hot rod as I enter the rear seat from the passenger side. When we're all in the car, Charlie lays rubber, leaving the driveway, and we head down Villard Avenue to the emergency faster than any ambulance invented in this here century. We arrive in no time flat. After Charlie gives me curb service, I walk humbly through the double doors, holding my right hand on my shoulder, and my arm right across my chest, as if I'm trying desperately to keep it together. The lady at the window is instantly concerned about my well-being, what with all the obvious blood about my person. She asks me have I been stabbed or cut, and I reply yes, after which she takes me straight back to the examination room, then disappears to find a nurse to attend to my condition immediately.

What I didn't know was that when you arrive in the emergency room and you are in shock, *you* are the last person to realize it. The door flies open from the push of a fluffy, five-foot-nine, two-hundred-and-fifty-pound, nice-faced brunette nurse in blue scrubs with serious dark-green eyes who takes her job extra serious and very professional. "Hello. My name is Helga. I understand you have been cut, correct?" she asks as she puts on a pair of latex gloves like she's going to enjoy the opportunity of giving me a cavity search. Once she accomplishes that task, she immediately asks me my name. At the same time, she takes a look at my self-inflicted wound and tells me to lie down quickly, as if something bad just occurred. I lie down on the examination table; she grabs some scissors and cuts the sweatshirt off of me without giving me a chance at taking it off myself. Then, all of a sudden, she says, "We must get you out of all your clothes!" Instantly and aggressively, she's snatching my pants off fiercely like I was rapidly sinking into a complete state of shock. Seconds later, I am buck naked on the examination table with the ambitious nurse taking my vitals, then handing me some cheap, flimsy, blue hospital clothing with the back out, asking the usual medical history questions before getting to exactly what happened to my shoulder. I tell her, "My ex was supposed to be replacing my clothes that she had previously burned up. So, when I arrived at her house, she played the part of denial, saying she didn't have any of my clothes and she had no intention of purchasing me any more clothes. She locks the door to keep me from entering. Then, allowing my stupid assessment of this crazy situation to let me justify trying to open a glass window door enclosed within a wooden frame using my invincible left shoulder, only then do I find out that she was just stringing me along by saying she was going to replace the rest of my clothes. Tammy had no real intention in the first place of replacing any more of my personal belongings. She purposely duped me. That's pretty much what's happening."

The nurse looks inside my wound and says, "That's pretty deep. But my main concern is, are you not in any kind of pain?"

After she examines the deep laceration, I explain, "The second my good neighbors Charlie and Sheila realized I was injured, they poured cocaine on my injury, causing immediate numbness and relief. And even though they were in the middle of celebrating their anniversary together, they still brought me to emergency. But that's what real friends do for one another." Then the doctor enters the examination room: long white physician's lab coat, six-foot-tall, olive-shaded Caucasian, black hair, blue eyes, a stern-faced smooth operator who looks very rested and eager to do some stitching. "How are we doing this evening, Mr. Williams?" he asks, as he examines the now-sterile wound, thanks to the very-thorough large nurse with an even larger heart and an appreciative, dedicated nature about making sure the doctor has everything he needs before starting to put Humpty Dumpty back together again. Starting off with these long needles of more numbing liquid. Since the cocaine was quickly wearing off, well, bring it on! Because that is one thing I don't fear after having been hospitalized; you get poked so much it makes no difference to you anymore. The doctor was curious as to how I came to be the victim of such an injury. I explain to him what I told his nurse. However, the doctor's reply made more sense. And that was, "Forget about your losses and move on with your life. So your ex put a lump on your head and burned your clothes? You're lucky you got away with your life. Stay away from her and move on." Those words echoed in my head long after the doctor put eighteen stitches shaped like an upside down letter L in my shoulder. And to my surprise, it didn't hurt. All in all, a not-very-painful episode in my life.

Charlie, so glad to be there for a friend in need, drops me off at my parents' late that night. And that's the night I started praying for change in my life, to better myself, to urgently get out of the slump I put myself into, and especially thanking Almighty God for good friends who are like diamonds in the rough. Charlie and Sheila! You are the best!

Two weeks later, the stitches in my shoulder have surprisingly all dissolved, leaving a scar that resembles a seven. After looking for a job all day downtown, I walk into the house and hear the phone ringing. I manage to grab the yellow phone in the kitchen before it stops ringing, desperately hoping it's a call about a possible job opportunity. I compose myself, ready to reply to the call in a businesslike manner. And bam! Out of nowhere it's the one person in this world who can actually ring my bell and make my day at the same time: Sherri. My spirit took an unexpected leap up ten heartfelt stories, up to the heights my soul had not yet reached. I am overwhelmed by the musical sound of her beautiful, distinctive voice. Not really known for being overly emotional, a big smile magically transforms my serious face. I realize what I am really missing in my life: my girl, my Sherri Amore, my loving, delicious, Snooky Nooky Poo Poo!

"How are you doing?" I ask, glad to be having this conversation. I switch to the cordless phone in the living room, sit on the couch against the wall, stare at the floor-model color TV directly in front of me. On the far wall, the big, front picture window is to my left, its light-green curtains open just enough to see Miss Mary's white house, the kiwi vine, and an assortment of lilac bushes, apricot trees, and red, yellow, and white roses spread out all over the front yard. She lives there with her husband, Al, who, from head to toe, is almost a dead ringer for Sammy Davis, Jr. They own a brown-and-white Springer Spaniel named Katie, and Charlie Bird, an African Gray parrot who mimics just about all sounds and voices. Katie prances around the cyclone-fenced yard sniffing the green grass, looking for a place to do her dog business. "Missing you," Sherri quickly responds, as I am rubbing my head slightly, feeling for that annoying lump that debuted on my head, which is acting like it's trying to make a comeback. "Honey, I am so sorry for what I did to you. I really miss you and, seriously, I want to start all over again with you. I can't stop thinking about you. I love you, Baby. I only want to be with you. Except I cannot handle living in Portland. The big city is just not me, Baby," she says, admitting her weaknesses, and that this relationship doesn't stand a chance of working in the Rose City Metropolis. Therefore, only one formula will fix what has been broken.

"I am so sorry. I will never, ever, do that again, Baby. I swear. I promise, Snooky Nooky Poo Poo," I reply, being very apologetic, calling her by the sweet pet name she just adores, especially after we've had mad, passionate, around-the-clock mega sex.

"Baby, I miss hearing you say that," Sherri says sensually, driving me wild by saying all the right things I really need to hear. Just the motivation my mojo desires. "I know you won't because I intentionally provoked you," Sherri volunteers.

"No excuses for me. It will never happen again," I swear to Sherri. "However, there is a solution to our complicated problem, Snooky. I've always dreamed of living at the beach." With that said, I figured I may as well go all the way out. "Sweetheart, since your desire is to live back in your home town, this would be the perfect opportunity for me—as in we—to experience the Oregon Coast for a change. It's not like I'm going back in the army anytime soon." I mention the last part to make the choice that much easier, since we don't have too many options on the table.

"You would do that for me, Baby?" Sherri asks excitedly, but still not quite convinced.

"Yes, I will. After all, you tried it up here in the city. Well, now let me try it down there. It can't be that damn racist down along the Northwest Pacific Coast, can it?" I ask her.

"You are serious. Aren't you, Baby?" Sherri asks, not believing what she's hearing.

"I love you so much, Snooky, that I can't stop thinking about you," I say, leaning back on the couch with this million-dollar grin on my face. "All I have to do before I make my move is let my probation officer know I am going to relocate to the coast, obtain gainful employment, spend some quality time with my kids and inform them that their out-of-this-world dad is relocating to the Oregon Coast."

Sherri tells me, "Honey, I am working at another convalescent home in Astoria. However, check this out. I will probably land a job at the Shilo Inn in Seaside, which is a beautiful hotel located right on the beach. My sister Kelly works there as a dinner waitress. I plan on getting a job at the Shilo Inn first, and then hopefully find a position for you, Baby. I miss you so much I sleep on your shirt. I refuse to wash because it smells like you." She's making me feel like I'm the luckiest man on earth.

"What did your parents say about the fight we had?" I ask, changing the subject, and wanting to know what I'm getting myself into, knowing I'm not in such great standing with them.

"They are not happy campers about it. But I told them I provoked you," she says. "What did your mother say?" Sherri's very concerned about what my mother thinks of her since they hit it off so well at the beginning of our crazy relationship.

"That I had no excuse for what I did, and I wasn't raised to do those kinds of things," I tell her.

"She doesn't like me. Do she?" Sherri asks, not knowing the half of it.

"That's not what is important. What's important is, what do we want?" I announce.

The next day, Pops voluntarily drives me over to the Southeast side of town to report to my probation officer. I inform him that I will be relocating to Seaside, Oregon. Then I spend some quality time with my kids who I love very much. Shamelah is eight years old and Deon is nine; both look exactly like me despite having different mothers. I buy them the Christmas presents their little hearts' desire. They think it's the bomb that their dad is moving to the beach, and they're already thinking about all the fun they are going to have when they come and spend the summer at the coast. It will be a blast! However, when I announce it to the rest of the family, some can't handle that I'm moving to Seaside because of the inferno of stereotypical hatred there that whites have for African Americans. This grips my loved ones' thoughts, especially the older generation, who grew up there in the fifties and couldn't quite handle it. Meanwhile, all my first, second, and third cousins love the fact that their cousin will be residing at the beach, which means only one thing: they are coming down there. No ifs, ands, or buts about it.

This particular weekend, my abnormal immediate family is all congregated at Mother's house for New Year's when I announce the shocking news. Aunt Marie, my mother's sister, and her husband, Uncle Walt are present, as well as Slim, Popeye, and Bud. My mother swiftly answers the ringing phone with an air of anticipation, hoping it's my grandfather, Bishop H.B. Daniels, Sr. "Hi, Daddy!" I hear my mother saying eagerly into the black, cordless phone. "I'm fine. He is right here. Eddie, telephone. You-know-who wants to talk to you," Mother says, gently handing me the phone. For every person in my family, there will be just that many opinions. But my Grandpa is a whole other story.

"Hello, Grandpa. How is you?" I say, as I walk down the hallway for more privacy and to be able to hear over the mid-level roar of everyone all talking at the same time.

"I understand you are moving to the beach," Grandpa says.

"Yes, Grandfather. I am moving to Seaside," I reply.

"Well, just know that I love you and you should go to church while you are down there. Okay, Grandson? I love you, and you take care of yourself," Grandpa says, short, but sweet, sounding very upbeat about my decision. He's always been a positive grandparent when it comes to me.

"I love you too. I will be okay, you'll see," I say, trying to reassure him. I hang up, walk back down the hallway and hand the phone back to my mother.

"When you leaving for the beach, Eddie?" Uncle Walt asks while picking up his drink from the table. I tell him I'll be moving the next weekend. "Tell Daddy a lie, and tell Mama the truth," Uncle Walter says. Clearly, he is a little tipsy and letting his emotions get the best of him. He knows he's not going to able to talk me out of this outrageous decision that will have an impact on the rest of my life. So much so that I can't even begin to comprehend the state of things to come.

"I am serious, Uncle Walter. I am moving to the beach," I say, letting him know I really am serious. I sit down next to him on the couch and he gradually puts his arm around my shoulder.

"I have one thing to ask, since you are moving down there to the ocean boondocks, Nephew. What is the most important verse in the

Bible?" Uncle Walt asks, taking a sip of his gin-and-grapefruit juice concoction, then setting it back down on the table.

"John 3:16," I snap back at him, like a choirboy in Sunday school.

"That is correct. You make sure you take good care of yourself. I am not even going to try to talk you out of it," Uncle Walter says, kissing me on the forehead. "I've already been through what you are about to do, Eddie. I have lived in some small, all-white-populated Oregon towns, like Estacada and Roseburg, with your Uncle Glenn when he was working as a counselor in the Job Corps. So I know, sometimes you have to find out for yourself."

My Aunt Marie says sitting there, looking just like her sister, my mother, but you won't hear my mother uttering great, racial platitudes, since she has experienced the obvious racism that has plagued Oregon for many years. "Eddie, I know you are a good man. But some white folks just don't like to see a good man like you succeed. They are the ones you are going to have to worry about," Slim says respectfully, while pointing his finger at me and showing his fearful, caring thoughts about me.

"I would like to say something, if I may," Popeye says, somewhat tipsy, which gets everybody in the small square footage dwelling to hush. He might as well, since everyone else is chiming in. It's all love. I am very touched that they all care so much about my well-being, and I am going to miss them. That's what makes me love them, more than ever. "Eddie, how's your head?" Popeye asks jokingly, which lightens up the mood as everyone laughs, including me. I assure everyone they don't have to worry about Sherri hitting me on the head with a telephone or burning up my entire wardrobe. In that respect, they all agree that would never ever occur while I'm with Sherri, since all of them are very acquainted with Sherri and Jeremy Blaine, as my mother continues with her intervention that has no effect on my final decision. There's more chance of a blizzard in Hell than me not going to the Northwest Pacific Coast. My mind's made up.

"I encourage all of my children to spread their wings, travel, and do things I didn't get to do. However, I don't condone my children going to places where they can be seriously lynched just because of the damn color of their skin," my mother says, finally adding her comments as she walks through the house, not at all in favor of my relocating to the beach. She has every right to voice her opinion, concerns, beliefs, and shortcomings.

"You are going to Ku Klux Klan land," my stepfather says, sitting at the table his legs crossed, sipping whiskey from a double shot glass. He's overly concerned due to some of the confrontations they've encountered: wicked racial situations in Lincoln City, which is ninety miles southwest of Portland. However, even in my pre-teenage years when our parents and grandparents would take us to Seaside, I can never, ever, recall one single incident out of all the numerous family getaways there. I even recollect having picnics at Cannon Beach, as well. Maybe that's why I'm not fearful of the well-known racism in small towns.

"Pop, the KKK is everywhere in Oregon," I respond truthfully as I stand up.

"Just promise your old stepdaddy that you'll watch your back and stay in touch," he tells me. I talked to quite a few cousins before my departure. Mostly, they all had positive things to say about Seaside, thinking it was slap-dookey-cool to have a relative living at the beach. Cool because of the simple fact that they have somewhere to stay, and believe-you-me, they are definitely going to make the trip. Nothing like a quiet getaway.

I'm chilling alone at my parents' the very next afternoon, sitting on the couch in the living room watching MTV. Paula Abdul's video, "Opposites Attract," is playing as the phone rings. Unthinkingly, a crude, non-devilish smile grows on my face as I pick up the phone and do a two-step, knowing it's my favorite wine, Sherri, on the other end of the line, anxious. "Hello. I am he that is moving to the beach," I say, with a smiley face.

"Hi, Baby. You're in a good mood!" Sherri says, excited, still in extreme disbelief.

"I'm coming to see you. I sure do miss some of you," I tell her.

"That is fine, Honey. I just called to let you know we are staying with a friend in Warrenton, temporarily. Okay, Baby? I still can't believe you are actually going to move down here, just to be with me," she says, excitedly. I made it just fine overseas in German Town; I think I can handle the Northwest Pacific Coast. My loving, caring, huge family might not like it, but it's my life. I've got to live it to the fullest. Sherri's doubtful voice was a dead giveaway, for a good reason. I suppose she wasn't a hundred percent sure I was actually going to relocate to the coast. If I can somehow forgive Tammy for assault in the first degree, surely I can forgive Sherri Lynn, the one who possess the combination to my heart. This old saying of yours truly, which I keep so dear to my heart, comes to mind. It goes like this: I can show you better than I can tell you.

6

. . . .

Welcome Coastal Jungle

On Saturday afternoon, the sun in the sky plays a game of peek-a-boo with the gray, billowy clouds. It's a January 13, 1990, Martin Luther King, Jr. Holiday weekend in Portland on a normal, partially overcast afternoon, temperature in the mid-fifty degree range for this time of year. George H. W. Bush is the forty-first President of the United States. The NFC Champion San Francisco 49ers and the AFC Champion Denver Broncos are to play in Super Bowl XXIV in New Orleans. The residual static of Jessie Jackson's African-American run for the highest office in America has psychologically spooked a lot of undecided Americans who fear unwarranted change, which re-enforces their intention of there never being a black president. And Mike Tyson is the undisputed Heavyweight Champion of the world.

Grateful to the Almighty for another day, I am enthusiastically overwhelmed. I depart from my parent's home and this town once again, dressed in blue jeans, a multi-colored, reddish flannel long-sleeve shirt I received as a Christmas present, my worn-out black Reeboks which saw better days a long time ago, and not to forget, my black Guess windbreaker. As I eagerly march toward my stepfather's truck, I glance at the beautiful, green, ever-changing neighborhood I grew up in, and realize there's a journey ahead of me that I must take. I'm on the front porch, telling my mother goodbye, once again. "I love you. Don't worry. I will be happy." Of course, her reply is,

"Please be careful," and giving me a good, tight embrace, which is quite frightfully different from when I departed from basic training, or when I left for Giessen, Germany immediately after getting hitched. I'm listening to the radio while Pops, being unlawfully silent and smoking a cigarette, drives me to the bus station. He's most likely trying to find the right words to say to me. Soon, being no longer able to hold his peace, he flicks the long cigarette ash in the ashtray just under the built-in radio on the dashboard. He turns left on Broadway, pulls up in front of the Greyhound bus station, and at that moment, lays his weighty wisdom on me as he brakes his excellently conditioned black-and-white rig to a stop in front of the main entrance. As he drops me off, he says a very heartfelt, riddled with little sorrow, "Don't take any wooden nickels," like he expressed to me prior to my leaving for Europe. He gives me curb service to the double-door front entrance of the red brick bus station in downtown Portland, which is in close proximity to the train station, located directly catty-corner behind Greyhound, in the Northwest side of downtown Portland. Taking a positive outlook, I mindfully purchase a one-way ticket at the counter with the large glass windows and walk with suitcase in hand to my departure gate.

From Portland to Seaside, Oregon by bus via Astoria is an approximate distance of eighty miles. The trip lasts all of two hours going by way of Highway 30 West, with nothing to see but low, rolling mountains, beautiful scenery, green foliage, and a slight dusting of snow in the higher elevations around Saddle Mountain. It's really nothing to write home about. However, I'm the only African American on the long, silver Greyhound, which, when you live in Oregon, can easily be described as the norm. There's about twenty-five people, young as well as old, in scattered seating on both sides of the bus, all going about their lives, headed for different destinations on this milk run of sorts, which stops everywhere along the Oregon coast: Scappoose, St. Helens, Rainier, Rockaway, Jewel Mist, Elsie, and the beautiful city of Manzanita. Astoria, Oregon is situated near the mouth of the Columbia River, has a deep-water port, and was the first US settlement in the Pacific Northwest. The current population of about ten thousand was no shock to me, as this is the status quo.

Mainly Americans of European descent live out this way in Oregon, which is commonly known as the Beaver State.

I was attending Peninsular Elementary School's eighth grade when our class embarked on a field trip to Astoria, Oregon in preparation for our next writing assignment: an essay about Fort Astoria. We visited a lot of historical sites and looked over numerous fur trading artifacts. However, the one thing that stands out in my memory is the Astor Column. Built atop Coxcomb Hill high above Astoria, it stands 125 feet tall and presents a panoramic view of Astoria and the surrounding countryside. Over there's the Columbia River flowing into the Pacific Ocean where the world's tastiest crab, sturgeon, oysters, clams, Ling cod, and salmon are there for the taking. There are plenty of forests everywhere, which provide habitat for rabbit, deer, elk, and wild geese. My charismatic persona weighs no more than 150 pounds, a lean-muscled wet dish rag, so I am no threat to them. I am not a promoter of self-hatred, a condition that's not consistent with my DNA! Hate is *the* number one waste of human energy. As we come into close proximity to our destination, you can smell the change; the elevation, as well as the salt-scattered air from the Pacific Ocean is letting us know we are truly on the Pacific Northwest Coast!

When you first enter Astoria, you're greeted by these huge, ornate period homes, carefully built everywhere on this steep, green, mountainous area. The driver slides into his last turn carefully, pulling into this tiny bus station on schedule as one of the passengers' headphones barely broadcasts Robert Palmer's "Simply Irresistible" into the shell of the bus. I somehow realize I am in the neighborhood where they filmed *The Goonies* in 1985. As the bus comes to a stop, now I can hear Milli Vanilli's "Blame It on the Rain" very faintly, coming out of this curly brown-headed, jeans jacket–wearing dude's headphones a couple of rows of seats directly in front of me. Then, out of my visual periphery, I quickly pinpoint Sherri's dookey-brown Datsun B210 parked on the other side of the street in front of some huge historical building. I wave to her, signaling in my own body language, in case she thought I wasn't going to make the change of buses. Well, think again, cause here I am! She smiles excitedly when she detects my chocolate, youthful silhouette inside the long silver bus and waves eagerly. Surprised, but no longer doubtful, Sherri literally ejects herself from the car, jumping mad-crazy as the car door swings open wildly. I maneuver myself in my seat so I can look at her again from the rear window of the bus, letting her know visually that I am not an illusion, just crazy, excited, mocha-chocolate Me, watching my gorgeous Lady of Eye Candy cross the busy street in downtown Astoria. I'm imagining she's moving in slow motion as I watch her crossing the street. The driver makes the announcement over the intercom that we may depart the vehicle and thanks us for choosing Greyhound. The passengers grab up their belongings, then stand in line in the aisle, waiting patiently, ready to get off. It's a grayish, cloudy day and I move toward the front of the bus with the rest of the passengers. I survey my surroundings, making sure I have all my belongings. I'm as excited as a dolphin in the Pacific Ocean. Sherri is run-walking alongside the bus to greet me, the love of my life, just a fine, delicious specimen of a lady sporting a tight-fitting, sexy black sweater jumpsuit that shows off her super curvy, gorgeous silhouette. She's a hot, thick brick house country-crazy woman who I'm very proud of. The strong smell of the salty ocean greets me as I step off the bus. I watch her heavenly smile that drives me buck wild as she delicately, innocently walks up to me and we instantly embrace like where're neurotic newlyweds who were shipwrecked, then separated for a year, missing each other crazily, now rejoined, kissing one another, not caring about who on this planet happens to be looking, or the unbelievers who can't fathom a loving biracial relationship. I'm no longer imagining what it's like to hold my Sherri Amour lovingly, proudly, in my arms once again. Well, the facts speak quite clearly for themselves.

Now, as to the rest of this love equation. This relationship's only major function is to be a successful one. It is strictly up to ourselves how much we really want to be together forever and to make it happen. This will be the ultimate test of our love for one another as, side by side, we embark on a journey into the cool, green, clean, weathered coastal beaches of the Pacific Northwest Jungle, rich in adventurous history, caves, mountains, lakes, coves, beach volleyball, golf, sand castle-building, fishing, and crabbing.

"See? I told you I could show you better than I could tell you, Snooky Nooky! How do you like me, now?" I ask, smiling, feeling automatically happy-relaxed, like a beach bum who doesn't have a care in the world. I hold her captive, insistently hugging, kissing her, can't keep my hands or eyes off this amazing lady who possesses the proverbial combination to my emotional Libra love-lock.

"I love you very much, Baby," Sherri says, hugging and kissing me again. I shuffle over to the bus hatch where the driver has already diligently set my suitcase down on the pavement. I retrieve my light-blue, weightless suitcase, then stroll with Sherri, our arms entwined around each other as we turtle walk across the street. I place my huge suitcase in the cramped backseat of the compact, dookey-brown Datsun and realize just how much I'd been missing that buzzing, muzzle sound of its four-cylinder engine.

"Well, Sweetheart, we are starting a new chapter in our lifetime of love at the coast. Are you really ready for this?" I ask, looking at her face-to-face, then quickly sliding my tongue up her right nostril. Sherri jumps slightly, then, realizing how much she missed my comical antics, smiles, lets it go, and I kiss her once again.

"Yes, Baby, now that you are here," Sherri says happily, no longer skeptical. "I did not know if you were really moving down here or not," she adds, starting the car and pulling away from the curb, making an illegal U-turn into the traffic, heading in a different direction from where the bus came into town. I must be turned around somewhat. I'll have to get my directional compass together and educate myself on my whereabouts now that I am residing here. It's about time I start paying more attention to detail, for there is no time like the present. It doesn't get any better than that.

We see picturesque houses near and far, tucked into the green-colored background here and there. Then we head south on well-known Highway 101, which extends through three West Coast states, starting from Washington, through Oregon, and finally through the Golden State of California. Suddenly, my seafood addiction kicks in and I experience an acute desire for crab with cocktail sauce, accompanied by some good champagne. That would absolutely make this Saturday all the much better, so I suggest that we celebrate with some fresh-out-the-water crab, which is just one of the dozens of my positive reasons for wanting to make the coast my second home for life. "I have already taken care of that request because I knew you wanted some, Baby," Sherri replies, grinning, holding my hand in hers. We go on pacifying each other like this until we arrive at our destination. We cross the lime-green Young's Bay Bridge, which spans the Columbia River and connects Astoria to Warrenton, otherwise known as the Lewis and Clark Trail. The blue ocean's salty water is so beautiful, and the scenery so breathtaking I look like I'm a tourist viewing squealing seagulls around the docks as sea lions clown with one another in their shining wet coats around the mouth of the river and the Pacific Ocean, where bald eagles, geese, and the occasional owl rule the skies over Saddle Mountain and the Clatsop Plains in this neck of the Great Northwest.

We are both all smiles and finding it hard to keep our hands to ourselves. Daydreaming Cupid is kicking our crazy animalistic natures into extreme overdrive, stubbornly stimulating our horny to the point where our can't-seem-to-keep-our-hands-off-one-another infatuation has us both wanting nothing less than unadulterated makeup, mad, mega-sex until we are raw, an unstoppable, hours-long love session until we pass out cuddling, held in one another's arms in dripping-wet, well-used sheets from extended mega lovemaking until the sun comes up, smiles upon our faces. Suddenly, we're no longer thinking about our bellies being full of fresh salad castled with ranch dressing. Or crisp, cracked crab dipped in cocktail sauce. Or delightfully force-feeding each other succulent seafood tidbits. Right now, our thoughts are running along the lines of just licking each other's fingers, which is acting on us like an ultimate, sensualistic aphrodisiac.

"We will be staying with a coworker friend of mine in Warrenton for a few days. Her name is Karen and I used to work with her in Astoria at a convalescent home. She lives alone in a very nice trailer park not far from here," Sherri says, rubbing her baby-soft hand inside the palm of mine, sending me all the right messages as she finishes crossing the bridge. She exits Highway 101 and turns onto the main street heading into Warrenton, which makes me pretty sure Fort Stevens is somewhere around here. I had performed military duties in the National Guard thirteen years ago when I was still a teenager and couldn't even vote in that year's presidential election. However, I was old enough to go to war and die bravely, just not man enough in age to vote in a regular election, thanks to discriminatory policies and practices. "Baby, I'm pretty sure I can get you a job at the Shilo Inn. There is an African-American man by the name of Troy who also works at the Seaside Shilo Restaurant. He says he can probably give you a shot at a job," Sherri says optimistically.

"Yes, all I need is one opportunity to prove myself, because work is simply nothing more in my mind than a gym to work out in. I can easily outwork any competitor around me like a whirlwind, working my way up to being their supervisor," I say confidently.

"I know you can, Baby," Sherri replies positively, downshifting the four-speed Datsun to a sudden stop at a four-way intersection.

Warrenton is quite the busy little fishing town, and coincidentally where Clara Cynthia Munson, the first Lady Mayor in Oregon's history, was elected. "You mean there are other chocolate people in the area?" I ask, surprised that there might be more of my persuasion around these here parts. Because it may come in handy one day. "Honey, Troy is the only African American I've ever seen living down here," Sherri admits as she finishes turning left into this paved, very clean and somewhat elegant looking driveway, going as slow as a sleeping slug on a busy highway. She's cruising well under the tiny turtle speed limit, which gives me some time to inhale this new locality. This is only temporary until we reside permanently in Seaside and become real, established coastal Pacific Northwest citizens. We lovebirds waste no time arriving at the Alder Manor Trailer Park in Warrenton—or should I just say our new, temporary home. Next to the sign identifying the trailer park is a 10 miles-per-hour speed limit sign. "I just realized something. I never lived slept in a trailer before. Or even made love in one," I say proudly, like I have saved myself for just this particular moment in time. Yeah. Right.

"Well, that's about to change, Baby," Sherri replies, smiling, tracing the inseam of my pants leg with her fingers as she pulls into a parking space and turns off the overheating engine.

We both exit the car and I notice the whole trailer park is nicely paved. And all of the trailers in this court are decent looking. We walk up the two little wooden steps of this light avocado green with white trim single-wide trailer. Sherri walks in front of me, swaying her female anatomy, captivating my mojo, purposely rubbing her luscious, moon-round backside against me. She then opens the unlocked, glossy-white front door, blowing my security-minded mind, and with just the car keys in her hand, freely walks in, not the least bit worried or concerned that there might be somebody up in there. This trust-culture of people down here is a very interesting, weird world tucked away on the suburban coast that actually lives up to the code of really living and being free. "Where is Jeremy?" I ask, checking out all the various plants in the window just above the kitchen sink. The frame of single-paned windows, as well as everything else in the kitchen is spotlessly clean. The round, brown, wooden dining table is accented with colorful placemats and farm animal–shaped salt-and-pepper shakers in the center. Dishes, pots, and pans are all put away so neatly in their rightful places, out of sight, out of mind. And it smells freshly fresh in here. This has to be the neatest, pettiest kitchen I have ever seen. "He's with Mom and Dad. They live in Gearhart, which is a small town next to Seaside, about eleven miles from here, Baby. He's been asking about you, wondering when you were coming," Sherri tells me, making sure I get the comment, hinting that we must go see Jeremy, and at the same time talk to Sherri's parents. "My ex-coworker friend Karen owns this trailer. She is gone for the evening," she says with a smile. Which means my first night at the beach will be spent alone, with my lady. "Here, let me give you a quick tour!" she says, pulling my hand tightly with hers. We walk to the back of the trailer into a bedroom. There are plants in the window in this room also, just above a double bed with a white bedspread and green pillows. There's a single nightstand next to the bed, perhaps because there is only room for one.

There's also a small dresser with a mirror attached, and a 13-inch television on top of a nightstand, which sits on a multicolored shag carpet. It's all very clean, very well-organized, everything in its rightful place. The entire place looks like a well-thought-out exercise in how to achieve a decorative interior; a sweet home, which could be used as a template on how to properly decorate a trailer. "This is nice. Is this where we are sleeping at, Baby?" I ask while checking things out. "No, this is Karen's room," Sherri replies as we walk out of the bedroom.

We go into another small bedroom on the other side of the trailer, located across the hallway from the petite bathroom that's big enough for one, maybe two people tops. "This is where we are sleeping," she says, kicking off her worn white flats, as if they hurt. The next moment, she's stepping out of her black bodysuit—sexy, soft, and naked, making me do what I do when I see her voluptuous, natural beauty that drives me wild and allows me to release in a way that best expresses how I'm truly in my comfort zone just being in her area code. I softly begin to sing the song that's in my soul: "You are so beautiful to me, can't you see. You're everything I hope for, you're everything I need. You are so beautiful, to me," while holding her hand ever so gently.

"I just love when you sing to me, Baby. You know how it makes me wet," Sherri says as she unbuckles my belt, unzips my jeans, and shoves me forcefully backward down onto the small double, maybe twin bed. She's smiling like I am the only Christmas present she had gotten. And the only one she really wanted. We make love for a couple of hours, like it is the very first and very last time. Then, buck naked, we get up to devour fresh, succulent Dungeness crab with cocktail sauce at the dining table until we are full, make love once again for hours, then cuddle up in the fairly comfy yet small twin bed, dozing off into a tranquil, deep, translucent sleep. I am graciously blessed with someone who really loves me the way that I love her.

I wake up crazy-hungry like a vampire starved for nourishment and thank the Almighty Creator for another day. I'm flat on my back, staring directly up at the room's decent white ceiling in a trailer park in Warrenton, Oregon on the Pacific Coast. As I carefully but aggressively rub the boogey sleep from my eyes, my ears are being amusingly entertained as they hone in on the sound of water being forced through a showerhead, rapidly pushing out pounds of pressure, trickling off into nothing but drip-drops, then slight movement, followed by the static music of a hair dryer ringing out this staccato, vibrato screeching noisemaker of a machine keeping me from sleep, waking me up completely out of my well-relaxed slumber. My nose detects the fresh, heavenly smells of shampoo followed by conditioner, the mingled scents deliciously crashing into my nostrils. There is nothing quite like the scent of the cleansed skin of a sexy human being's body, especially when she's your favorite, trusted friend in the whole world who has my back one hundred percent, full of support, and who energizes me to the point where I can't do anything but a better job of successfully chasing down the American Dream.

Not by any means necessary, but by utilizing the positivity at hand. I'm pleased to initiate forward motion as long as it's positive, and this time it takes the form of having abandoned our negatives in Portland.

"Good morning, Baby," Sherri says, so very wide-awake as she happily enters the bedroom. I roll over so I'm facing the doorway. She leans over as if she's trying to restrain herself, wanting to get back in the bed with her long, dark, dried, sweet, fragrant-smelling brown hair falling lightly on my face as she sensually plants love kisses all over my face, and loving every moment of it. She's all ready to go, dressed for work in a white, long-sleeved blouse with a dull dark-blue below-the-kneecap denim skirt that doesn't do justice to my tender lady. It is a uniform created in the early 19th century simply to achieve that special librarian look; a work of art all its own. But this is the Coastal Pacific Country winter look, I suppose. This particular outfit could definitely benefit from a complete wardrobe overhaul. It does not do a body good.

However, one thing is more than sure: this attire cannot possibly give anyone the wrong impression. "Good morning, Sunshine," I reply, smiling like an unsaturated nymphomaniac, though my unrelieved, overly full bladder may have something to do with the throbbing I'm experiencing down there. "Today is my big tip day at work," Sherri states happily, then barefoot back to the bathroom, stares attentively in the mirror. Watching her with the door ajar, I realize how much I love her and am genuinely missing her already. She puts on her makeup in the unique, petite bathroom while my eyes secretly, fiendishly undress her. She is totally unaware of how happy I truly am, being with her.

"Why is today a good day for tips?" I ask curiously, sitting up in the bed.

"Because Sweetheart, it's the Shilo Inn's Martin Luther King, Jr. Holiday Seafood Sunday Brunch! And it's actually really good," she replies as she puts on her blue apron, then walks back into the room sliding her stockinged feet into her shoes without bending over. Then she pins her gold Shilo Inn nametag with the black lettering to her plain white blouse. Her first name is spelled correctly: S-H-E-R-R-I. She is the only Sherri I know who spells her name that way, and I love it because of its smooth pronunciation. It's like a fine wine, an appetizing name that slides silky smooth off my lips. "I won't be gone long, Sweetheart. I am going in extra early so I should be off the floor by early afternoon and back home with you, Baby. Unless something comes up," she says, reassuring me like she has a plan of some kind. "Fix yourself something to eat, Baby, there's food in the refrigerator. Don't be shy. Help yourself"—still leaning over me— "And, I will bring you something home from the Sunday Brunch, and a job application."

"That's a good plan. Bye, Baby, have a nice day," I say, still naked, standing up to give her a sendoff kiss, staring happily into those sexy green eyes and definitely as early-in-the-morning-aroused as the day is long.

"Mmm, it looks like somebody is very glad to see me!" she says happily, looking down at my hammered, proud, erect state. Sherri just a-smiling away, "I have got to get going, Baby." However, somebody else in this equation begs to differ as my heartbeat continues to engorge my throbbing probe profusely.

"Please go! He does not want you to leave!" I say jokingly, hinting down at my extended concrete-hard penis with my hands on my hips, like some kind of nude, earth-tone superhero with my weapon in throbbing readiness for some more of Sherri's sweet, succulent cherry pie.

Which, by the way, you could never get me to eat a real cherry pie in this lifetime. It's never going to happen. Like eating watermelon, it just does not agree with me. "Bye, Baby, have a nice day," Sherri says as she walks away from me sensually, out the front door, driving me crazy, laughing softly to herself.

Then, with the chill of the morning freezing my special purpose, I take my Naked-King Eddie skinny, chicken, chocolate butt back to bed PRONTO! Five-thirty in the a.m. is way too early around this here locality. I head back to the empty-sounding bedroom, realizing there is a lot more mattress space to sleep now.

Later in the morning, I wake up, shower, and leisurely get dressed. By mid-afternoon, I'm sitting on the couch in the living room watching television after having a smoke outside. All of a sudden I get a good dose of heart-pounding startle! Someone unfamiliar opens the back door, and not being at all quiet about it, walks into the house as if they own the place, sets some keys down on the counter in the kitchen, then some kind of package on the dining table, which I can't see. My astonishment disappears when I realize this must be the owner of the trailer. A nice-looking lady peeks around the wall which separates the living room from the kitchen. "You must be Eddie," she says, not alarmed in the least, as if she knew very well that I was here in the living room and it's no big thing to her. "I am Karen, the owner of this trailer," she says with a smile, sashaying slowly toward me as I stand up. Not being shy about it either, she literally inspects my anatomy, looking me up-and-down like I'm a chocolate-freaky-cake, mail order sex toy Sherri has just bought to use at their command. You know, the "I'm a sex-package equipped with a white, delightful creamy surprise" kind of inspection. She has beautifully clear olive skin, brown shoulder-length hair, and sexy lips. She's very attractive, nicely built, and somewhat similar to Sherri: thick, brick house with a nice, tight silhouetted package. Consequently, they both could easily be mistaken for half-sisters, as well as first cousins, or maybe just some long-lost, distant relative, which could explain their looking very much alike, though not being officially related.

"Oh, yeah, nice to meet you,", I say. Then we go through the formality of a somewhat lengthy, rather aggressive handshake.

Karen's brown eyes are smiling; she's not at all shy and apparently has no shame about purposely sizing me up, ready to put her hands on me, wanting to show me that she's obviously working in more freakish, nasty ways than one. In all honesty, if things had been different, I would have let her have it yesterday, Pacific Standard Time, without giving it a second thought.

However, that's not the case here. "Did I startle you?" she asks, giving me that "What you waiting for, come get it!" looking woman-signal, at the same time, finally, reluctantly, letting go of my hand, despite the obvious sexual advance. She's definitely making an overly friendly impression, which prods me into gathering up my scattered scruples. *Snap out of this!*

"Yes, I could easily have shit myself," I say jokingly. She keeps checking me out, smiling, staring sexually, kicks off her shoes, takes off her jacket, places it on the back of a dining table chair, apparently hypnotized by my full, thick, chocolate lips, which is turning me on simultaneously in a *very* wrong way. I'm trying extremely hard to ignore her obvious, seemingly spellbound sexual advances, which only makes me want to give her my mahogany lamppost, have her absorb the cream of my honey right here, right now. More so now than ever, as if she had this all planned, waiting to sexually swoop on me like I'm Sherri's gigolo she shares with all the Homie Ladies around the way! "Here you go," I say to Karen, and can't help but smile at her while handing her the remote. She takes it, and my hand as well, which I slide smoothly out of her grasp.

I tell her, "I'm going outside and have myself a smoke," to calm myself down. I am obviously beside myself, but I don't say it. I walk out the door into the cloudy cold overcast, close the glossy-white door behind me, walk across the small, wooden, deck-like porch, then down the two steps, looking over at the neighbor's yellowish, older-model trailer. I reach nervously for a smoke out of the pack. I've been down here less than forty-eight hours and already somebody's trying to get me to cheat on Sherri. No way! No how! I love Sherri, and don't need or want anybody else! Karen must be out of her country-crazy, cute-ass mind to think I'm going to go smooth up in her. She can think about it all she wants to; it's definitely not going to happen.

After a half-dozen drags, I don't have the urge to finish the whole cigarette. I butt it out on the wooden steps, promising myself that I can handle the situation with ease, if I so choose, then go back inside the very warm, clean, comfy trailer. I purposely walk loudly a couple of steps inside the trailer, and looking down the hall, I see Karen, naked as a peeled banana, standing next to the partially opened bathroom door in the hallway, giving me a free show. Then, she slowly steps into the shower, making sure I see her very beautiful, olive-naked body in its natural entirety. Her overwhelmingly beautiful body has definitely got my attention; her lovely anatomy has successfully slapped a gorgeous imprint into my photogenic mind. "You see something that you like?" Karen asks me, as I am frozen stiff for a second. Her body is calling my naked sword, which is wasting no time extending. Though this is her abode, she can do what she pleases. I give her an "A" for effort. Maybe this is just a test, or better yet, maybe this is the real McCoy? If Sherri were to come home now, she may think something has happened. Damn! That would destroy us! It would disrupt the whole plan. Besides that, I informed my probation officer that I would be very successful at the beach and that the change was going to do me every bit of positive good.

Right on schedule, I'm saved by the sound of the dookey Datsun pulling into the driveway, the transmission downshifting to second gear, then hearing the car park. The car door slams, steps echo on the small, wooden porch, then Sherri enters the trailer with a plastic container of seafood and closes the door behind her. She has no idea what is actually taking place here. Or is this something that Sherri may have orchestrated? I doubt that's the case, since she never really shared me with anybody else intentionally. So, retract that thought because that has never been the case, and I am pretty sure it never will be. Karen's casual slipping naked into the shower will likely cool that temperature down, even though her flammable body heat is enough to turn a cold shower to steam.

Sherri will still continue to keep it real. "Hi, Baby!" she says, greeting me with a luscious smile. "Hi, Sweetheart," I reply as she sits down next to me, scooting me over on the couch, leaning over, giving me a hands-on, really good smooch.

"I made 150 dollars in tips today, Baby! We were so busy!" Sherri says, frantically reaching in her apron. "I also think they fired somebody, Baby, so they could possibly be hiring someone soon." Sherri hands me the single-sheet Shilo Inn job application and what looks to be an inexpensive ink pen. Positive thoughts start to formulate in my head as I immediately start to fill it out on the antique-like, wooden coffee table that's within arm's reach in front us, where Sherri sets down her apron and the plastic to-go container, which holds an assortment of seafood: crab, lobster, shrimp, and mussels, as well as some prime rib, liver, condiments, and a few well-chosen desserts. All this on top of what's in the Frigidaire from the previous evening of fabulous, fresh crab. "This is a good thing!" I say happily, smiling as the hair stands up on the back of my neck and arms, detecting a mind-bogglingly deep cosmic feeling in my bones, energizing my spirit as I fill out the basic information on the application. I realize I am just one interview away from landing some kind of potentially gainful employment, since I always ace my job interviews with my extensive experience and natural motivation. I learned when I was fourteen years of age that it's not how many times you go down, it's how many times will you get back up in the labor force.

After I thoroughly fill out the application, I move onto the plastic surf-and-turf container, demolishing all of it except for the watermelon and cantaloupe slices, which are very gross, allergic pooh, and the nasty liver. Sherri doesn't seem to have a seafood appetite, probably because she's burnt out on it already, what with living down here every day, repeatedly eating the same things. "But there is something I have to tell you," I say, attempting to get this situation out in the open pronto where it belongs, so there won't be a throwback in my face should the truth be known.

"Why are you looking at me so serious?" Sherri asks me with a puzzled look on her face. "What did I do? You ready to go back already?" Sherri asks, with a look of despair, assuming I have had enough already.

"No, Honey. There's nothing wrong with us. Karen is your friend. And she's flirting constantly with me, and she isn't ugly, not by a long shot. But walking around buck-ass naked? "I truthfully confess, feeling relieved I've got that out of my system so there is no misunderstanding.

"Oh, really? Well, Honey, she did give us a rent-free place to stay," she replies, not at all shocked or concerned about the situation at hand.

"Well…so you want me to do her?" I ask, being dramatically serious, looking into her beautiful green eyes, not quite understanding how this will work out. But something's got to give or it's the end of Karen's house party.

"No," Sherri says with a capital N, finally grasping the severity of the situation at hand. The present freaky situation finally dawns on Sherri's reasoning, which gives me her undivided attention.

"Because that's definitely what she is thinking!" I reply as the bathroom door opens and the steam from the shower rushes out into the narrow hallway. Karen exits the bathroom, wet hair dripping, looking relaxed, wearing only a white, fuzzy towel. She heads for the kitchen barefooted, opens the refrigerator and gets some juice or something, looking very normal. Then she goes to her room and puts on a short, silky colorful robe, doesn't bother tying its belt, and comes into the living room cocky as hell. She's being very obvious, as if whatever she sees is what she wants, but being very straight up about it.

"Hello, Sherri, how was work?" she asks, strolling into the living room with her silk robe untied, not giving it a second thought. It's her casa.

"It was very busy, Karen. However, I had a great shift today. So, how is your day going, Karen?" Sherri asks, just to get a response, which may be more than what she bargained for. You can't be too much bolder than that.

"Oh, pretty much the usual. You know, same-old-same-old routine. But that's what cold showers are for, aren't they?" Karen replies, drying her partially wet, brown, stringy hair with the towel she had wrapped around her. She says this smiling, making her sexual disposition well-understood in spite of Sherri being somewhat kind-of-a-friend, eagerly hinting that we can all have mess-around sex. Sherri is no longer having any false doubts about her so-called roommate's conduct in front of the two of us, dripping wet, very comfortable, without a care in the world.

So, being the game-changing genius that Sherri Lynn is, she turns the tables instantly.

"Anyway, Baby, you are going to need some more shoes. Especially if you get that job at The Shilo Inn. Honey, those shoes have had it,"

Sherri points out. "Come on. Let's go to the Young's Bay Plaza Mall and buy you some new shoes." She stands up like she has her second wind and is ready to roll. But it seems to me like Sherri was in some kind of a hurry. We exit the trailer, unaware that we are being watched. I put my black jacket on, knowing very well those are rainclouds in the dark-lit sky.

"Is that your way of getting my attention?" Sherri asks, as I follow behind her, clowning, being comical, in close proximity down the wooden steps, then up to the Datsun like an overly hyper horn dog, passionately in heat. Sherri just shakes her head happily. "You are so crazy," she says, smiling as I begin to dry-hump her backside. Then I turn her around and give her the biggest love-smooch while embracing her like she's a million-dollar bill.

"What was that for?" she asks, questioning my extensive affection.

I volunteer, "I was just in the moment and very glad to be living on the Northwest Coast! I just love you the way you are!" I say while smiling at her, ignoring the nosy elderly next-door neighbors, staring at us in dismay. I'd bet they have never seen a mocha-chocolate man and a light-skinned Caucasian woman in love before. "We have an audience," I say, as I wave bravely at the shock-filled couple in their late eighties or early nineties. Then Sherri joins the fun, turns around and starts kissing and humping me in front of the elderly couple until the old man gets up, quickly strides over to the window and closes the curtains, as if we have offended the human race to the point of sheer disaster. Sherri and I start and continue to laugh reflexively, taking forever just to get in the car, almost weak from so much fun. We don't consider anything between us could be viewed as wrongdoing.

We exit the trailer park and cruise up Main Street, heading east as I try to somehow regain my sense of direction. I really need to learn my way around the coastline. "Are we close to Fort Stevens?" I ask, looking all around. Places look familiar since I had been here in another decade, doing something positive for my country.

"Yes, we are very close. Have you ever been to Fort Stevens?" Sherri asks.

"I was there about sixteen years ago, when I was in the National Guard. We came out here for some weekend training. That was before I was in the army," I say proudly. We arrive at the Young's Bay Shopping Plaza and Sherri parks in front of the clothing store. "Now, this is the mall?" I ask, noticing the shoe store two doors down.

"Come on, Baby, let's take a look," Sherri says as she opens the car door, grabs her purse, and slams the door without locking it. Once again, she puts the pedal to my mental metal. I am simply floored that she does not lock her door. Security around here is definitely obvious. To a certain extent, locking your door in this town is a waste of time, and not exactly the priority it would be in the city.

"Is this the big mall plaza thing down here?" I ask, scanning the rural-looking, single-level, concrete structure that houses a few stores, offices, and warehouses. "Yes, this is about as big as it gets here," Sherri tells me.

We head into the not-so-busy shoe store holding hands. To my left is a short, Caucasian man with black hair, wearing dark pants and a wrinkled white shirt stacking boxes on the first aisle of women's shoes. His back is to me and he glances over his shoulder at me, looks away for a split second, and almost drops the shoe boxes he's holding. He quickly swivels his head back toward me, eyes bugged practically out of their sockets in utter surprise, as if he's seen a ghost of some kind, either that or he's been brainwashed to the point where he thinks I am the Black Grim Reaper. Then, this young, five-foot-four-inch, dishwater-blonde lady cashier in a white, long-sleeved blouse and a navy-blue skirt makes the mistake of glancing at me, once, then again, and gets that deer-caught-in-the-headlights look on her face. I glare at both of them, well aware of their ignorant alliance of prejudiced assumptions. Then the huge, six-foot, 230-pound, sandy-haired store manager in tan corduroys and a white short-sleeved shirt comes out from way in the back in extreme panic mode like he's been alerted to a horrific problem that is baffling his staff. They can't quite handle this outrageous situation of preconceived ignorance.

To say the least, I'm irritated to the point where I do not feel comfortable spending any money here in this racist establishment.

And it's Martin Luther King, Jr. Weekend, my role model who I look up to, who stood up against racial injustice, literally, so I can't go for that! "May I help you?" the manager asks, walking directly up to just me.

"No, thank you," I say, smirking back at his face, all the while thinking, *Get a real job!* Sherri is grabbing me by the hand, leading me out of the clutches of the brainwashed staff. She's totally oblivious to what's really going on, or maybe not. Sherri pulls me by the hand, still in her uniform and flats, cruises to the men's shoe aisle and grabs a very funky looking, light-brown shoe off the top shelf.

"Honey, what do you think about these?" she asks. I give her the thumbs down. Work shoes need to be either dark-brown or black. These can go hastily back to the manufacturer for a complete standard overhaul, like some people I just made contact with. They did not get the memo. I started looking for some sturdy shoes that could withstand restaurant funk, while looking presentable at the same time. Then I notice another employee peeking around the corner of the aisle, as if he's undercover and trying not to be seen. "Here we go again," I say to myself, exhaling bad-tasting anger. Eventually, I decide to rise above this plateau of self-inflicted fear and ignore the store employees, no longer allowing their unjustified, misguided attitude of ignorance get the best of me. My fresh new start is in the City of Seaside, not in this Johnny-come-lately town. Warrenton is just a stepping stone of no worries. We won't be living here, anyway. I finally see some reasonably fashionable shoes that I could wear to work.

Ripping the Velcro on my old, prehistoric pair of shoes, I reach for their replacement: a pair of black, sturdy work shoes, marked size ten-and-a-half on the shoe box. I decide to wear my new ones out of the store and put the overrun shoes I was wearing in the shoe box. I tie up the laces on the new shoes and strut back and forth in the narrow aisle, making sure they are a comfy fit. I signal to Sherri that I have found the proper shoes for the workplace. Now I would like to pay and get the Hell out of this place!

As we walk up to the checkout counter, Mr. Huge Manager takes over the cash register, looking visually concerned about how I am going to pay for the items on my feet. Sherri immediately steps into the picture, reaches into her apron, and pulls out those Sunday Brunch tips, whipping out three twenty-dollar bills, and hands them over to the dressed-in-Muffin Man-looking-clothes manager. Realizing he's made a big mistake, he says, "Have a nice day." However, no apology. His upbringing dictates normality.

Sherri and I walk down to the clothing store where she immediately heads into the women's department, which is right in front of us. I start for the back of the store where the men's section is, when all of a sudden I am aware of being followed by three employees: two men and a woman. I arrive in the men's department and notice they have some nice things. I find it hilarious that the employees are watching me so hard, because while their eyes are riveted on me, they have no idea that a blond woman dressed in petite jeans, tan knee-high boots, and a light-tan leather jacket opens the swinging glass door directly behind all of them, walks to the very first rack of clothes, and steals two very expensive petite leather dress coats. Looking past the employees, I see the blond thief put her index finger up to her lips. She's signaling to me, silently begging me not to alert the employees and to keep her theft a secret.

I am so struck by the popcorn-eating entertainment of the moment that I am no longer stressed about being racially profiled in this store. It'll serve them right for being so brainwashed, so bamboozled, and so extremely ignorant, all at the same, sad time. So much for this Martin Luther King, Jr. Holiday Weekend! I've already been racially profiled and accused of stealing when the person who's really doing the stealing is transformed by multiple blind eyes.

"They have some nice clothes in this place," I say to no one in particular, smiling, still looking all around, shaking my head. Since the idiotic employees are still not getting it, I comically clown-signal to Sherri, who's over in the lady's section, that we should come back after I get my first paycheck. "Once we've gotten on our feet, I'll buy something nice and special for my Baby Snooky Nooky Poo Poo. By all means I will," I announce.

"You are absolutely right," Sherri says, putting the white blouse she is holding back on the rack. We exit the store and as I get in the passenger seat, I find that my feet are feeling good in their new shoes. Sherri starts the car, takes off out of the parking lot, and makes a right turn onto Highway 101 South, headed for Gearhart where her parents live. "After I get off work tomorrow, we can go and apply for some apartments. I'm also waiting to hear back from Debbie, a waitress at the Shilo. She says there may be an opening coming up. Jobs are pretty hard to come by during the off-season, but between Spring Break and Labor Day is a good time to be working at the beach," Sherri says.

A few minutes later we pull into the parking lot of Seaside Upholstery. "This is where my parents live. The shop is in the front and their house is in the back," she says as she turns off the ignition. The grass is growing wild over the spacious yard. There are big trees scattered here and there, but the one closest to the house has the end of a very long rope tied to one of its lower branches, and the other end knotted securely around a tire hanging about a foot off the ground.

Jeremy sees the brown Datsun and without hesitation, runs excitedly out the entrance of the storefront and jumps into his mother's arms, obviously missing the one person in the world who means the most to him. "Hi, handsome!" Sherri says, giving Jeremy a big kiss on the cheek. He wipes it off with his hand, as usual.

"Who is that is over there?" she asks him.

"Eddie!" he says, staring at me, trying to do a Donald Duck voice. I can tell he's happy to see me, and I am certainly happy to see him. We go into the smallish-looking single-level house, but which seems sizably larger on the inside. There is a rocking chair on each side of the living room and a couch in the center, which faces the nice-sized television positioned against the spacious wall.

There's also a long, fairly wide stainless steel–decorated kitchen, a chef's delight. Just beyond this kitchen, down a short hallway, there is a narrow door leading to the storefront; an extensive upholstery shop with lots of square footage, complete with a wooden horse and a huge assortment of tools of the trade. Sherri's mother, Donna, coffee cup in hand, comes into the living room from the shop wearing white tennis shoes, blue jeans, and a white sweater with a blouse underneath.

"Hello, Mom," Sherri says, greeting her mother, as I stand waiting, holding Jeremy.

"Hello, Sherri," her mother responds, smiling sweetly.

"Mom, you remember Eddie, don't you?" Sherri asks, taking Jeremy from me and easing him down very carefully onto the clean, contemporary carpet.

"Yes. Hello, Eddie, how are you doing?" Donna asks, smiling and sipping her coffee.

"Good, ma'am. I'm just trying to take all of this in. It's very beautiful country down here," I reply, smiling, looking all around, getting my sense of direction and a feel for the place.

"Where's Dad? In the shop?" Sherri asks, walking toward the shop, waving me to come along to speak to her father and check out the upholstery shop at the same time.

"Yes, he's in there. Eddie, go on in there and say hello," urges Donna. As I walk through the doorway leading into the shop, I am wondering if I could possibly work in this shop, or maybe even take it over someday. I'm in daydreaming mode as I walk into the huge, high-ceilinged room with its large storefront windows which face Highway 101 and afford a view of the bowling alley and restaurant directly across the street in good old Gearhart, Oregon. There are a number of beautiful couches in different stages of restoration being worked on, as well as other pieces of furniture that have already been finished, and all the materials and tools you need to run your very own upholstery shop.

"Dad, you remember Eddie, don't you?" Sherri asks, introducing me as we walk into her father's world. Ron has his back to us and is busy adjusting some springs on the frame of one of several couches around the shop that are positioned on wooden sawhorses. Sherri's father looks somewhat like Chuck Connors. You know, the Rifle Man?

"Hello, sir. How are you doing?" I ask, showing her father respect, even though I am not his favorite human being at this particular moment in time. This is due to my behavioral infraction of putting my hands on his daughter in a highly incompetent fashion.

"Well, Eddie, I'm doing just fine," Ron says, slightly stuttering, stopping what he is doing and turning around slowly, like he has been anticipating this particular moment for a while now. Without my getting another word out, Ron asks bluntly, "I understand you have made a decision to live down here on the coast?" He is definitely not a happy camper right out of the starting gate, his sarcastic tone mincing no words, hinting that this is the one place I am not going to get a Welcome Wagon–style welcome. Here's another obstacle I have no choice but to overcome in my current situation. Maybe my apologizing will guarantee a non-violent relationship?

"That is correct, sir," I say, looking straight into his eyes like a man.

"Well, I got to get this here work done, so why don't you guys stay for dinner?" Ron says, being civil, which will give him time to prepare for the moment when he lays into me about my inexcusable behavior toward his daughter—which I totally agree with. He very well has the parental right of expecting me to conduct myself in a respectful manner since Sherri is his daughter. It would be unnatural not to expect that part of his fatherhood to be upset with me. I have a daughter myself, and I would be just as upset if it happened to her.

Sherri looks at me, nodding slightly in agreement. We exit the shop, allowing Ron to get back to finishing up his work. The sun is very low in the horizon and it is quickly getting very cool.

Before dinner, I decide to take a walk around outside to enjoy the elements of the mummy-quiet country atmosphere and have a smoke. Out near the back of the neighboring acre lot, I notice a yellow cottage—a shack of a house, actually—and to my astonishment, inside the front window, there's an elderly woman staring out at me, who looks like she's the Little Old Woman Who Lived in a Shoe. So, being the polite mocha-chocolate human being that I am, I wave my hand at her. Insanely baffled, the old lady's eyes bleed out of their sockets. She's wearing an old school scarf on her head, but I can still see the annoyance on her face the second she takes notice of me and my polite manners. She immediately shuts the curtains with an attitude of hateful, unadulterated malice. I can't stop myself from laughing at the mini-spectacle of it all. She was quite humorous in her awkwardness. She probably spies on everyone from the windows of that little doll-sized cottage, which appears to be no bigger than a single garage. I'm thinking she's probably suffering from an advanced case of cabin fever. Sherri comes out to join me, and I inform her of the new neighborhood friend I just made, who is going to have to get used to seeing me around these here parts.

"Mom says they want to keep Jeremy here until we get a permanent place. What do you think?" she asks, while watching me blow one smoke ring through another in the evening air.

"How do you feel about it, Baby?" I ask her, while trying to find a place to butt out my cigarette, finally just dropping it on the ground and grinding it out with the sole of my new shoe, of all things.

"I think it's the best thing for all of us. That way we can find something quicker," she says, while pressing her body up against me, sending sensual messages to my manhood. Just when Sherri has me totally aroused, Donna comes to the door.

"Come on in, you two, dinner is ready. We don't want it to get cold," she says, stepping back inside. I quickly put my hand in front of my super-unexpected erection and start chanting, "Monkeys are tickling my armpits, monkeys are tickling my armpits!" Sherri starts laughing at me as I keep repeating the monkey chant until my single-minded Eiffel Tower subsides in my jeans. Fearing her parents might accidentally make the acquaintance of my Sherri-induced uprising, or her mother seeing the imprint of my Eiffel Tower trying to escape its jeans prison, I did what is like kryptonite to me as far as any unwanted erection is concerned. After Sherri stops laughing at my imperfections, we hold hands and let each other know that we are in this for the duration.

We walk back into the house, wondering what dinner is going to taste like. I try to keep a positive outlook because Sherri can cook for me anytime. Her meals are always seasoned to perfection. I sit between Sherri and Donna at the round, mahogany dining table, which is in excellent condition. We start eating dinner, which tastes delicious, superb, however the silence doesn't last long. From which direction shall I be struck first? "So, Eddie, how do you like it down here so far?" Donna asks, smiling politely.

"Well, ma'am, it's going to be quite an adjustment, but I think I will do just fine," I answer.

"I'm not trying to discourage you Eddie, but people here don't, in any sense of the words, highly favor mixed relationships," *Translation;*

Please take your black ass and go back home! I don't look for it, but somehow racism finds me, as usual. 3

"Mom!" Sherri protests loudly, slapping the dining table. "Everybody's not like that at all! It's just your presumptuous generation!" Sherri preaches loudly in her capacity as ambassador for the utmost equality, hoping to be victorious in her stand against inequality on the Pacific Northwest Coast in Gearhart, Oregon, for the man she truly loves, unconditionally. Which is just what I needed to hear, what with it being the Martin Luther King, Jr. Holiday Weekend, and me feeling like a discarded human being, thanks to actions sanctioned by the Immoral Majority. "Look," Ron says, "everybody's *got* a right to live, but some people just don't see that as *being* right. Like a lot of my customers. They have a very racist agenda."

"So…there's no sense in asking you for a job?" I ask bluntly, looking Ron straight in the eyes as he chews his food. I drink a sip of soda, use my fork to take a bite of salad, then chew my food with my mouth tightly closed, waiting for a logical response to a very discriminatory lifestyle that reflects liberty for some, but not for all.

"No. I could actually use the help. But my accounts…the racist people I deal with…I just can't take that chance," Ron says truthfully. "Therefore, I would appreciate knowing, since you are going to be living down here, and since I'm a local businessman, that you know how to conduct yourself in a respectable manner."

"Excuse me? What exactly does that mean?" I say, putting my fork down, realizing I am practically a stranger in this man's house and an alien to this part of his world. I really and truly want to hear his explanation.

"If you are going to live here, you can't be talking any jive, Eddie!" Ron says as he rises to his feet in his cowboy boots, jeans, and long-sleeve plaid shirt. "And I would appreciate if you please don't pimp-walk on the street in downtown Seaside or hang out on street corners!" he says, illustrating his point with the piss-poorest impression of a so-called pimp, walking back and forth in the living room, looking for the entire world like a crazy, crippled, generic cowboy who, for no good reason, has had his rodeo license revoked.

"Dad! Stop that!" Sherri shouts, trying to protect me from these false, presumptive attacks.

"Now it's my turn, sir," I say calmly. "Number one: with respect, I have an extensive upbringing that you can't even begin to comprehend. It's called being raised to have what are known as manners. Number two: I have never in my life been, and will never in my lifetime be, a pimp. So…please. Don't ever from your mouth call me that word again. Know who you are talking about, please, before you label anybody, anything, sir. Number three: I love to work for my money. I have done just that since I was fourteen years old. Understand, Mr. Man. The Oh Wow! Typical Stereotype they put in your brainwashed, bamboozled, hoodwinked head is fear of me! Evidently, because I must be a descendant of the Original Man. For only number two man, logically, will fear number one. I served my country honorably in the army. I have two years of college in Fire Science. Both of my parents work for the Multnomah County Sheriff's Office. My father is a corrections officer, six foot two, 240 pounds, and in whose presence, not in your wildest dreams would you be running your mouth that way. Number four: my maternal grandfather is a bishop in the city of Portland. I was raised in the church all my life. I am a Christian who maintains a high level of respect for my fellow man. I don't have the luxury of being a hateful human."

"What are your intentions toward my daughter?" Ron asks, staring me in the face.

"To be the best man she's ever had in her life, and to take good care of Jeremy!" I snap back at him, meaning every word I said, staring back at him in all seriousness and respect.

"And how do you plan on not assaulting my daughter?" Ron finally asks.

"I will never in my life stoop that low again! I sincerely apologize for my inexcusable actions," I say solemnly, looking both of Sherri's parents directly in their faces, not asking for forgiveness, just the opportunity to prove that my word is my bond. I'm imagining with all their everyday involvement in racism, I have really stepped on my own jewels. In their persuasion, putting your hands on any so-called white person is an abomination. For a so-called black man to put his hands on a so-called white woman, even if she is killing him, is blasphemous damnation.

"He has a shot at working at the Seaside Beachfront Shilo Inn," Sherri chimes in, sitting next to Jeremy, feeding him out of her plate.

"What are you going to tell them in your interview about your criminal record?" Ron asks, nitpick-grilling me, searching for any negative, undesirable circumstance that would discourage me enough to turn around and head back to Portland, the city where *my* kind of people belong and are not allowed to live to equally at the coast.

"I am going to tell them the absolute truth. I've been convicted of a felony only once, and I don't plan on any more in my lifetime. Sir," I reply firmly.

"Dad? What is wrong with you?" Sherri asks abruptly, "You have a long criminal record yourself. What makes you so different?" She's not understanding, by a long shot, what makes it acceptable for her Caucasian dad to think the way he does. Which is called awkward equality. However, that would be not acceptable for me.

If I did the same thing, that would be the judgment of a consistent career criminal. "Yes, Ron. Who are you to talk?" Donna interjects, finally joining the debate.

"Well, all right, then. Here's the deal: I will try to help you out anyway I can. Just treat my daughter right. Do we understand each other?" Ron asks firmly.

"You have my word on it, sir. I will treat her like a queen and protect her and Jeremy with my life," I swear.

The air in the room is unevenly thick, like someone had set off an atomic flatulence explosion at the dinner table on this fine holiday weekend. "Jeremy, you getting enough to eat there, Slick?" Ron asks, changing the subject, still not quite sure about me or my positive intentions.

Jeremy just nods his head, still eating, not at all concerned about adult comments, conversation, or actions. "Sometimes, it's not what you know, but who you know," I say. "Your daughter is very persistent, and where there's a will, there's a way. However, in this particular arena, the rest is totally up to me. And I actually do very well in interviews. That's all I really need. I always seem to get hired once I am given a fair chance,"

I add, making my point regarding fearful discriminatory practices of hate-mongering. After the initial, minor confrontation of really getting to know where folks are coming from, everybody quietly finishes their meal and drinks their sodas, sitting around full and friendly, at least one silently hoping I pack my bags and head back to the city.

I stand up with my empty plate and walk to the kitchen where I rinse it off and set it down in the sink carefully, somewhat irritated by the bamboozled, ignorant stereotypes produced by media cycles of repetitively injecting racial fear into the masses. Yesterday I was ready to go outside and smoke a cigarette, get some air, calm my spirit down so I can process this incurable societal dysfunction. *I can show them better than I can tell them*, my inner voice says to me.

What the hell is next for me? If it is this bad down here for a chocolate man, then Troy *has* to have an outlet like music or something to keep him from jumping off a cliff or going crazy. As I look up at the stars, I hear the sound of the door on the porch sliding open, then closing, then someone slowly lurking in the mild darkness of the moonlit night is walking toward me.

Sherri's footsteps on the gravel give away her approach as I continue to inhale the smoke of my addictive nicotine pacifier, hoping that it truly is a relaxer right now.

"Hi, Baby, you okay?" Sherri asks, her voice betraying extreme concern as she walks toward me, making the gravel speak in the dark.

"Yes, I'm okay. It's just the transition," I reply. "We all are going to have to go through it, and it might get just a tad bid rough around the edges. Besides, he wouldn't be a good dad if he didn't grill me like that, but I'm not ever going to kiss his or anybody's ass. That's where I draw the line." This is the no-ass-kissing-zone. I'm a hard, down-to-earth-ass worker and that's where it ends.

It turned out to be an unexpectedly cemetery-quiet drive home. My first weekend at the coast was an eventful one and I am still thinking about the educational racial dinner class conversation with her exceptionally interesting parents. But I wanted very much to ease Sherri's mind that I am not going anywhere. I don't scare that easy.

The next morning, I hear Sherri getting ready for work as I lay in bed, wanting to go to work as a well. So I'll keep thinking positive thoughts. I open my eyes and look at the ceiling, thankful the Almighty Creator is allowing me to see another day. I'm going to stay away from Karen's freaky temptations, but damn! She looks deliciously gorgeous, a vision of a light-skinned, beautiful oasis of nakedness. Yeah, we need all the help we can get, so we can get the hell up out of *here*. Sherri comes back into the room already dressed in her uniform, leans over and gives me a goodbye kiss. I turn over and drift back into a dreamful level of sleep. Hours later my erotic, sex-oriented dreams where I'm always flying are replaced by the aroma of breakfast being cooked, waking me up. Karen is just so wrong for this move since I'm devastatingly, baseball bat-hard as Plymouth Rock. I feel the urgent need to drain the major buildup of fluid in my bladder and my options are limited.

If I tiptoe quietly, maybe she won't detect me and my extreme Eiffel Tower. I need to go real bad, but having this particular full-blown piss-hard-on is quite a difficult, painful, infamously directional thing; two opposing pressures are at work here. I want desperately to relieve the one-eyed organ, and at the same crazy damn time, I also need to avoid Karen like the plague. I quickly put on my jeans, open the bedroom door, and head straight for the petite, craft-decorated bathroom. Once I start unloading liquid, my Eiffel Tower pressure is a torment like constantly hitting myself in the forehead with my own fist. I'm finally done with my business, relieved, relaxed, and apparently somewhat horny. I'm unexpectedly startled as I step out into the hallway, Karen catching me way off guard. To my surprise, she's standing there at the end of the hallway with her robe untied once again, giving me a photographer's dream pose of her incredibly smooth, honeysuckle-smelling skin, a sexy vision of the tantalizing, intoxicating fine wine of her anatomy. "Good morning. Eddie," she says, holding a fairly new, black-handled spatula, gazing down at my midsection with a sinister grin, boring a hole in my mystery package with her eyes, having a real ball. She is obviously not in the business of giving up easily and is probably thinking she's got me worn down to the point of being ready for some hot, volcano-erupting, sexual-healing, sweat-slicked therapy. She's constantly challenging my non-cheating nature by going for the jugular vein to convince me to see things her nasty, submissive way.

She's trying to convert me into a dog who just wants to bury his bone. In her.

"Are you hungry for some breakfast, Eddie? Or maybe there's something else you would like?" Karen purrs, attempting her very best at making me weak in the knees. She sees that I am indeed hypnotized by her outlandish sexual advances.

"No, thank you," I reply, walking toward the kitchen. She's standing in front of the white stove, sexy as ever. I stop in the hallway, my Eiffel Tower now under control; the thought of monkeys does it every time. I'm grinning back at her nonstop, no longer feeling tempted by her smooth, freaky flesh or her intense sexual advances. Her attempts at turning me on like it's a sex-hunt game have backfired and I finally find myself turned off by her.

"Coffee?" she asks, turning toward me, purposely letting her multicolored, short silk robe swing open even wider, revealing everything she's got. Let it be from head to toe. Now that I know how dedicated she is to tapping into my obvious, animalistic nasty nature, I'm enjoying her flirtatiousness and curious to see just how far she will truly go.

"Yes," I say as I walk over and sit at the dining table.

"You know, Eddie, the only reason I flirt with you so much is that there is an extreme shortage of men out here," Karen says truthfully. "Sherri knows that to be true. Why else do you think you are really here, honey?" Karen spills her game, going on about if she had only known how cute I am, blah, blah, blah.

I hear Sherri pull up in the driveway, kill the engine, then slam the car door loudly, right on schedule! *Thank you, Almighty Jesus*, I whisper to myself. She comes in announcing, "I have some good news, Baby! We have a place to stay in Seaside just one block from the beach and four blocks from the Shilo Inn. And you have an interview with Troy tomorrow at nine a.m. at the Shilo Inn, Baby. I convinced Troy he'd like it if an African American was working alongside him, which he personally thought was a fantastically good idea!" Problem solved!

Yes! My impressive job history on the application caught their eyes, plus we have a place to stay in Seaside one block from the beach? Interesting how much difference a day makes.

Positive opportunity slides into one's journey, and now we are moving closer to our destination in life. "When can we move into this place, Baby?" I ask, ready to evict ourselves from this abode and our sultry roomie's haunting me with sexy advances, almost close to temptation.

"Today. All we have to do is go get the key, honey, and meet them," Sherri replies, seriously rubbing up against me.

"Do they know about me and my melanin skin?" I ask quickly.

"Yes, Baby. They are Hippies," Sherri answers happily.

"Well, in that case, we haven't left yet? Let's bounce, Baby!" I say, getting to my feet as I map out a plan into action in my head. But first, be thankful for everything.

"Thank you very much for letting us stay here, Karen," I say and give her a hefty kiss on her soft lips, and an innocent, but heartfelt hug. Then, it's scurry into the spare bedroom to gather our belongings, put them effortlessly in the car, and we're ready to relocate to Seaside, Oregon.

Karen calls out as we drive away, "Don't be a stranger!" and stands there, staring out her open front door. We are into the next phrase of this interesting series of events, relocating to the city by the ocean where I've always dreamed of living some conscious part of my life along the Oregon Coast: working, fishing, crabbing, camping, hiking, swimming, boating, kayaking, surfing, four-wheeling...

7

· · · · · · · · · · · · · · · · · · ·

Living in Seaside

I t's still early afternoon twenty-five minutes later on a partially cloudy, windy kind of a day. We depart Warrenton with Sherri steering the dookey-brown Datsun, listening to the radio station playing "Jack and Diane" by John Cougar Mellencamp. We cruise through Gearhart on Highway 101 south, heading for the next town. The green-and-white city limit sign says Seaside, Oregon, Population 5359. It's only eighty miles west of Portland and known as the end of the Lewis and Clark Trail. It's also one of the most visited beachfront party towns in the United States, with its beautifully smooth, flat beaches that are excellent for volleyball tournaments and sandcastle-building competitions. There are jogging and bicycle paths, an amusement arcade with land, and water bumper cars; family-oriented ocean-fresh seafood restaurants, live music, an aquarium, and a gorgeous cove for digging clams or fishing. As we enter the city proper, we see a deep-gray, castle-like restaurant with flags lining the right side of the highway called the Pizza Palace. Tillamook Head offers a heavenly view of the Pacific Ocean as we arrive at the Flying Dutchman Motel on Fourth and North Downing. The beachfront homeowners rent out their gray-painted, furnished cottage units to tourists during the peak season, which lasts from Spring Break to Labor Day weekend in the pre-fall. Although this time of year, business is completely turtle-slow, so to make up for some of the lost revenue in the off-season, they rent out the vacant units to the locals who live in the surrounding areas on a monthly basis throughout the entire winter. Sherri and I exit the car, happy for the change, and walk to the front entrance of the motel, which faces west toward the beach. We hear the Pacific's waves crashing on the shore as we continue to the front door, walking into the ocean breeze while seagulls on cruise control glide through the friendly skies, having raucous conversations with one another. We are very excited to finally have a place of our very own. I knock on the weathered, grayish-looking door, and this delightful woman greets me with a great big smile that, at last, makes me feel like a human being who is welcome down in this neck of the woods. She stands five foot four, has fluffy, long, flowing sandy blond hair framing her roundish face, stunning baby-blue eyes, and is wearing a light-pink sweater over a white blouse and blue jean dress. She opens the door of the brown, cabin-style wooden home. Now this is more like it, more like Martin Luther King, Jr. Holiday Weekend, allowing freedom to ring.

If you are from the Pacific Northwest, one fact is definitely clear: so-called white people—which term I personally don't care for—are either Caucasian, or just logically speaking, European Americans. All I see are light-skinned people, not the common term, "white American." Truthfully, there is no such thing as a white person. White is simply verbal shorthand for White Master, while the color black is commonly used to describe Black Property during the days of slavery in the 1800s. Therefore, all people are not racists. They just haven't gotten the memo yet. You have to investigate carefully if you want to find the *real* people, who mostly are like precious, rare diamonds-in-the-rough of things. In other words, don't judge a man by his skin covering. That's only the presumptive recipe of ignorance, deception, and a waste of precious time, and is always particularly louder than empty, spoken words ever could be.

"Welcome! Please come right on in! My name is Debbie. You must be Eddie?" she says, allowing us to make our way into the humble, yet hospitably friendly, stylish home.

"Hello, nice to meet you, and thank you for helping us. You don't know what this means to us," I reply, looking back at her with a pleasant smile.

"Please, come in and sit down. Make yourselves at home!" she says as she graciously invites us into the living room. "Sherri said at work you guys have somewhat of a situation?" she asks, smiling, closing the door behind us. We are both hit with a one-two-punch combination smell of a lovely lavender fragrance mixed with honeysuckle. Yes, indeed, it is quite the Welcome Wagon welcome, if you know what I mean. We breeze in around the coffee table and sit down on the cushioned, green-patterned couch. Her home is very cozy: immense decorative plants hang in each corner of the room, there are flowers in vases, and plants run along the ceiling and the corners of the room. There's a blue, denim-covered recliner nestled close to the medium-sized window that has a slight view of the ocean. Gold-colored plant stands are covered by flourishing potted cactus plants, all of which are in bloom. "Sherri, let me go and get my husband. He's out back in the garage," Debbie says, as she breezes gracefully by us with a seemingly permanent smile on her face. She appears to be a very happy soul. We don't even have time to check out the various flowers and vines hanging down from their pots before she returns. "This is my beloved husband, Joe. Joe, this is Eddie, and his lady, Sherri," Debbie says, making introductions all around. I stand to greet this remarkable man who is giving me an opportunity to prove myself: six feet tall, olive-skinned, thick mustache, medium straight hair, wearing jean overalls, a dark plaid denim shirt, black boots, and fragile-looking John Lennon glasses. I shake his hand, glad to be in Seaside and in good company.

"I am so glad to meet you, man," I say, overwhelmed on the occasion of finally making positive headway after moving down here just seventy-two short hours ago.

"Yes, thank you, Joe. And on such very short notice too," Sherri says humbly, shaking his hand after I let go of it, smiling big, glad to put Karen's antics behind us.

"I am glad to meet you too, Eddie. Sit down and make yourself at home. Please, take a load off," Joe says as he sits down in his rocking chair pointed toward the window that has a partial view of the ocean. He swivels around facing us, smiling as he massages his thick mustache with his fingers.

"You nice people are definitely not from around here?" I ask, sensing by the way they carry themselves that they feel really good about us moving out of Warrenton.

"No, Eddie. That is so correct," Joe says. "We are from beautiful Wasilla, Montana. So, whereabouts are you from, Eddie?" Joe asks, focusing his attention on the cigarette he's smoking.

"I am from Portland, Oregon," I answer, mentally exhausted from the hustle-bustle trouble-drama of living in the metropolitan area. "I needed to relocate for a while and make a positive change in my unfulfilling life. So I moved to the beach where I've always had a desire to live, since my immediate family frequently visited here when my parents were still married, a very long time ago."

"So, you have something of a temporary housing problem?" Joe asks while rocking in the chair slightly. "Well, I have a unit. It's actually a studio-slash-cottage with an old school-style Murphy Bed, a shower, toilet, and a TV. Nothing fabulous. However, you pay the rent, let's say about four hundred dollars a month, utilities included, and you are free to stay up until Spring Break when business starts to pick up again and we will call it good," Joe says, as if it's a no-brainer. However, I don't have the money ready to fork over to him right this very minute. But I already know this charming, caring couple are not really concerned about getting a payment up front, since they understand our current hardship. They are going to waive the rent until we get on our feet.

"It sounds like an excellent plan to me," I say, turning toward Sherri, who is more interested in inspecting the cottage first before she makes her final decision. "What do you think, Honey?" I ask Sherri, who's grasping my hand. I know this offer is ultimately a blessing that we can't refuse, and our only option.

"Let's all go and take a look at where you will be staying," Joe says, and we all stand up at the same time. He leads the way through the kitchen, makes a pit stop at the very wide, practically new refrigerator, opens it, pulls out three bottles of long-neck Millers, shuts it, and hands one to Sherri and then me as we continue on. I shuffle anxiously behind Joe, eager to see what's behind the front door of where we will be staying for the duration of the winter. We follow him down a hallway, then on out through the huge garage door. Once outside, we crunch across a gravel driveway about five to eight yards from their main house and over to four small, identically painted cottages scattered about the spacious lot. There's plenty of parking for all of the tenants' cars and lots of room to work on vehicles. He walks past the first cottage to the next one and pulls out a single key from his front jeans pocket, inserts it in the knob of the weatherworn door, and opens it with a slight push. I can tell it's been quite a while since it was last occupied because the cottage has developed its own unique aroma. I find myself hoping it's not a dump. But then again, at this point, who really cares? The beach will officially be my backyard for at least the next sixty days. By then, I'll have had time to explore alternative places of residence that will be in my name. At first glance, it was actually not that bad of a cottage. It could have been way worse, and I still would have taken it. Joe, Sherri, and I do the inspection stroll, checking out the interior of the weather-beaten gray cottage. The walls look somewhat freshly painted, and the cottage is actually older than I first thought. A dresser sits in one corner next to the window. There's a small stove that matches the size of the small, almost antiquated refrigerator. Joe then walks over to the widest wall in the cozy unit and pulls a lever that unlocks the Murphy Bed, allowing it to unfold and swing down out of its wall recess and come to rest on the worn, greenish-blue, low/no pile carpet balanced on its metal legs. Sherri, slightly hesitant, tests the bed for stability and comfort by pushing down on the aged mattress with her hands, then sits down and scoots backward onto the center of the bed with her shoes hanging off the side. She seems satisfied, then gets back up, walks over to inspect the cheesy, off-white, a-tad-smaller-than-your-everyday normal-sized refrigerator, as well as the small, glossy off-white stove. With the exception of the red countertop, the entire unit is color-coordinated; the walls, ceilings, appliances, kitchen sink, and cupboards are all painted a uniformly dull, off white.

"See? All the comforts of home," Joe says, standing next to me with his arms folded, holding his beer, casually chilling, not really too concerned one way or another. He's waiting to see what I have to say as I watch Sherri open every cupboard and door, turn all the appliances on and off, including the mini-sized stove, which caps off her inspection of the place.

"Does the heater work, and is it electric?" she asks, looking up and down, re-inspecting the mini kitchen that will work just fine for the two of us.

"Yes, it does, and yes, it's electric," Joe replies. "All utilities are included in the rent, so you don't have to worry about that." Joe winks at me, closing the deal.

"Well, this looks good to me. We will take it! Thank you very much, Joe. You really can't understand how much this means to me," I tell him, humbled, with a smoke screen grin on my face as I set my beer bottle down on the small red countertop.

"Well, folks. We just like helping good people like you and Sherri," Joe says, obviously with something else on his mind. I chug down a swallow of my beer while Sherri is turning on the oven to see if it's functioning properly. "But there is one more thing we need to do to seal the deal. Here's the key. You got to go and get one made. Fair enough?" Joe says, dipping into his shirt pocket with two fingers, feeling around until he pulls out a skinny twig of a joint and hands it over to yours truly. I put it in the corner of my mouth, bend down to the flame Joe's already flicked up in his lighter, fire up that pale, anemic-looking joint, and start smoking on one of the finest of all natural herbs in the world. And, coincidentally, forging a nonverbal contract between two men regarding our law-abiding consensus.

We chattered for a bit about the time we both spent in the service until the joint was gone. "Well, I'm going to let you folks get settled. I realize it will be a while before you can pay me, and that's understandable. Just pay when you are able to after you start working, all right? She's all yours. I will talk to you guys later," Joe says and heads back to his nest. I am so excited all I can say is, "Thank you, Almighty!" to celebrate residing one-half block from the Pacific Ocean.

Moments later, like any other couple in their right lovers' minds' would, Sherri and I get into a very festive mood just by knowing we are one step closer to having our own place. We quickly unload our not-so-very-many personal belongings from the car, and Sherri changes into something more comfortably suitable: a gray sweatshirt and blue jeans. Just minutes later, we're locking the door of our little cottage and strolling around the huge, graveled lot as the wind starts to blow frantically. No longer a visitor, but now a local citizen of Seaside, Oregon, I am walking to the beach, holding Sherri's swinging hand, wanting just to be happy in loving her, excited that we have a cozy cottage for two and need no transportation to work due to its close proximity to the sandy, ocean beach.

Early the next day, I enjoy the salty morning air, blessed to see another day, walking alone on the concrete promenade, feeling like I'm on cloud nine, gazing out over the Pacific Ocean, the biggest bathtub known to man. Seagulls are landing on the clear, sandy beach, resting before they start searching for food. I'm confident I'm going to have a good day since the forecast calls for partial clearing. And the sun does decide to greet me, so I hustle down the sidewalk past the tall buildings, noticing that lights have been strung out along the entire length of the promenade. I walk further on, past more hotels facing the ocean until I reach the turnaround point of the walkway. About thirty yards to my immediate right is the Seaside Beachfront Shilo Inn, painted in shades of pretty blue and gray, the colors of my favorite football team, the Dallas Cowboys. Sherri left the cottage way before me and is already in there at work. I find I'm going to be almost a half-hour early for my job interview. However, the early bird catches the worm. To kill some time, I watch the seagulls along the beach hunting in the sand for their morning meal. To my immediate right is the city's aquarium and I can hear the seals flopping around, splashing in the water tanks, making obscenely loud, deep-throated noises. Standing in front of a very old gray building, I watch the waves in the distance crash against Tillamook Head's thousand-foot cliff, the top of which is excellent for hiking over the approximate four miles to Cannon Beach. I'm pumped and eager to roll as I enter the four-star restaurant and lounge through the automatic main lobby doors. The front desk faces away from the beach and is on my right as I walk in. Off to my left is the restaurant and lounge and as I cross the lobby, since it's my first time being in the place after seeing it advertised regularly on television, I can't help but notice the elegance of this here hotel. I walk to the entryway of the restaurant and am cordially greeted by this blonde, blue-eyed Caucasian lady with a bright smile, wearing a uniform somewhat similar to Sherri's, who just happens to dart by us carrying a tray as she attends to one of her tables in the beautiful dining room. The windows of the dining room afford customers a spectacular view of the great Pacific Ocean, the traffic turnaround in the center of town with its landscaping and statues of Lewis, Clark, and Sacajawea, and in the distance, the cove guarded by Tillamook Head. "Good morning. Welcome to the Shilo Inn Restaurant. How may I help you?" asks the gorgeous blonde with the bobcat hairstyle, Hollywood legs in white stockings and navy-blue skirt, black flats, and a name tag in black letters on her white blouse identifying her as Shilo Inn Waitress Carolyn, who is sporting a nice, warm, welcoming smile.

"Hello. Good morning, Carolyn. I am here for a nine o'clock interview with Troy," I say proudly, rubbing my hands together, then holding them behind my back, assuming an at-ease position, standing straight and smiling from ear to ear, which influences the waitress to smile back in a decidedly non-innocent manner.

"I will let him know you have arrived. And whom shall I say is here to see him?" she asks, playfully nosy, and yet sexy, continuing to give me that cheesy smile.

"Eddie Dee Williams is my name," I tell her.

"I will be more than happy to get him for you, Eddie Dee," Carolyn replies, still smiling as she switches away in that tight-fitting blue skirt. Out of curiosity, I watch my Snooky Nooky Poo Poo exit the kitchen carrying trays of food into the too-busy-to-notice-me dining area. She serves her tables efficiently, which are occupied by dozens of people enjoying their meals, as well as the panoramic view of the rugged coastline. I decided to wear my grey slacks, a black dress shirt with a black jacket, and some black dress shoes, the right one of which aggravates an old injury to my foot I sustained while in the army. It hurts like hell, but I don't show it.

Troy approaches me in the lounge with a big smile that sends a thrill of goodness over me, validating my faith that things are going to get better, all in their good time, so I maintain my composure and not let the devil-worshippers get to me. "My name is Troy Hunt," he says. He's the first person I have seen since I moved here who looks like me, and it feels good and comforting to know I am not alone. He's six foot four, mocha-chocolate, a medium-built 240 pounds of muscle with a mini-afro, big smile, wearing an iron-blue shirt, black denim jeans, brown loafers, and a black employee badge trimmed in gold like Sherri and Carolyn's. However, his badge says Shilo Inn, Troy Hunt: Purchaser. I am very much impressed. He looks down at me like he's your average NBA player. I am anxious, as well as glad, to shake his hand enthusiastically, finally meeting this chocolate American.

"My name is Eddie Dee Williams," I reply, being genuine and not putting up a front. I always believe in being myself. Right now, I'm feeling upbeat and full of confidence that I will have an equal opportunity interview.

"That's like Billy Dee, right?" Troy asks, flashing a million-dollar, perfect-white-teeth smile, with not a gap in sight. I'm pretty sure the clipboard he's holding has my application Sherri submitted not long ago on it.

"No, sir," I reply, smiling cheerfully, giving him his due respect since he's my senior. "Eddie Dee is a comedian, singer, and songwriter. Billy Dee is an artist, singer, and actor. No disrespect intended." I am feeling pumped and ready to get it on!

"Oh…well, all right. Come on, let's go downstairs to my office," Troy says, smiling as he leads the way. We go through the employee doors to the back of the kitchen, passing the somewhat busy waitress' station, stroll by the dish tank located on the right side of the kitchen. And then there's the cooking line, where I hear this distinctively crazy-kind of-tingling-giggling laughter that strikes a very strong chord with my sense of humor; it's out of this world! And it's coming from this cook to my left: a blonde-haired, blue-eyed, stout, muscular Caucasian man who's talking to another dude with his back to me. He's built like the present Heavyweight Champ, Mike Tyson. *He and I are going to become great friends*, I say to myself. Then Troy leads me to the banquet elevator adjacent to the dish washer, saying he'll give me the grand tour of the property later. The somewhat flimsy looking elevator's orange doors open, and we step inside. He hits a button on the panel and the elevator takes us down one flight to the basement, where Troy leads the way again. Just out of the elevator, we make a sharp left down a hallway with a checkerboard-tiled floor, where Troy stops at the second door, slides a key into the lock, and opens the door to his private office, which is located down the corridor from what looked like a dry storage pantry. He gestures toward the chair in front of his desk and he takes the seat behind it. As I sit down facing him, I hear the voice in my head saying, *The time has finally come! It's ShowTime!* And it's all up to me now.

"Well, now, Mr. Williams. Tell me about you," Troy says as he tilts his seat back, relaxing into his wooden office chair, which does nothing but strengthen my own self-assurance that much more of my having a fair and equal opportunity of landing adequate employment on my first interview.

"I moved down here to look for a job and to change my dysfunctional life. I'm tired of the city. And I have me a very nice country girl. I am not going to sit here and lie to you. I've been in trouble *once* in my life and I'm done with all that. Jail is not going to be my lifelong slavery. I'm very intelligent and I was born to do well. My grandfather always used to say, 'Number one grandson, it doesn't matter how many times you fall. What matters is, how many times are you going to get back up?'" I say, with all the righteous charisma and dignity I can muster, putting us both on the same human page, since I detected that he could relate to where I am coming from. I went on to inform him of my college education, honorable discharge from the army, my service industry experience in the restaurant sector, four years of hands-on experience as a production glass worker, extensive janitorial experience with my grandfather and stepfather, along with my year of employment as a firefighter cadet with the Portland Fire Bureau at Engine House Seven.

"Why should I hire you?" Troy asks, still leaning back in his chair, awaiting the right answer, unaware that I know exactly what he wants to hear.

"Because you want somebody who accomplishes an overabundance of work and doesn't complain about it, who can kick ass at any given moment and get the job done in a timely fashion, and sing about it like it's nothing more than a workout," I answer quickly, realizing he's trying to figure out what I'm really all about. So I decided to let him know exactly where I am coming from. That way he will see that I am real. However, it's going to take a short while to convince him, but I am always up for a good challenge.

"That's right, Sherri's your girlfriend. And you're a singer, are you?" Troy asks, as if checking to see if I'm bluffing. But on the other hand, maybe he has a plan for us to gig together sometime.

"Yes, I grew up singing in my grandfather's church in Portland since I was zero years old. I have my own, original soulful style, but I can also imitate a lot of other singers, comedians, and celebrities. My range is humongous and an ultimate blessing from the Almighty," I reply happily, confidently adjusting myself in my chair.

"What kind of songs do you sing?" Troy asks, seemingly more relaxed now.

"A very good question. I sing anything but that devil-worshipping music. I can't go for that," I tell him. He chuckles as he reaches into his top desk drawer, pulls out a single cigarette and holds it between his fingers, but doesn't light it. I understand that the interview is now over.

"If it was totally up to me, I would hire you right now. But first, I have to speak to the other supervisor, Chef Dennis McKeown, and I'll get right back to you, Eddie," he says. He then shows me the way out of the maze we took to his office up to the lobby. He walks me to the main entrance of the hotel and informs me that he will most certainly talk to me later as he shakes my hand.

I'm through the front door of the Shilo Inn and head for the sidewalk leading to the turnaround with the statues centered in the middle of it. As I'm walking toward the historical marker, I notice a sign to my left for the aquarium. I have some time to kill, so I decide to go check out the animals of the water world, which I have not done since an eighth-grade school field trip to Seaside and Astoria, and the aquarium is just a short distance away. I walk down the promenade, looking through the inn's windows at the people eating in the restaurant. The next set of windows offers a view of the hotel's guests, diving and splashing in the indoor pool. I notice the seagulls cruising the sky with the greatest of ease on this partially cloudy day. I can't think of a better place to live. I sit for a while on this bolted-to-the-ground, weather-beaten bench, watching the ocean waves crash into the cliff. Then, all of a sudden, the wind really picks up some speed, so I quickly make my way to the aquarium.

As I enter the gray, chiseled stone-block building, I see a caretaker feeding some seals. A few seconds later, a blonde, innocent-looking young Caucasian girl runs toward me, stops dead in her tracks a couple of steps away, and just stares, surprised, like she realizes she went the wrong way. Staying a safe distance from the somewhat frightened little girl, I motion to her with my index finger to go back the opposite way where her mother is. Then, out of the blue, a woman I guess is her mother rushes over frantically and snatches the child up in her arms. The second she lays eyes on the color of my skin, she's petrified, instantly rushing to judgment when she sees me: she knows who really commits *those* sorts of crimes. I look at the racist lady as if she is the most dysfunctional person I've ever seen. Her face tells me that she knows for a fact that African American men like yours truly kidnap Caucasian children and do unspeakable things to them. It's just that old, assumed ignorant bigotry when a light-skinned female is brainwashed to the point where she just knows something bad will happen to her child when a dark-skinned man is around. It's that same ignorance that gives true criminals the benefit of the doubt, simply because justice suffers from the Caucasian Trusting Code that has proven crucial to allowing one's own persuasion to prey on one's own race, year after year. Just like at the clothing store when that white woman stole those leather coats while watching me, the dark-skinned man, being singled out immediately as the assumed thief about to commit a crime, in a store run by employees who pay no attention to their own privileged persuasion. Like an annoyed damn fool, I start to explain that my finger is pointing the little one to go the other direction, while her mother is evolving from Ignorance Land. Do all light-skinned people down here have an ignorant racist panic button or what? Guilt-ridden racism makes seemingly normal people real damn-dumb, decision-making hoodwinked humans, who have a hell of a time snitching on their racist upbringing. This has to be an exceptionally tiresome dimension in which to be doomed to live a white lie as a fearful, paled American—ready, willing, and far beyond able to prejudge a situation to an obscene level of supreme racism.

Well, there really is no sense in letting misfortune get the best of me. Besides, I had a very good interview today and decide to distance myself from this ignorant, brainwashed human. W-H-I-T-E weird humans ignorant to equality.

I'm heading for home, which is now less than seventy-seven very windy feet away, and I can hardly wait to get inside. I open the door with my key, step into the cottage, close the door behind me, and just stand for a moment, savoring, soaking up the cool, calm quiet. I change into some more comfy clothes and turn on the TV. Since there is no chair, I sit on the squeaky, well-used Murphy bed while watching *The People's Court*. Sherri comes home and tells me she thinks things went well today, but Chef Dennis wants to interview me as well. A couple of days go slowly by until I finally meet with him and have a fabulous conversation and interview. I tell him the absolute truth, which he appreciates, and I'm pretty confident I've got the job. He's five foot five, medium build, olive-skinned, Italian—black hair and mustache, a cool-natured equal opportunity type of guy with no hang-ups, and very fair and respectful. Now it's time to be thankful, to be patient, to wait for that phone call, to start my new job, so I can rent us an apartment, or maybe a house at the beach if the price is right.

By Monday, I haven't heard anything from Troy or Chef Dennis, either. But it's the start of an upward trajectory, something much more, because you never know what's going to happen next. As long as you are breathing, there is still opportunity knocking at your door. Sometimes, you just have to open it and see your way through it. I'm thinking to myself, *I'm very blessed. I am.* Sherri blasts through the cottage door like she had a number-two accident, drops the brown paper bag and her rolled up blue apron on the bed instead of the counter, ready to lovingly pounce on me. It's the start of her weekend off from the Shilo Inn. "Baby, you got the job! You start tomorrow at eight o'clock in the morning!" she announces loudly, straddling me in her unattractive white see-through blouse and blue skirt uniform, her hot undercarriage heating up my already obvious addiction to her mind, body, and soul. "You also need to bring two pieces of Oregon identification," she says, rocking back and forth gracefully in my lap, sensually, purposely playful. "You did it, Baby!" she sighs, kissing me continuously on my chocolate lips, like a beautiful queen kissing her king, making me feel marvelously glad that I made the decision to relocate to Seaside and start fresh.

"No, Baby. We did it!" I say, smiling between kisses, hugging her like we just won the lottery, ready to celebrate the joyful good news of my new employment. After Sherri changes into her jeans and sweatshirt, we take our daily stroll, hand in hand, down the promenade, enjoying the waves crashing on the shore as the dull, overcast sky is still in play. Knowing that the only appropriate dinner for us is fresh crab, we head back to the dookey-brown Datsun parked in front of OUR cottage. Sherri drives while I familiarize myself with the surrounding area. We stop for seafood shopping at the Crab Buoy on Highway 101, across the street from the gas station. Once we're back home, Sherri teaches me how to properly crack the tasty, fresh-out-of-the-water crab she has just boiled in a pot on the glossy white stove. We toast ourselves with glasses of champagne Sherri has brought for this very special occasion, telling each other how much we really love one another, and consequently turning up each other's natural heat, which naturally turns into an hours-long lovemaking session, until we finally fall asleep, resting in each other's arms.

Before the antique clock can sound the alarm, I jump out of bed and into the hot, burning shower like I'm still in basic training, then shaving, thinning my goatee, brushing my teeth, deodorizing myself, and getting dressed for work like I'm a human Energizer Bunny. For my first day on the job, I decide to wear a sky-blue, short-sleeved shirt, dark charcoal-gray, straight-legged denim jeans, a brand new black belt, my new black shoes, my black windbreaker, and some dark-gray socks. I try to do all this without waking up Queen Sherri Lynn, but the plan fails miserably. Her blinking eyes finally settle on the outdated, three-by-five-inch, brownish, portable alarm clock/radio sitting on the reddish countertop, which is plugged into the socket close to the stove and refrigerator. It's plain, red-lit dial face glares back at us: 6:00 am. "You are up *way* too early, Honey. I wanted to snuggle some more with you, Baby," Sherri breathes, sleepily. Standing by the side of the bed, fully dressed, and ready for the world, I tell her, "It may be six o'clock in the morning, but I am pumped up! I can't help it. I need a good workout! I need to do something constructive! Besides, it keeps me in shape. I will never, ever catch this body lazy. As far as I'm concerned, work is play, and playing is just lots of work. But once you get your job duties down, it becomes playtime! Because the repetition of the daily grind becomes second nature. Baby, I have to go wrestle the meat and bring home that bacon!" I gently lean over the bed to give my Snooky Nooky Poo Poo good morning kisses all over. As an equal exchange of affection, she tries to pull me back into bed. And I am starting to get aroused. On top of all that, I am overly eager to start functioning intelligently in the workplace as an everyday, motivated Citizen of These United States. "Honey, Baby,", I truthfully say, "There is absolutely no way we are going to just lay here and calmly, quietly snuggle, and nothing else is going to happen."

"Oh, Honey, just come lay down with me?" she purrs, and she lifts the bedclothes, exposing her natural, naked flesh, which I interpret as my delicious, dessert/breakfast. I study the red-lit clock face on top of the small counter, doing the math in my head. It's only six twenty-five, I don't have to be at work until eight. And I only live five minutes away. Yep! That adds up! *You are doing too much*, I think as I attempt to slide between the sheets on the narrow side of the squeaky, metal-frame bed without undressing, easing myself onto the well-used mattress, attempting to lay down flat. "Honey, I can't snuggle with you when you've got those darn, thick clothes on. Take them off, please, Baby! I want to feel your warm body!" Sherri whines, moving toward me slightly, giving me her pouty, baby-of-the-family face. I do a quick, unsexy strip and get back in bed where we make love for at least another hour. Then I wash up all over again, get dressed all over again, kiss my Snooky Nooky Poo Poo good morning all over again, then head out for work. I stroll down the promenade into a chilly, partially sunny Monday morning, watching a few early morning joggers and speed walkers get their exercise. I am truly excited about punching that clock, as ready to make money as a crazed Energizer Bunny. So excited, in fact, that I was twenty minutes early anyway.

After walking to the Shilo Inn on this slightly overcast day, which is soon to burn off, I enter the main doors and take the first hallway to my left, down the carpeted corridor furnished with mini loveseats for the comfort of the guests staying at the inn. I pass through the employee door and down a short corridor, then into the large kitchen where the dish tank is directly in front of me, then down the hallway to a small break room, where I am supposed to wait for Chef Dennis, or Mike, the Kitchen Steward. "Good morning!" I say to Troy, as I stand up to shake his hand.

"And good morning to you," he replies. "You are early."

"The early bird always catches the worm," I quickly answer.

"I heard that!" he replies as he takes me into the restaurant through the employee entrance. As we enter the kitchen, once again I hear this amazingly hilarious, high-pitched, lovable laugh coming from the dude on the cook's line; you know, the kind that makes you want to laugh too? It seemed to cover me with a sense of safety, like everything down here was going to be okay. There are some good people around here. I've just got to find out where, and who they are. Now Troy and I walk a couple of steps to a long, narrow room, one wall of which supports a long, collapsible metal table with three small, circular glass ashtrays almost overflowing with cigarette butts on it, and a few yellow phone books. Troy, dressed in a burgundy sweater, Bach slacks, and loafers, respectfully asks me to have a seat and fill out some forms with personal information for the United States Government. I sit down, not wanting to get comfy, and fill out my new-hire paperwork. Without a word, Troy abruptly leaves to make photocopies of my identification. He returns just as I finish filling out the rest of my paperwork, and I hand him the entire packet. He flips through all the forms, making sure they are complete, and as he hands me back my identification, he asks, "Well, are you ready to meet and greet?"

"Let's do it," I answer confidently.

We leave Troy's office and make our way to the kitchen and over to the cooking line where stands my future friend, the man with the outrageous laugh of the century. "Mr. Jim Dunkin!" Troy says, smiling, getting Jim's automatic attention.

"Yeah, what's up, Troy?" Jim asks, as he's simultaneously wiping his hands with a yellow rag and reading an order on the metal ticket wheel in front of him. He turns around, quickly flips an egg in a small, very well-used, black-handled sauce pan as he continues building a breakfast plate.

"This is Eddie. He is from Portland and he's now working for the Shilo Inn. Fix him something to eat, please," Troy says, politely respectful, before he takes off with my paperwork. I am standing there, checking out the dishwashers, making mental notes on how they operate their machines, checking out their entire setup. Jim Dunkin is all decked out from head to socks in a white, ironed uniform, complete with a white cook's hat, and is the owner of that amazing laugh I heard earlier.

"What would you like to eat?" he asks, wiping off the cutting board on the line.

"I'm really not hungry right now. I have to work up an appetite, if you know what I mean," I say with a smile. "Okay. Then I will fix you something for lunch.", Jim says, returning the smile as he gets back to work.

I head for the break room, where the kitchen steward is going to give me my first challenge. While I'm waiting, some more employees file into the room: Mike, six foot two, medium build, mustache, wearing a white-striped sweater and brown slacks; Marty, five foot eight, face full of freckles, black hair, a busboy who briefly introduces himself saying hello, then immediately darts out of the break room back to the restaurant floor to do something he forgot to do. Then, this other cook named Gary comes in, five foot nine, long black hair in a ponytail held captive by a hairnet, medium-to-slender build like yours truly, dressed all in white. After him, in walks a guy who seems to be character-cool as all outdoors-like; a stand-up, leveled-headed copasetic dude of the planet who's solid. He turns out to be Mike, the kitchen steward I'm waiting for. We introduce ourselves, and he lets me know he's the hiring and firing supervisor of the dishwashers and janitors. He then takes me on a tour of the entire property that winds up in the basement. We enter the hallway that leads to Troy's office, but stop one door short on the same side. He opens this door wide, and I can see that it is just what I thought—a dry storage room. But one with a difference: this room has never been cleaned or had anything put in its proper place. I see cases of canned sauces on the floor, cans piled on boxes, metal shelving not being used efficiently, and on and on. Michael explains he wants this entire room cleaned up and rearranged, which is nothing but a challenge to me. I definitely have my work cut out for me as I survey the disarray I have to get in order. "So, since you have so much experience, I will just leave you to it," Mike says, giving me solo time to do my exercise thing on this minor workout.

"Well, thank you for having faith in me. I will not let you down. You will be impressed because I can show you better than I can tell you," I tell him proudly. Mike then starts the clock, leaving the project totally up to me.

The first thing I do is locate an extra garbage can in the banquet prep area down the hall from the elevator. Then I open up an internal can of kick-ass and start breaking down empty cardboard boxes and stacking them at the end of the hallway. When I finish with that, I do a quick recon of the basement to gather all the supplies and equipment I'll need to do the job right: broom, dustpan and brush, rags, sponges, liquid floor cleaner, TSP, wringer bucket, mop, check. Next, I brush and wipe off the tops of everything I'm taking out of the room and stack it against the walls of the hallway. After I brush and wash/wipe down the shelving units, I give the room two thorough sweepings, corners and under the shelves included, a preliminary wet mopping, a scrub mopping with floor cleaner, then a final rinse with clean water just to take the stench out of the room. Troy walks by, looking at some invoices on his way to his office just as I am finishing up organizing the food products according to their expiration dates. With his head still buried in his paperwork, he asks me from the hallway, "How's it going, Eddie?"

"Take a look for yourself," I reply. "Everything is put away in order, organized so you can see exactly what you are looking for, which makes it easier to order inventory. This way you won't spend any unnecessary funds." He steps into the storage room a little hesitantly, but once he sees the extent of my job, he begins walking slowly around the entire room, looking, checking, and inspecting. His jaw literally drops like it is the most dramatic makeover he's ever seen. He almost looks like he's in shock.

"It smells clean and fresh in here. I am truly impressed," Troy says softly, still walking around slowly, inspecting, looking all around. "Very impressed."

With the dry storage room out of the way, I inspect the prep area in the basement, and the large banquet area. I notice the interior walls in the banquet area need to be scrubbed down and the garbage cans need to be drastically sanitized, like yesterday or last year. After completing these two eyesore projects, I venture over to the banquet dishwashing and prep area to inquire and inspect what urgently needs to be done. I'm working up an appetite and ready for some nourishment. I have to wipe the sweat from my forehead with the back of my hand. I'm grinning at how much progress I've made in such a short time, inwardly proud of my accomplishments so far. I toddle around the corner into the huge banquet kitchen, where there are four large, long solid wood cutting-and-prep tables, a couple of huge mixing machines, and a deep, stainless steel double sink. There's a guy dressed in a white cook's uniform being semi-quiet as he cuts up stale bread into croutons. I see him smile at me as I make my way over to the long table. I put out my hand and say, "Hello, my name is Eddie Dee Williams."

He puts his cutting knife down on the counter, takes off his tight, yellow Playtex glove to shake my hand. "Hello, man. My name is George," he says, smiling. Another cool brother from another mother, I'm pretty sure of it, and my senses say all-the-way-human.

"Do all the cool, sophisticated human beings who live here in the City of Seaside pretty much work at the Shilo?" I ask, knowing this is not the case from the get-go.

"No bro, it's just that there is a humongous number of people that work here, but are generally, for the most part, cool," George says. "However, there *are* quite a few racists, too, so you want to be careful," he adds, seriously. He's blonde, around my height and weight, the laid-back, mellow type, and has long bangs that he flicks backward without using either of his hands. "What the hell brings you down here in Seaside, bro?" George asks in a curious, hyped up, fashionable way.

"My girlfriend is from out here, her name being Sherri. She is one of the new waitresses on the day shift. Besides, I always wanted to live on the Pacific Northwest Coast since my family used to vacation down here occasionally when I was a young lad. That's when we were a mother-father-married-with-children family and life was good and happy," I tell him.

"Well, I don't know who she is, because I haven't been working here long, either," he explains. "But, yeah man, we should get together and kick it."

"Definitely, we got to get together soon," I say as I leave the kitchen. After my inspection, I walk around for a bit looking for Mike so he can do his own inspection. I knock on the door to Chef Dennis's office, someone says, "Come in," and I see Mike and Dennis are chatting. The boss's office is only a six-by-eight-foot room with a lot of safety posters plastered all over the white wall, which you can barely see due to the overkill of posters—safety announcements, long-past events, and outdated advertisements. Dennis is sitting at a contemporary stained-oak desk so littered with paperwork, forms, and other office paraphernalia that you can barely see the wood grain. It could easily use a makeover. He is sitting, leaned back in his chair, relaxed, chatting with Mike. "Eddie! Good job today! You're just who we've been looking for," Dennis says, complimenting my work today. "You can go ahead and punch out. You keep working like that and I will make sure you get forty hours every week. Yes, I have no problem with your work habits. You work like you are two people."

"You keep this kind of momentum up and you are going to go places, Eddie," Michael also chimes in with his constructive compliments.

"Thanks. I'm glad you like my work. It's good to know," I say as I exit the office. I grab my time card out of its slot on the wall next to the elevator, lean back around the office doorway and ask them, "What time do you want me here tomorrow?"

"Same time, same place. Have you had anything to eat today?" Dennis asks, realizing that I had been so busy I forgot to eat.

"No, I haven't," I answer, as my stomach seconds that motion with hunger pains, reminding me I haven't eaten since I had that crab for dinner last night. My overeager excitement about my first day at the grind somehow derailed my appetite without me giving it a second thought.

"Well, what would you like, a cheeseburger or something?" Dennis asks, motioning to me.

"Yes, I would, please," I respond.

Dennis walks over to the kitchen line casually and yells out for one of the line cooks. "Make the new janitor a cheeseburger, please."

A few minutes later, Jim Dunkin brings my cheeseburger: lettuce, tomato, pickles, onion, and fries on this masterpiece plate to the break room. I inhale the well-done cheeseburger like I haven't eaten all month. Once I'm done, I also drink a whole glass of ice water in two or three huge gulps. I thank Jim for the chow, grab my jacket, exit the break room, and start for the employee exit. I sink my plate in the main dish tank, asking "Was sup?" to the amigo who's working there. I walk out the employee exit door, reach in my pocket for my cigarettes and lighter, fire up a fag, and experience a moment of blissful contentment. Then it's down the concrete disabled ramp, ready to get home. I stroll leisurely to the turnaround, viewing the statues of Lewis, Clark, and Sacajawea, the beach, the Pacific Ocean, Tillamook Head in the distance, then down the promenade, glad to be out of the City of Roses. I watch the few people at their beach activities, carefree, wandering along the sandy, windy, but pleasant coastline as I amble down the promenade, enjoying the scenery on my way to the cottage. Just a matter of minutes away.

8

. . . .

We All Look Alike?

few days later, while I'm enjoying my mini-stroll to work
on the promenade to the Shilo Inn, feeling blessed to see
another day, a male passerby on a late-model, full-sized
Schwinn bike, who apparently lives down here and to whom I was
not paying attention, says to me, "Hello, Joe," as he rides by me in
the opposite direction toward Twelfth Avenue. I turn to look at him
riding away, wondering in amazement, *Who the hell is Joe?* because my
understanding is that there are no African Americans in Seaside other
than Troy and me. *Hmm.*

A couple of hours after this awkward start to an unusual sunny
day, my shift turns into a trust test, which leaves me feeling a little
uneasy, unfortunately. As usual, I arrive at work in my upbeat, good
mood before going through my early morning inspection rituals: check
the schedule for banquets, straightening and sterilizing the reach-in
and walk-ins from the dinner shift, discarding empty boxes, rotating
produce, scanning the expiration dates to prevent waste and spoilage,
and keeping all the floors clean and sterile throughout the entire
back of the restaurant. While sweeping the walk-in refrigerator with
a narrow, industrial broom, I notice a five-dollar bill on the floor in
plain sight. For the benefit of the unenlightened, this is a classic ethnic
investigation to see if I am honest enough to return the money or
keep it, like any true criminal obviously would. So, I immediately pick
the money up from the clean, concrete floor, and without hesitation,

march straight to the chef's office, giving the lie to the stereotypical beliefs that have haunted my persuasion ever since my ancestors were set free from the chains of the abomination of slavery. I knock on the partially open door. "Excuse me," I utter before entering the office. Dennis is sitting at his desk somewhat relaxed, while Troy is seated in one of the two chairs against the far wall next to Michael, the kitchen steward, who's in the other chair. Both of them have suspicious looks on their faces. I'm holding the money in my hand as I say, "I found this in the walk-in, Dennis. Somebody must have dropped it," then hand the bill over to the chef.

"Good job, Eddie," Dennis replies, smiling. "Most people would not have done that. You are a good person. Keep up the good work." He nods, leaning slightly back in his high-backed, wooden desk chair. I exit the chef's office smoothly, yet bewildered, shaking my noggin as I head down the hallway to complete my daily duties, realizing that I am actually being thief-proof tested! I am not a happy camper and feeling slightly humiliated about their money entrapment scenario. But, I proved them wrong, and that is what I do best.

A few minutes later, Terry shows up in the hallway along with a few of the other employees—Julie, another waitress, John, Marty, Jim, Larry, and Swede, all listening while Terry tells me this joke. He starts by assuming the position: leaning forward with his hands over his head a couple of feet apart, palms flat on the shiny, light Bach-painted wall, while spreading his legs, like he is being frisked before being arrested. He puts his full, sandy-haired head down on his chest and loudly asks me, "Eddie, who am I?"

"You are a black man being arrested," I reply, holding a slightly damp mop, standing, watching, listening to Terry's bit, awaiting his punch line.

"Nope, that's not it! You give up, Eddie?" Terry asks, turning around, facing me. Being six foot tall, he's looking down at me, and says, "Nope, that's a black man being spray-painted in Heaven! Get it, Eddie?" Along with everybody else who heard it, I laugh at the joke, which was quite humorous. "You are all right for a black guy, Eddie," Terry says, laughing, patting me on the back, as if I had won him a bet. See, when you have too many racial hang-ups, this is one of light-skinned Caucasian people's ways of breaking the ice, so to speak, to see if I have substantial anger issues. Later on that same afternoon, I decide to ease my positive-thinking mind by letting go of the early morning theft/entrapment/separation test I was dealt and have lunch with Sherri, who's in the break room.

"Hi, Baby, how's your day going?" I ask, smiling, excited to see her sweet, pleasant face.

"Hi, Baby," she replies as she downs her clam chowder out of the miniature soup bowl, like she's starved for nourishment. "It's steady, not real busy, Baby. Everybody seems to think you are very nice and a good worker," she says as she finishes her soup. Then, two more waitresses enter the break room, and Sherri introduces me to Melinda and Carolyn.

"Hi, Eddie, pleasure to meet you. So, you are Sherri's chocolate man!" Carolyn says, smiling at me like I'm a Hershey's chocolate bar just waiting to be tasted.

"Hi, I'm Melinda. Nice to meet you," the other waitress introduces herself. Both of them are bleach blondes. Melinda is a petite, gorgeous five foot four, and Carolyn is a well-seasoned, five-foot-seven, blue-eyed blonde lady who appears to be really easy to get along with, who I met the day I came up to the Shilo Inn for my interview. Jim brings my burger plate and I quickly introduce him to my lady, Sherri.

"What are you doing after work, Eddie?" he asks, standing in the break room doorway, taking a quick five from the cooking line after the lunch push, the perspiration on his forehead soaking into his white cook's hat.

"What's up?" I ask.

"You want to go and have a beer after work?" he asks, leaning inside the doorway of the break room. "That is, if it's okay with your lady?" he adds, putting the question out in the open—the "can I come out and play for a little while" scenario, like he's trying to find out whether I need a hall pass to go to the bar.

"Eddie Dee Williams does not need my permission to go and have a beer with you!" Sherri says seriously, turning to face Jim, making it perfectly clear ours is no ball-busting, shackle-chained, apprehensive relationship.

"Well, bro, what's it going to be?" Jim asks, unaware that I've been waiting for an invite to the bar to socialize, anyway.

"Sure, why not? Does the place we are going to have pool tables?" I ask.

"Yes, it does. We should go to the Beach Club just down the street from the here," he adds, and walks back to the line.

"Honey, I will see you when you get home," Sherri says, kissing me goodbye since her morning shift is over. Jim and I cross-reference our schedules, then decide to meet around 4:30 p.m. at the Beach Club, which is only two small city blocks from the beach front Shilo Inn.

Hours later, it's time to call it a day. I punch out, well-exercised, walk through the employee exit, past the Shilo Inn's dumpsters, and onto a narrow street with no sidewalks named Ocean Way Avenue. This merges into Downing Avenue which intersects with Broadway, the main drag into the tourist town of Seaside, and is lined with a collection of storefronts businesses. It's a clear, early evening on the coast, with the sun still shining as I stroll down Ocean Way Avenue. I'm enjoying the walk without a care in the world and I arrive at the next intersection, just one block from the Beach Club, when all of a sudden, BAM! A hot rod beefed-up, canary-yellow Chevy Nova with wide racing tires and its engine roaring comes toward me at supersonic, devil-bat-straight-out-of-scorching-hell velocity! I can hear the shifting of gears and the engine roaring loudly, like an untamed lion as the driver of the car tries to run me over. At the last second, my adrenaline enables me to react, dodging, and running super-fast out of the way, avoiding the deranged, demonic vehicular posse's Angel of Death, who is desperately attempting to end my livelihood. "Get out of town, nigger! Or die, nigger!" an obnoxious, lunatic man threatens me, yelling from the passenger seat of the car as they fly past after missing me. Another passenger yells out, "You fucking porch monkey! Die, nigger!"

This is a racist vehicular lynching, my intellect informs me as I'm standing there, bent forward at the waist, my hands on my thighs for support, panting feverishly from my unexpected need-for-speed sprint. The driver guns it toward First Avenue, then makes a furiously fast right turn at the intersection, obeying the traffic sign that says,

"Right Turn Permitted Without Stopping," spinning away at an extremely high rate of speed, past the Seaside Convention Center and disappearing into the darkening early evening.

It doesn't take rocket science to realize I have an authentic hateful racist situation on my hands! They were actually trying to kill me, and I don't exactly know what my options are in this town! Should I report it? Would that do any good? They were traveling so damn fast I couldn't see what they looked like! All I saw was a hot rod with long, stringy hair sticking out the open passenger side window.

My heart is still beating as hard and heavy as a seven-piece drum set, just like the time back in 1980 when my cousin Donny was driving his black 1973 Cadillac Coupe to Lincoln City in the rain. Patricia, Angela, and I were in the car with him when the wipers just quit working. We got off the highway at the wrong time and the wrong place, running smack into a Ku Klux Klan meeting. There they were, dozens of them, dressed in all-white Klan uniforms in the middle of a large field, forming a big circle around a huge, blazing wooden cross. Once we'd made the wrong turn and they saw who was in the car, they started running toward us, yelling at us loudly, "Come here, you coon niggers!" in the suburbs of Stayton, Oregon on an unpaved gravel road. Donny froze fearfully in the driver's seat, barely managing to ask me, "What I should do, Eddie?"

"Get the hell out of here!" I yelled, as I mashed down the gas pedal heavily with my foot on top of his, getting us the hell out of there. And I haven't been back there since. I'm definitely going to have to be careful in Seaside from here on out. Wow!

Cold-sweating, feverishly devastated, I'm scanning my surroundings, looking left, right, all around, making sure the enemy has vanished, using my ears to detect the sound of a souped-up engine. I continue across the Beach Club's gravel parking lot, my guard up and on high alert, walking toward the entrance, still a little shaken, still somewhat shell-shocked. I can't wait to have a cold glass of beer to calm my distraught, overheated, psychologically jangled nerves. I grab the handle of the front door, pull it open, and walk in. There are approximately a dozen people in the establishment. The inside is beautifully designed, with stained-wood paneled walls throughout, two regulation-size pool tables, and to my immediate left, a jukebox against the wall, next to the hallway that leads to the restrooms. I make my way toward the bar, which is outfitted with six black-and-silver bar stools. As if I haven't been through enough already, I experience another shock when, out of the blue, a man comes up to me who I do not know at all, acting like we are old acquaintances.

"Hey, Joe! Hey, man, how are you doing?" the strange man says, as I sit down on the black, cushy stool, staring at him, still in an upheaval from what just went on outside. I glance at the mirror behind the bar to size this guy up, and there in its reflection, looking directly at my head, is a sandy-curly-haired, five-ten, medium-build, bad-disposition face dressed in blue jeans and a short-sleeve, plaid dress shirt. So, how am I supposed to react to this confused individual who has inherited a case of misinformed identity? As I spin slowly around on the stool, letting him get a really good look at me, my heart is still racing somewhat. It's hard to swallow those damn scary racial death threats and keep them down. However, I'm not going to let that, or anything, get the best of me. I'm built of stronger stuff than that. I shall be all right. It's not always going to be this way. "What did you just call me, sir?" I ask, realizing he has made a mistake. And it's happened for the second time today. He's now actually standing, as if he wants to perform some bad activities on me, so I am going prove to this individual that I am not a Joe, since he is absolutely, positively, sure I am.

"Joe, don't act like you don't know me! You owe me money, and you know that," the man says, grumbling, whispering the word "spook" as he approaches very close to my face, pointing his finger to assure himself he's right, and that the real world is just completely cross-eyed wrong.

"Look, man, I don't want any problems with you. But I am not Joe," I say, reassuring him as I stand up from the black, cushy stool, and face him in a peaceful, yet ready-for-whatever way, simply and calmly attempting to educate this individual to the fact that I am not who he thinks I am. "My name is Eddie Dee Williams, and I work at the Shilo Inn. You have the wrong person, my friend," I add, stating the simple truth as I rub my hands together, not trusting the present combination of his ignorant attitude mixed with his obvious intoxication. Spotting a foreseeable unpleasant future situation, my coworker friend Jim, still in his white cook's uniform, scurries over from the pool table to the bar and stops next to the inebriated stranger. "Jim, will you please inform this man that I am not this Joe individual he thinks I am, and who owes him some kind of money?" I say, not wanting the situation to escalate to the physical exercise level.

"Hey, man? Look, his name is Eddie. Not Joe," Jim says, standing his ground as he faces the stranger.

"Do you know Joe?" the man asks an intelligent, but out-of-this-world-crazy question.

"No, I don't. But I do know *his* name, is Eddie," Jim states firmly, pointing his finger in the dude's face.

"Hey, man. That's *not* Joe. And I know who Joe is. Believe me, they look nothing alike," the somewhat tall, partially bald bartender says from behind the bar as he's filling an ice-cold, glass pitcher with beer from the tap.

"Look, man, since you don't believe me, ask Troy Hunt the very next time you see him. Seriously, you should do that," I say, suddenly understanding that someone my size and close to my complexion has been here and done way too much toward putting me in a potentially very serious situation.

"You mean Troy Hunt, the big, huge black guy?" the strange, decent-looking man says to me, calming down as he realizes who is in my corner.

"Yes, him. He is the person who assisted me in obtaining my job at the Shilo Inn, and he can easily straighten out this issue, since you don't believe I am a truthful person," I say bluntly as Jim returns to the pool table to play his next shot. "Listen, man, the very next time you see Troy, just ask him about Eddie Dee Williams," I say seriously.

The stout-build, average-height guy staring at me in distrust finally says, "Okay, I will do just that," and he drains his beer, sets the empty mug on the bar beside me, checks me out a couple more times, then finally walks away, deep in thought, shaking and scratching his head. Still somewhat unsure, he stops, turns and glances at me one more time, then decides to exit the bar.

"Hey, man, thanks for saying something. I really appreciate it," I say to the bartender as I finally sit back down on my stool.

"No problem. My name is Rob," he says, as he extends his hand, shakes mine soulfully, comfortably. He's six foot, stocky, slightly bald, and wearing a tight black short-sleeved shirt, blue jeans, and getting right back to business, asks me, "Now. Eddie. What are you having?"

"I will have a Miller in a mug, please," I answer, wondering what's going to come at me next.

Jim is a good pool player. He and I play a few pool games of eight ball, have a few more beers, and have a very good time. We decide to call it a night quite early, since we both have to work tomorrow morning. The four short blocks from the bar to the cottage go by very quickly as I walk down Downing Street, make a left turn onto Fourth Avenue, go up just a half a block, and on the right-hand side of the street I see the large-lettered Flying Dutchman sign hanging on the front awning of Joe and Debbie's cozy home and office. I greet Sherri as I enter the warm cottage and tell her about my being mistaken for some other chocolate American named Joe a couple of times now, and my run-in with some ignorant racists, which could lead to more problems down the road. Sherri, being Sherri, changes the subject, and says that since we both have the day off, her mother wants to take us clam digging, because I had mentioned wanting to experience some coastal outdoor activities. "Right, Baby," Sherri says, standing in front of me in a silky, white nightie, smelling that delicious way she does, putting her arms around my neck, causing me to forget whatever it was I was concerned about, relaxing my nerves until I realize all I want is to dig some clams, go whale surfing, be captain of a pirate ship...

It's partially cloudy a few calendar days later, with a small fog bank posing on top of Tillamook Head, making it look mysterious. Business has been declining at the Seaside Shilo Beachfront Inn as slowly as frozen molasses, so downstairs in the banquet prep room, Sherri suggests to me and George that we all go up to Astoria after we get off work. Since I was still going through bigotry withdrawal, she thought it would be a good idea if we went up to Astoria and find a club with an open mic. Now, don't get me wrong, I love to sing and would love the exposure, and perhaps even start an R&B band down here. However, it's just not that simple. Anyway, Sherri, George, and I, being fellow coworkers, all take turns showering at the cottage and changing into our evening clothes. Sherri drives the dookey-brown Datsun as we venture up to Astoria, to a club that supposedly has an open mic night. We arrive at the club, which is located in the middle of a block in downtown Astoria. The inside is a double-tiered affair with fake palm trees, some round wooden tables with wooden dining chairs, a tiny section of booths in the rear, right by the restrooms, and a rather sizeable, well-stocked with hard alcohol, full bar. The accompanying stage is already occupied by musicians—drummer, bass, rhythm guitar, and a lead singer jamming out some blues and rock and roll, a brand of music which I love. There is a healthy turnout of people, so I strongly doubt I will be allowed to do my singing thing. Us crazy three casually sit down at a table twenty feet from the stage and dig the laid-back atmosphere. Everything seems to be cool, but you never can tell. George and I each order a pounder of beer, while Sherri chooses a mixed drink. We listen to the live music for a while, then Sherri strolls up to the stage in her white blouse and tight blue jeans to speak with the long-haired guitar player onstage. She makes several trips up to the bandstand, after which it becomes evident she has successfully pissed off the guitarist to the point where he gracelessly tells his drummer friend, "I'm not going to let that spook jam with *us!*" I ignore the vulgarity and keep drinking my beer, maintaining my composure as Sherri returns to the table, utterly unaware of what was said. I'm not at all surprised. After all, this is still Oregon. Offended but patient, I realize as time passes, a few more singers, and then some more musicians, take the stage, that they're ignoring Sherri. We finally recognize that they are obviously just blowing us off, which bothers Sherri and my friend George, who mentions how racist to some degree people truly are. I can see Sherri is wanting to give them a piece of her mind, but I lovingly reassure her, "It will happen, Snooky, just not tonight. That's all it be."

"About how long have we been waiting?" George asks, impatient, and now tipsy from drinking on an empty stomach, smoke from his cigarette curling up in front of his face, eyes slanting closed, then opening slowly, looking as if he's smoked an ounce of the strong but highly misunderstood medicinal cannabis sativa. "I don't know, bro," I reply, flicking cigarette ashes in the tray on the table.

"Honey, I'm really not feeling well," Sherri says, looking very pained, leaning out of her chair, laying on me for some comfort. Naturally, I place my warm hand on her forehead, which is absolutely clammy. She appears to have a slight fever and looks quite sadly pale. Unanimously, and without debate, we decide to leave this establishment and get back to Seaside, Oregon, putting an end this dry run.

We exit the bar to the parking lot, where we find the weather has turned into icy-temperature crap, thick drops of wind-chopped, freezing rain nagging against our faces, rushing us into the car. Sherri confesses that I have to drive back to Seaside. I remind her, "Listen, Baby. DWB, you know, Driving While Black, *especially* late-night driving, just might be a very bad idea for someone of my persuasion." George knows he's intoxicated and admits he cannot drive. "I don't feel up to it," Sherri says all pouty, leaning on me, holding my hand tightly. "I know you don't want to drive, but you have to, Baby. I feel very sick, like shit, Honey," she pleads. I finally give in and settle Sherri in the passenger seat, then go around the car and quickly into the driver's seat. George is pretty buzzed, gets in the car a little unbalanced, then lands successfully in the back seat. Of the three of us, George is the regal legal, the only one with a legitimate license to drive. We pull out of the parking lot and head home down the highway, doing the within-the-city-limits thirty-miles-per-hour speed limit. Unknown to our happy little band, the Astoria Police have been following us. I haven't even driven a quarter of a mile before they hit the siren and turn on their flashing red lights. I dutifully turn on the right turn signal of the dookey Datsun, slow down, pull over to the curb, and stop. I know I'm going to get a ticket for no license, and the cop might very well make us walk all the way home. I just don't really know. Damn! I knew I should not have been driving. I had that funny feeling.

"Honey, is the police going to arrest you, Baby?" Sherri asks, looking sick as well as very worried. As I'm rolling down my window, the medium-to-large-build, clean-shaven, black-haired officer gets out of his vehicle with his flashlight and walks up to the driver side of the car.

"Everybody just be cool!" George says, sitting behind me, tipsy in the backseat. The officer's eyes get bigger when he shines the light on my skin. Then he notices Sherri in the passenger seat.

"Do you know how fast you were going?" the officer asks very sternly.

"Not quite that fast officer," I reply, being respectfully honest while looking the officer in the face.

"Let me see your driver's license, sir," he asks in a commanding voice, leaning down toward the window.

"Sir, I don't have a valid license," I tell him truthfully. "My girlfriend just got sick a couple of minutes ago, my friend George, directly behind me, was the driver, but is very intoxicated, and that's why I am driving the vehicle, officer."

"Do you have some kind of identification, sir?", he asks in a forceful tone, as if he's trying not to hear any excuse for anything. "Have you been drinking?" he asks, going through his routine-ritual-line-of-questioning.

"I had a one-pounder about one hour ago," I say as soberly as possible, carefully reaching into my wallet to give my identification to the officer.

"Sir, would you please step out of the vehicle?" the officer says.

"Honey!" Sherri shouts, showing her concern. "This may not be just a simple traffic stop. This might just be one of those nights."

"It's okay, Honey. Just let the officer do his job," I tell her as I grab the door handle and step out the car, carefully showing no attitude whatsoever.

"Do you have any weapons or drugs on you?" the officer asks, as he's patting me down, frisking my jeans pockets, then my short jacket.

"No, officer," I reply, rain dripping from my hands onto the dookey car. I immediately feel the damp, cold, freezing night right through my dampening jeans.

"Are you sure you don't have any drugs or weapons on your person, Mr. Williams?" the officer asks me redundantly.

"Yes, officer," I say, as I'm standing there, getting very wet, squinting my eyes just to be able to see through all of the rain that's blowing into my face, thanks to a strong westerly wind, which is also making it quite difficult to breathe.

"Do you know what a sobriety test is?" he asks.

"Yes, I have heard of it,", I reply, now shivering vigorously from the windy, freezing-cold, stinging, aggravating rain that's blurring my vision.

"Have you ever taken one?" the officer asks me, facing away from the main street, planning...something. But I don't get it. Unless he really believes I am drunk. Or...it's time to make his quota? Oh joy.

"No, I haven't," I reply peacefully, realizing what is about to occur next: The Test of Sobriety!

"Okay, this is how it's going to go," the officer says, as if I am in a remedial reading class. "Now, I want you to say your ABCs backwards, please?" the officer commands, staring in my eyes coldly.

"Well, let's see—z, x, y, w, v, u, t," I say, not thinking, just singing the alphabet backwards, which makes it very easy to say backwards.

"Okay, now lift your left foot off the ground and stand using only your right leg,", the officer commands, very serious about his sobriety.

"I can't perform that action due to a military injury sustained while on active duty in Germany that has left me stricken with a foot condition," I explain to the obviously close-minded officer, who's not even trying to hear that veteran jive about my right foot condition.

"If you don't do it, I am going to arrest you. Do you understand?" he says.

"But, officer, I can't do it because I sustained this injury in the military," I say, sincerely stating facts which he couldn't care less about.

"Well, then, Mr. Williams, you are under arrest for DUI. Turn around and put your hands behind your back," he commands, pulling out and opening his handcuffs, putting one cuff around my left wrist, the other on my right, then pushing me face-down on the hood of the car.

Curious-minded George and Sherri exit the Datsun excitedly, like that's really going to make a definite difference in this I-told-you-so-situation. Who do they think they are, really? They can't successfully change the police officer's mind about arresting me. Don't they know they could easily get themselves arrested for interfering with a police officer—which I know won't happen, because he has the individual he wants, and that would be me. It would behoove them to just get back in the car because he is not going to release me out of bondage. This is still the state of Oregon. Some things might not ever change. "Officer, why are you doing that?" George slurs, slightly stumbling, not realizing there are double-standard racial rules.

"What's going on? Why are you arresting him?" Sherri asks as she gets out of the car, moving very slowly, not really getting that's it's okay.

"Both of you get back in the vehicle, now, or else you will be charged with interfering with police business," Officer Calisto commands loudly, not in the mood for their mischief, restraining me as he tightens the handcuffs so they make that latching-clicking sound, biting, gnawing, pinching perversely at my skin as he continues to frisk my pockets a second time for weapons and drugs. The officer hauls me off the liquid-covered car as the rain falls freely on my face, guiding me into the patrol car head-first. After slamming the door forcefully closed, the officer marches over to the Datsun and informs Sherri that she needs to drive home, not at all curious if she has a valid license. Once the dookey-brown Datsun has evaporated out of sight, Officer Calisto, who's been in no hurry whatsoever so far, finally decides to take me to jail. On the way there, he has the audacity to start asking me questions, which I do not feel like answering. I have the constitutional right not to snitch on myself, and I've already said enough. To live is to hopefully learn. Once we arrive at the Clatsop County Jail in Astoria, he puts the vehicle in park, kills the engine, gets out of the patrol car, shuts his door, and then opens the rear door. I get out, careful not to bump my head. "Come on, let's get this over with," the officer says, leading me to where I am to be processed properly and charged with DUI—Driving Under the Influence. After I am processed and fingerprinted, he advises me that I am to take a blow test. If I refuse, my license will be suspended for another year. We're in this tiled, funky-built room with an out-of-date hunk of machinery for drunk-driving violators to blow into. The miniature, clear, vacuum-looking hose is connected to a machine that probably hasn't been calibrated since President Nixon was disgraced out of office.

"Officer Calisto, since you asked all of your questions and got all of your answers, I have some questions for you. First, why the hell did you arrest me?" I ask the mean-looking officer, staring right into his face, to see if he has the balls to tell the truth. "Second, why did you let my girlfriend drive home when you knew she did not have a license? And you knew darn well I was not intoxicated," I say, stating the facts. "I just want the truth, like you did," I add, looking at him like he can't be a man about his position.

Then he says beautifully, "I am an Italian with a badge. And you're black! Boy! Now, blow in the machine," Officer Calisto commands, threateningly loud, like I am his personal property.

"No. I refuse to be talked to like I'm some dog! Can I please go to my cell now?" I say, morbidly pissed off, as if there is anything positive I can really do about the situation.

"If that's the way you want it," Calisto says, playing rugged head games. I am pissed out of my comfort zone to the point where I don't know what to do. I am a damn racial target and there's pretty damn much nothing I can do about it. After several hours of being locked up, I'm finally released from jail. Sherri was there to pick me up in the Datsun, feeling dreadfully bad that she made me drive in the first place.

Still feeling hoodwinked a few days after the incident, I just go work every day, then proceed to go straight home, realizing I'm really not up to being harassed or judged. Once a week is enough for me. However, I am not ever driving again until I am positively legitimate. A couple of days later at the Shilo Inn, my coworker, Jim Dunkin and I are in the break room munching down on delicious teriyaki burgers with grilled pineapple in the company of the newest addition to the Shilo Crew, busboy John Trent, who just happens to be Marty, the other busboy's cousin. He's a stocky young man, five foot seven, blond hair, blue eyes, cool-crazy as all outdoors, levelheaded, very spontaneous, and has been working a week now. The weather is particularly nice this time of year; it's peak season, otherwise known as Spring Break, when the town and the beaches are packed for the next couple of months. Oregonians can't wait for the weather to get gorgeous so they can enjoy all the natural wonders the great Pacific Northwest has to offer. One never knows when the bright yellow star will shine. And when it does, you have no choice but to get outdoors and enjoy those addictive ultraviolet rays, which have traveled all 93 million miles from the sun to this here planet classified as the Earth. "Bro, you said you wanted to see something beautiful? We should hike up to Tillamook Head," Jim suggests, which sounds like a positive thing to do.

"Yes, why not? I would like to see it," I reply, excited and game ready.

"I want to go and hike up there with you guys, if that's all right with you?" John, the new busboy, asks.

"It's slap-dookey-cool with me, my most excellent dudes. Let's do it right after work," I suggest to Jim and John. So, after work John, Jim, and I meet outside at the turnaround, walk all the way down to the promenade, then over to a beautiful cove where huge, glacier-dragged rocks are battered by timber logs that the ocean waves crash against them.

"Once we get up there, bro, we should be able to see Japan, right?" I ask, being funny.

"Sure, Ed," Jim replies. "If you want to call Cannon Beach Japan, go for it."

"How many miles is it to get all the way across to Cannon Beach?" I ask John.

"It's about four miles to Cannon Beach," John says.

"Are you serious?" I ask, looking up at the furious, frighteningly dark-gray storm clouds moving inland off the Pacific, as if they were riding a silent, magic carpet. "Because it looks like it's about to start pouring down rain." We hike up the hill from the cove, and less than two minutes later, it starts to rain.

"Well, this sucks!" Jim says. "This is not the way I planned it."

"Yeah, let's turn around, dude, this isn't good! A storm is definitely coming!" John replies.

"Hey, brother Ed! Want to hear a joke?" John asks me, being polite.

"Of course. Let's hear it!" I answer.

"Why do Mike Tyson's eyes water during sex?" John asks Jim and me, then spits some tobacco juice, and we both start laughing loudly.

"Why?" I ask, still laughing.

"Maze!" John replies laughing, making a sour lemon face.

We head back down the hill, still joking, laughing, and having a good old time, only to be met by a most unwanted welcome wagon; at the bottom of the hill is a Seaside Police patrol car. Not again! This can't be happening! Not twice in one week! No, there must be some other reason, they're probably looking for somebody else. Maybe. Once we are down the hill, the officer gets out of his patrol car, his flashing blue light on top of the car still flickering in a circular motion, but no siren. The six-foot, stocky, clean-shaven, light-skinned, Caucasian American officer approaches us professionally in his blue police uniform, looking like a no-chip-on-his-shoulder officer. I'm thinking, *Maybe there's an unknown city law against laughing too loud, or an excessive noise ordinance?* He appears decent-looking. He's about ten feet away from us when he gets straight to the point, no mincing words, no time for bullshit, except for what flows out of his mouth as he abruptly says, "We received a complaint about some strange-looking people up here," pointing his index finger, singling me out of the three of us. "You have some identification on you, young man?" he asks as a formality, not taking his brown eyes off me. Since he has already stated that I am out of place, there's no telling what's going to happen next in this little scenario. I slowly, carefully, and respectfully hand him my plastic-coated State of Oregon identification card, which I had already retrieved from my black leather wallet when he began his little stroll over to us. He visually analyzes it all the way back to his clean, late-model patrol car with the Seaside Police logos on the doors and the diamond-grid shield in the center of the interior of the vehicle, which separates the police from the criminals, once the bad guys are in the car.

"Hey, bro. Sorry this shit has to happen to you, man. This sucks," Jim whispers as he's standing next to John with his hands behind his back, shaking his head slightly, wondering the same thing we all are wondering: *What the hell?*

"Man, it's not your fault, just as long as I don't get arrested twice in the same week," I reply nervously, smoking a cigarette, trying to lighten the mood.

"Yeah, man, sorry you got to go through this bullshit, bro," John says, spitting some residual tobacco juice onto the beach.

"Mr. Williams, would you come here, please?" the officer asks. I walk up to him and he tells me I am under arrest. He asks me to put my hands behind my back so he can handcuff me. "Do you have any weapons or drugs on your person?" he asks.

I tell him, "No. But that shit doesn't matter, I'm still going to jail again. Officer, why am I being arrested?" I ask, being genuinely curious.

"Failure to comply," he responds bluntly, while frisking me for weapons and drugs. Then he opens the rear door, puts me in the patrol car headfirst, swings the door shut, gets in the driver's seat, closes the door, and drives me to the Seaside Police Station, leaving my newfound friends behind, who look at me being driven away like I don't belong in the backseat of a patrol car and that the cops got the wrong guy. I arrive shortly at the small but newly remodeled police station on Holliday Boulevard. The officer pulls the patrol car into the police parking lot and I can see the Thriftway Store next door to my left. We enter the station through the front door where I am totally surprised; he does not fingerprint me or put me in a cell. My arresting officer lawfully orders me to go up front and sit in the wooden chair next to this nicely stained, polished wood desk in this big open area, which looks more like a detective's office, except this is very clean, not like what they have on television. Well, this will be twice this week. Now what? One can only wonder.

The officer in charge of the desk has sergeant stripes on his uniform sleeves, and Barnett on his professional name tag; dark hair in a medium buzz cut, mustache, thick eyebrows, nonchalant, leaning his chair back against the glossy finished, smooth brown wall, a non-threatening man who bears a striking resemblance to my all-time-favorite actor, Jack Nicholson. He's on a long-distance call, speaking into a Bach-colored receiver that's connected to a rotary-dial phone, inquiring into some legal matter concerning, maybe, yours truly. "He is right here. I'll ask him," Sergeant Barnett says. He covers the mouthpiece of the phone with his hand, effectively muffling the voice transmitter component of the phone, giving me the benefit of the doubt and wanting to hear my explanation first before passing judgment upon me. "Your probation officer in Portland wants to know what you are doing here," he tells me.

That's why I was arrested? Because of him? I ask myself. Well, here's the story. I am feeling confident about my disposition right about now, for The Truth Will Set You Free! I humbly state, "I am living down here because I am employed at the Shilo Inn. I informed my probation officer the very last time I saw him that I had reunited with my girlfriend and was going to relocate, and that I would most likely be working here at the Shilo Inn in Seaside, Oregon. I have been working as a janitor for the Shilo Inn since last month," I proudly tell the nice sergeant, who silently rewards me for a good-ass answer by making faces and comical hand gestures as he reports all this to my probation officer. He's being classily blunt about me doing the right thing in challenging the probation officer's validity of having me arrested. I haven't left the state or committed a crime. I'm just working my forty hours a week, minding my own business and attempting to enjoy my freedom. "He says he works at the Shilo Inn, he's got a job, just like he told you he was going to," the nice sergeant says as he smiles, then winks at me, and gives me the thumbs up for my intelligent explanation. A few seconds later and Sergeant Barnett and my probation officer end their conversation. Bring it on! Two more years to go!

"Well, Mr. Williams," Sergeant Barnett says, "you managed to successfully piss your probation officer off gloriously, so he's going to expedite your probation file to Astoria." He rises from his chair, grinning, having been thoroughly entertained at my expense, strides out from behind his desk with key in hand, and respectfully asks me to stand up, which I do immediately. He removes my handcuffs and informs me that I am free to go, the smile never leaving his face.

As I exit the police station experiencing extreme bitterness, I also begin to recognize that I have triumphed over a system fraught with weaknesses and injustice. I walk out into a massive coastal rain shower, with 20 to 30 mph wind gusts blowing nasty, super gloomy gray clouds across the sky. I walk bent over, dodging the fierce wind that is blowing against my 155-pound, lean-muscled self. It's an excruciating storm from out of nowhere made of hail, rain, and sleet! Excellent! I walk my bent-over anatomy down Roosevelt, and by the time I get home, I AM DOUSED!

9

· · · · · · · · · · · · · · · · · · ·

Mr. Nigger!

Incredibly shocking news! Television's *Sports Edition* announces on the set in our cottage that Mike Tyson, Heavyweight Champion of the World, has been knocked out in the tenth round in Tokyo, Japan a few hours ago by Buster Douglas, who now is the reigning Heavyweight Champion of the World! Translation: Anything in life is possible!

A few blissful days later, after rain showers have river-danced away from the unexpected sun's rays, blue skies give me a soothing reassurance that everything is going to be just excellent.

Luckily, Sherri has the following day off, and she needs it desperately: the dookey-brown five-speed Datsun finally bit the dust after throwing a rod yesterday when she was headed to the Fred Meyer in Warrenton. Sherri's father picks her up at the cottage and informs her that the Datsun is shot. However, he has a friend who is getting rid of a black 1977 two-door Chrysler Cordoba with very high mileage that's still in decent condition, so they are going to pick up the vehicle this morning. The first day I ride shotgun in the Cordoba, the cops pull us over just for the melanin in my skin. The Seaside City police are making U-turns and pulling us over repeatedly, like I had stolen their wives or something. Sherri's sister, Kelly happily loans me a bronze ten-speed in excellent condition that has a security chain lock with a key wound around the top of the bicycle seat post. Sherri and I go to work separately since we always get racially profiled by the Seaside police whenever we're in the car together, and for no citable infraction. This seems to happen every other day like clockwork. Now the stickiness of our problem thickens as we are turned down for housing three times this week. It appears that forward motion is not our best friend right now. We're still functioning, even though we know we're surrounded by racism. As we contemplate our options, the inevitable conclusion is finally reached: renting a house to a so-called black man in Seaside, Oregon, just isn't going to happen. Sherri says it does not frustrate her that much. However, I beg to differ. She was already offered all these nice houses with the landlords ready to hand her the keys, and yet she cannot live in any of them with yours truly due to the melanin in my skin, along with my cousin David T. Duke illegally using my name, renting a townhouse he had no business doing.

Seeing as it's my day off, I sturdily decide to stroll to the Twelfth Avenue store. Returning to the cottage, I butt out my cigarette, enter the abode, turn on the nineteen-inch, color Motorola television set, sit down on the Murphy bed, open a can of Miller's and relax, watching the *People's Court,* when the front door flies open and Sherri rushes in like she just robbed a bank. She's holding onto the doorknob hard, and in a panic says, "Baby, the landlord called! Come on, let's go! They said we can rent the house!" hurriedly, but not at all quite thinking this out logically.

"You really have no understanding of the concept of naïve, do you, Snooky?" I ask seriously. "Listen up. Please believe me, I don't want to see you get hurt. I really do believe in you and I love you. You're wonderful in every way and you're positively my everything. However, if the landlord wants to see me in person before they bother to give you the keys to this luscious house, we are definitely screwed. That's an in-person racial check to see if I am of Mexican or African American descent. It's just that simple. Look, Sherri. If there is one thing I've learned about life in the world of racism, it's that when Caucasians want to see your face after they promise you the key to their house for rent, it's not going to happen. They are racist, plain and simple, short and sweet. They want to see my persuasion, and that's an automatic chicken shit-covered red flag, Honey!" I add cautiously, trying to reason with her so-called superior upbringing, that she refuses to sideline by not paying attention to the visual facts. Nevertheless, my sweet Sherri Baby is so naïve, yet so optimistic, and still doesn't quite comprehend how racism works, or the traumatic psychic toll it's about to take on her mental attitude regarding life. She's about to learn the horrifically ugly truth about racism, and believe me, it's not going to be pretty when she finds out that H-A-T-E stands for Having-A-Traumatic-Error, brought to you by the fear of equality.

"Not everyone is racist!" Sherri says defensively, at the top of her voice, looking at me crazily, pacing the tiny floor. I really don't want to be right this time.

"I know that, Snooky Nooky. Now when did I ever say that? I'm thinking about you!" I say, making my logical, mathematical point without a second thought, knowing in my gut what the future holds as Sherri attempts to put words in my mouth. "C'mon, Baby, please tell me something I don't know. In any situation, I try very hard not to rush to judgment. However, life has dealt me an extremely full hand of accredited rollercoaster-retarded racism," I say by way of explanation.

"Well, I think we should head out there anyway," Sherri says defensively, pushing the envelope with even more persistence to prove me wrong—which is impossible, or else she would have had the key in her hand yesterday. She doesn't realize in the midst of all of this, at this particular juncture I genuinely desire her to be so right.

"Fine," I replied, unappreciated. "I will go with you!" I reply in an elevated tone, irritated, realizing that we are having our first conflict of mindsets. I take a deep breath, let it out slowly, which instantly calms me down. Even though I'm not trying to go there, I'm feeling somewhat ridiculed and insulted. "However, there is only one logical solution. I can show you better than I can tell you!" I add confidently. After making my crucial point, I sit back down on the bed, causing the bedsprings to screechy noisily, bend over to put on my shoes, and prepare to teach a class in Racism 101.

Fifteen cemetery-silent minutes later, as "She Drives Me Crazy" is playing faintly on the car radio, Sherri wastes no time in driving us to our destination. She turns left off Highway Twenty-six West into a long, very private gravel driveway. I am 1000 percent sure this is a dry run, but I decide not to say a word; the proof is definitely in the chocolate pudding, with me being the chocolate. The clock is ticking. At the end of the driveway I see a magnificently beautiful, perfectly designed, three-bedroom, two-bath ranch-style house with a creek running through its spacious backyard; an exclusive home in a location fit for any family. A smiling lady comes out of the front door, and Sherri exits the black Cordoba joyfully as the round-faced, five-foot-six, brunette, fluffy-figured woman wearing a maroon dress comes down the walkway. She and Sherri exchange gracious hellos; however, when I exit the car smiling casually, the homeowner's face instantly transforms into a mask of hostile rage. "We've changed our minds! You get the hell off of my property now!" the woman shouts. I knew this bullshit toxic racism was going to occur, and I'm not at all shocked. The question now is: How is Sherri going to handle this devilish discrimination syndrome, which is deeply embedded, even in her very own family? Especially since she has already admitted her maternal grandfather is a straight up racist, making this present situation no breaking news bulletin to her. "We are no longer renting this property out! Please get the Hell off of my property!" the stiff-necked, mad lady shouts loudly.

"Excuse me!" Sherri says, diligently reminding the judgmental female racist, "You called me! And you said we can rent the house!" She takes a few steps up the driveway toward the deviant landlady, who has since backpedaled to where she is standing between the screen door and the beautiful doorway on the wide open porch, yelling loudly, non-stop, trying to outshout Sherri. "Just get the hell off my private property! We just changed our minds! Now, please get off of my property before I call the police!" she threatens, as she points in the general *get the hell out of here* direction. I'm resentfully thinking, *We could have saved the gas coming around here to deal with this ignorant-ass, racist landlady if Sherri had only trusted me.*

Sherri stands there in the long, heavily graveled driveway, mortified, confused, riveted, obviously not realizing she has no options, and staring at the beautiful home she cannot reside in. Had I been Caucasian, we would have been packing up to move into our new home yesterday. She slams the heavy car door after getting back in the driver's seat, looking very disturbed, like she's been shot in the middle her soul with an invisible dart. We leave the property as quiet as mutes until Sherri heavy-foots the gas, spinning the rear tires and sending up a blast of gravel back toward the house. "Can she legally do that? She can't do that!" Sherri asks, extremely irritated. She still doesn't understand what happened. "She can't legally do that, can she?" she pleads, demanding an answer. First and foremost, *I told you so* comes into my mind. However, given the situation, I decide it's best to say nothing. Just let it marinate in her soul. She does not have to go through this. She has the option of throwing in the towel and calling it quits. However unfortunate it may be, this the curse of the manufactured racial hate aimed squarely and exclusively at my melanin cells. As I look blankly out the passenger window, I'm asking myself what our next move is, wondering how much can Sherri take before the unspoken and ever-present possibility of her reversion to her so-called traditional persuasion is set in motion. "Would you please say something?" Sherri shouts at me, frustrated and appearing very upset. However, there is nothing I *can* say. The car radio lilts out Phil Collins's "In the Air Tonight" as I contemplate how to logically respond to Sherri's request. But there is no logic to it. I can only think; constantly dealing with a goulash of bigotry, police DWB (Driving While Brown) racial profiling, hate, prejudice—which you never had to in your so-called superior life—will righteously kick your ass, depending on how much you swallow before you wind up choking on it. Strong gag reflex or not, it's still an acid-bitter pill to swallow.

The next week, I am overly-glad to be at my place of employment, not only because of the money, but because they *know* me. Sad to say it, but I am treated far better at work than anywhere else in Seaside. I walk to work casually chilling, no worries, enjoying the lukewarm breeze, realizing these troubling days are going to be way-in-the-past, and Sherri and I will be in our own place soon, someplace, wherever that is. My young coworker friend, John Trent the busboy, takes me been-there-done-that advice about an older woman's fondness for a younger man and scores a bucket in the YES column.

"Ed, I would really like it if you could stop by the house of this older lady I've been plugging. Her name is Sonya," John humorously brags as he walks into the break room, where I've just pulled everything out, swept, mopped, and wiped down the walls. I'm just putting everything back in its proper place so it no longer reeks of the prehistoric fragrances of coworkers and nicotine. Terry, wearing a long-sleeved brown shirt and blue jeans, exits the elevator and walks into the break room, saying, "Hello, John. Howdy, Eddie! Got a good one for you!" he starts. "Why is Stevie Wonder always smiling?" he asks, smiling dreadfully himself, since he knows John and I usually laugh at his obvious jokes.

"I don't know. Why, Terry?" I ask, falling into the routine.

"Because he doesn't know that he's black!" Terry announces proudly, laughing as he exits the break room to check for room service orders.

"Yeah, Eddie Dee, she lives right by your place. I want to introduce you to her, if that's alright with you?" John asks, giggling. "How about right after work?" he adds. I kick it around mentally for a minute, calculating this little scenario, thinking, *Go by, make some new friends, drink a beer, and then stroll down to the cottage.*

"Sounds like a plan," I reply enthusiastically.

After work, we head over to Sonya's house on Third Avenue, which is only a block around the corner and hardly any distance from where Sherri and I reside in the weathered, gray-colored cottages. Sonya's apartment is set way back on the property and put together in this boulder/rock construction design like a hidden fortress, so you can barely see the entrance from the street. John opens the worn silver screen door, steps up to the front door, and knocks eagerly. He's being radically cocky and conceited, laughing, proud of his previous successful evening delights when this gorgeous lady quickly opens the door—five foot eight or nine, thick in all the right places, attractive eyes, bleached platinum blonde hair, who invites us into the dwelling. Being polite, I follow John into the living room of her private apartment. John introduces me to Sonya, who replies, "Have a seat on the couch. Would you boys like a beer?" I give John a thumbs up, *I approve* wink. I take a seat on the dark denim-covered couch that sits against the wall next to the front door. John and Sonya both disappear into the kitchen briefly—to retrieve the beer, I suppose—when a little barefooted boy no older than three comes into the living room wearing a diaper and a

T-shirt. "Hey, nigger!" the toddler says to me clearly, without mistaking his words. I sit there, stunned, shocked, humiliated, and disrespected. All I can do is just stare at this foul-mouthed little child, who is clearly suffering from a dysfunctional upbringing, and who has just validated my own knowledge and experience that racism starts being learned at a very early age. I knew right away he had been taught that word, and knew well enough that it was not appropriate. He said it so freely, even though not aware of what he's really saying, which makes me psychotically nauseous.

"Hey, nigger! You know you are supposed to speak when you are spoken to, Mr. Nigger!" he says again casually, though louder, as if I had disrespected him by ignoring his antics and not responding to his vulgar language. As he walks away toward the hallway, a blonde-haired, blue-eyed little girl, dressed the same way as the boy and who could almost pass for his twin or younger sister, playfully enters the room to see what's going on.

"Hi, nigger!" she says, "I said, 'Hi, nigger!' How are you doing, Mr. Nigger?" the brainwashed child says again, just as plain as a grownup. Sonya comes back out of the kitchen, showing no embarrassment and not apologizing for their behavior in the least, explains that the children's father taught them the word. Which clearly means I am in a very racially biased, hateful-ass, nigger-calling people's home, which I cannot tolerate, and I must break camp immediately.

"Would your friend like a beer?" Sonya asks John, who's glancing at me, sitting on the couch, after having been knowingly disrespected verbally by these two nigger-calling children. I am very pissed, desensitized, and finding this entire situation painfully appalling.

"Brother Ed? You ready to bail, Brother?" John asks, knowing never to call me Edward, since my birth name is Eddie, not freaking Edward. I instantly catapult myself to my feet by pushing my fists down into the creepy couch, so pissed off I can't come up with any respectable way to say goodbye appropriately. It's good riddance to the max as I dismiss my anatomy from that pathetic, racist dwelling without wasting any of my words.

I can't shake the fact that I was dehumanized by some so-called, not-so-innocent little white kids. Their symptomatic ignorance only lets me know that my enemy is in very close proximity to where I am standing, and they won't ever have to entertain the thought I'll be coming back to that abode.

"Eddie, dude, are you okay?" John asks, trying to catch up with my fast, not-quite-running-walk. I cross the street, keeping my distance from the silhouette of John's shadow on the sidewalk, turn the corner, purposely leave him behind. Now I'm headed directly for Fourth Avenue and Downing as I pace myself to hit the next corner, then I am home free. In my mind, I'm desperately trying to find a way to somehow smother this painful, vulgar ignorance; however, John keeps constantly, unnervingly pestering me. I want so much to release my anger, only lashing out at John is not going to solve this excessive plague of ignorant racism I've digested since I peacefully arrived here on the Pacific Norwest Coast.

"NO! I'm not the hell okay!" I shout, walking even faster, which should have been easily apparent to John, unless he is naïve about injustice, or he thinks that it's a joke of some kind, or that maybe he's blind to it and doesn't recognize the severity of the situation. Whatever the case, I certainly won't be attending any housewarmings down here in these parts, especially if it's a racist house. It's just not a safe thing to do. "No, John. I am not!" I reply looking back, highly disgusted with John. Then I turn my head forward again quickly, not messing a step. "That was a very dangerous situation back there! Please! Don't ever take me to some KKK, Aryan brotherhood shit like that again! As a matter of fact, don't do me any favors! You could very well get me killed around here!"

"Sorry about that, bro. I did not know!" John says, unconvincingly. I know he's lying.

"That's very hard to believe since those young children speak the word *nigger* clearly and so damn well!" I state, still highly irritated. "I will see you at work, John." I wave my hand halfheartedly at my young friend, and as I head up the street to my cottage, I notice my stout, six foot neighbor—the one who never says a word and lives next to our cottage—just staring at me. He's dressed in pseudo-biker attire and his look is evil, ignorant, like he has a problem with yours truly. However, I ignore him for now, walk into the unlocked gray cottage, and start explaining to Sherri about the little Caucasian kids calling me *nigger*, not once, but a few times in their white supremacist-educated, dysfunctional, hateful manner.

The very next day after working eight hours, once again we're going to visit little Jeremy for a while at Sherri's folks' house in Gearhart, Oregon. It's an enjoyable break and, afterwards, we head back home. We pull into Seaside, and Sherri's driving up Holiday Avenue, which is a two-way street with no sidewalks until you get closer to downtown. As Sherri drives the Cordoba past the back side of Seaside High School, a lone cop in a police patrol car passes us, looking directly in my mouth. His keen eyes light up like fireworks, as if he somehow knows I am America's Most Wanted Fugitive making an illegal U-turn in the middle of the street. He turns on his flashing lights and chases us down like we are attempting to elude a peace officer. I tell Sherri, "Pull over. We are going to be harassed, once again," as the officer pulls up, parks behind us, gets out of his patrol car wearing a wrinkled, dark uniform. He has dark hair, a medium build—definitely not Italian, probably a rookie I haven't met yet. Well, no time like the present. He approaches the Cordoba, walking slowly, hand hovering over the butt of his holstered gun. As he walks up to the driver side door, Sherri turns off the ignition. Then he sarcastically asks her what her name is and where does she live.

"Hey, you have some identification on you, young man?" he asks, keeping his narrowed eyes on every move I make as I'm retrieving my identification from my wallet. I hand it to Sherri to hand to him as he leans into the open, driver-side window. "Mr. Williams, where do you live?" he asks, being analytical nosy.

"He lives with me on Fourth and Downing Avenue at the Flying Dutchman Cottages, right behind where they are building the new Ocean View Motel," Sherri tells him, giving the officer enough rope to literally hang himself.

"What does your friend do? Is he your pimp or something?" the officer asks boldly, staring at both of us while definitely putting his ignorant foot in his jellyfish mouth.

"No, he's not. We both work at the Beachfront Shilo Inn. If that's what you want to call a pimp—well, then, you go right ahead," Sherri says stylishly to the lame officer, who really doesn't get it very well.

"Do you have any warrants or drugs or weapons on your person, Mr. Williams?" he asks persistently, ignoring Sherri, his eyes all over me. For some reason, he asks me the same question he previously asked one more time, attempting to catch me in a lie. Avoiding upsetting Sherri, he goes back to his patrol car, gets in, and runs a routine warrant check on me in an attempt to somehow lock me up, like I am somebody he's had a previous run-in with. This is getting really frustrating. It seems like every other day we are getting pulled over by the Seaside Police, like clockwork. Sherri's mother commented a month ago that they don't approve of biracial relationships. The evidence is as plain as the proverbial writing on the wall. Then, as predictable as the last half-dozen times this month, the officer never mentions his reason why he pulled us over. The ethically challenged officer returns, hands me back my identification, warns me to stay out of trouble, and tells Sherri to "Have a nice day." He turns around and heads back to his patrol car, never once stating any probable cause, like an infraction. It's just another one of your random racial profiling stops, anytime they damn well please, especially when I'm in the front passenger seat with a Caucasian woman.

The very next morning, Sherri announces, "Happy Valentine's Day, Baby!" before the alarm clock goes bonkers. I'm still half-asleep as we lay face to face in our romantic Murphy bed, and she's kissing my pillow-soft chocolate lips with those petite, elusive light-skinned chicken lips of hers, which I've become lovingly accustomed to.

"Happy Valentine's Day, Snooky Nooky Poo Poo!" I reply, smiling, realizing it's also Oregon's 131st birthday since becoming the thirty-third state in The United States of America, February 14, 1859. "Oh, by the way, Baby—Happy Beaver Day!" I add humorously, trying to get a rise out of my Lovebird. I explain to Sherri today is Oregon's birthday, which also just happens to be known as the Beaver State. I quickly slide myself out of our cozy, warm bed, looking forward to a busy day and the possibility of racking up some substantial overtime.

Later on the job, I find myself oblivious to the warm breeze as it dries the perspiration I've worked up from unloading and stocking trucks full of dry storage items, emptying all of the garbage cans on both floors of the kitchen and banquet prep areas, and taking all the disposables to the Inn's blue dumpsters out on the narrow, side road called Ocean Way. Before leaving for the day, I step into the freezer to retrieve the single long-stemmed pink rose I bought Sherri, along with the Valentine's Day card I picked up on my lunch break. I open the side door and walk down the handicapped ramp on this particularly weird Wednesday of an evening, and on the back burner of my mind, there is still the reminder that Sherri and I will have to move soon, vacating the perfect location where we now reside, one block from the beach. However, right now I've got to stay positive, not give up, or let the situation staring me in the face get the best of me. All this is running through my mind as I pedal my bike with the single pink rose carefully rolled up in newspaper inside my black jacket. I cruise casually through the gravel up to the cottage, still sweating somewhat, park the bike just to the side of the door, which I open, never thinking of using the key since the door is never locked, which just knocks my socks off, being from the city. Shutting the front door, I notice there are some lit burgundy candles and a bottle of champagne on the round, wooden dining table, and the aroma of steak cooking. But the real surprise is the two huge steaming-hot lobster tails fresh from the oven, ready to eat. I have excellent timing. Then I see Sherri's beautiful body, barely dressed in this provocative, red mini-nightie, finger and toenails painted a shimmering shade of glossy burgundy, instantly turning me on like a virgin. Her long curly hair is combed slightly over one of her green eyes, and she's scented with peaches and cream. I greet my Snooky Nooky Poo Poo warmly with a Valentine's kiss, card, and her rose. She hugs and kisses me softly in return, and hands me a new yellow, waterproof Walkman, complete with headphones, since my last one drowned when I fell in the Pacific Ocean after work one day. Now I can listen to my cassettes of Prince's *Batman* movie soundtrack, and Bobby Brown's *Don't Be Cruel* album. Sherri thanks me for the rose and card, and we both sit down at the table, which is covered with a Valentine's tablecloth bought from the party store. We have two chairs now, instead of just the one. After I say grace, we devour a king's and queen's exquisite five-star, candlelit Valentine's dinner of green salad, New York T-bone steak, those enormous lobster tails, baked potatoes with sour cream, and my favorite vegetable, asparagus.

Of course, demolishing our incredible eat-until-you-drop Valentine's dinner only leads to me having to sing her favorite song to her, Stevie Wonder's "My Cherie Amour" if I am going to be successful at getting my dessert as well, if you know what I mean— and I think you do! After I finish that one, then I sing "Forever," one of my favorite songs by Prince, who, by the way, is my number-one artist after Michael Jackson. Sherri, ready to joyously jump my bones, spontaneously suggests we sneak out into the night to the beach wearing just the matching, maxi-length salt-and-pepper coats she stole from that racist-ass-operated clothing store in Warrenton. After getting naked as the day we were born, we put on our brand new long coats, our old, well-used tennis shoes, and quietly slip out of the cottage after midnight. We instantly hold hands, walking side by side, step for step together, giggling like we're some tourist couple, sneaking out to the sand to make Valentine love under the stars with nature's soundtrack of blowing wind and waves crashing on the shore, trying to match the intensity of our getting buck-wild on the beach. On the sand, just the other side of the cemented promenade on Fourth Avenue, we continue to giggle at one another, courtesy of our combined champagne/surf 'n' turf buzz! Both of us are somewhat tipsy, as well as goofy, and drop our maxi coats on the sand. Obviously, we are twisted nudists, going at each other like we're slow-motion mud-wrestling on the ground, where we have craftily prepared a sex-pallet of our new coats, Sherri laying down, tempting me to surround her anatomy with my mocha-chocolate skin, and totally disregarding the wind chill factor. Actually, only Sherri's super-heated aggressiveness matters at this particular moment in time. For I am like the waves that rock! Wow! Me oh my! Her legs point toward the stars and we are so into loving each other, we don't even bother stopping when these two elderly, light-skinned, late-night old ladies momentarily watch us play Valentine's Volleyball with each other. They start to move off slowly, still watching, thinking we would stop, which only turned us on! After our release factories are finally satisfied on the seashore, we make our way back to the cottage through the sand, laughing and skipping. Still fired up from having so much fun at the beach, we had to go for round three, then round four, making the frame and the squeaky springs of the Murphy bed sing like a heavy metal band as we come to another explosive climax, then doze off into a blissful slumber.

The very next morning I cruise smoothly on the stylish, lightweight bicycle down the promenade, turning left just before the Shilo Inn onto a concrete sidewalk that leads to the main entrance. I slide the bike snugly into the rack located right by the side entrance of the inn, undo the chain lock, unwind it off the seat post, thread it through the frame and both wheels, and snap it closed to secure the bike. I enter the kitchen by way of the employee door and see Benjamin at the dish tank, filling the dishwasher with water, getting ready for the morning shift. "What's up, Benjamin?" I ask as I turn toward the time clock, grab my card, and punch in.

"What's up, Eddie?" he replies. Then I notice there's a new cook at Shilo Inn. He's flipping two eggs in two skillets, one in each hand, like there's nothing to it. "What up, dude? Are you hungry?" he asks, smiling seriously. "My name is Kenny."

"My name is Eddie," I reply as we exchange handshakes. He goes back over to the range, grabs two plates, and begins building two beautiful breakfast plates. In no time flat, he sets them down on the warm plate area for the ordering waitress to pick up.

"Damn! You're good, Kenny," I tell him. Looking at and smelling all that good food makes me somewhat hungry. Kenny, nicknamed Spin, stands five-ten, has sandy blond hair, blue eyes, kind of a slender build, and comes off as a hippie/cool redneck, but a cool-people sort of guy.

"Have you figured out what to eat yet, dude?" he asks, as he wipes down his station with a bleached towel.

"How about a pancake with an egg on top, please?" I request.

"You got it, my brother, coming right up!" Kenny says, as he grabs an egg out of the carton and a plastic container of pancake batter. I thank him and head off down the hallway to the walk-in freezer to check that there's no ice on the floor and the big blocks used for ice carvings are stored in a safe part of the freezer and away from possible damage. Then I empty the two garbage cans in the waitress stations, and when I get back to the break room only five minutes later, I've barely sat down to read *The Daily Astorian* newspaper, and here comes

Kenny with my plate. "Thank you very much, Kenny," I say as I feast my eyes on my idea of a delicious breakfast.

"No problem," he replies, while lighting up a cigarette. "In all my years cooking, nobody has ever ordered that—a pancake with an egg on top. *That* is some weird shit! And I love weird people!" Kenny admits, chuckling. Since I had not put away the condiments from yesterday, there was still some syrup on the break room table, just waiting for yours truly. "Hey, Eddie, I got to go back to work, but all my friends call me Spin," he says.

"I will talk to you later, Spin. Thanks again," I reply as he puts out his cigarette and heads back to the line.

After finishing my plate, I decide to have a smoke in the break room before I start work. Then Swede—the white-haired white-goateed prep cook, wearing a white cook's hat and a white cook's uniform—who always has a funny joke—comes up to me and says, "Hey, Eddie, a blonde's walking down the road with a healthy looking pig under her arm. As she passes a bus stop, somebody asks, 'Where did you get that?' The pig replies, 'I won her in a raffle!'" We both start laughing our butts off. Then, as Swede disappears downstairs, Terry, who runs the room service orders, enters the break room. "Eddie!" he shouts, grinning at me. "Why are blacks so good at basketball?"

"I don't know. Why, Terry?" I reply, bracing myself for the punchline.

"Because they are good at stealing, shooting, and running!" Terry replies, leaning on the back of the brown metal chair, laughing. And I had to do the same. He's funny!

10

· · · · · · · · · · · · · · · · · · ·

WTF?

Troy comes through the break room doorway in a blue shirt and gray slacks, lottery-smiling very weirdly. "Well, good morning!" I say eagerly, turning my head as I'm sitting in one of the brown metal chairs next to Steve, the cook. I exhale the smoke from my cigarette while I butt it out in the clear ashtray sitting on the table.

"Hey, Steve, how are you doing?" Troy asks Steve, boisterously happy.

"I'm good, Troy. How about you?" Steve asks, nodding, his white cook's hat on his head, grinning as he also puts out his cigarette.

"Eddie, when you get the time, could you stop by my office, please?" Troy requests nobly.

"No problem," I say, as Troy steps into the elevator and heads upstairs. Steve, who we call Steveo, is a real nice Caucasian guy from Portland; five-eleven, stout build, dark hair, clean-shaven except for his moustache, and an excellent cook who's been working here for a while. "Hey, brother Ed. Whenever you want to go fishing, just let me know," my friend Steve says, smiling as he stands up from the brown table in his white cook's uniform and white apron around his waist, turns toward the kitchen and heads back to the grind after taking his short break.

"I will just do that," I reply, only half-thinking about fishing, while the other half of my attention is focused on whatever Troy wants to see me about. I methodically complete my most pressing sanitization duties for the early morning and bring the entire kitchen up to an acceptable level of cleanliness, then decide, since I now have a little time on my hands, to stop letting my imagination run wild and find out what's on Troy's mind. I walk down the clear, clean, minty-fresh hallway, and as I approach his office, I hear him talking to someone on the phone about a meat order of prime rib. I tap lightly on the wide-open door, but he is looking down at an invoice as he's talking on the phone. He eventually realizes I am standing there, waiting for him to invite me in, and he gestures with his right hand to have a seat in the chair in front of his desk. I sit down and wait until he finishes his conversation, then he stands up, leans over to push the tan-colored door shut, and sits back down in his desk chair. He pulls two cigarettes out of his blue shirt pocket and hands one to me. "I had you come down here for a number of reasons," he starts off. "First things first. Thank you, Eddie, for being a very hard worker. You have met and easily surpassed everybody's expectations of you.

"Well, thank you very much," I reply as we shake hands, and am now really wondering what exactly this is leading up to.

"Eddie, Michael Banick, the kitchen steward who trained you, is going to be leaving soon. He already gave his two-week notice," Troy tells me as he leans back his chair, "Mike also made a strong recommendation, basically about who he thinks should take his place. How would you like to be the kitchen steward of the Beachfront Shilo Inn, Eddie Dee Williams?" he asks me, smiling, then chuckling, happily showing his almost-perfect set of piano key–white teeth.

"Well, of course. Yes, I wouldn't mind," I reply, but add quickly, "but isn't Buddy Mack next in line for that position?" I'm already wondering what type of backlash wall-of-resentment will arise from this sudden, out-of-the-blue promotion.

"Eddie, you have to understand that Shilo management doesn't exactly consider Buddy to be cut out for the job,", he says. "But they strongly believe that you *are* the one for the job. And for the last three months, Buddy hasn't been pulling his weight and seems to be expecting you to pick up the slack, like you're some kind of slave," Troy says, looking me in the eye seriously as he smokes his cigarette.

"Okay, then. I will say yes! However, let me discuss this with Sherri Lynn, since forward progress is what I am all about," I reply casually.

"Number two," Troy continues, "I have been observing you. I am impressed with what I see in you, and I would like to take you under my wing. I've heard you've been having some racially related tribulations here in Seaside, already." He then advises me to not even try looking for a nice house down here since it's so the racist there's no possibility that it's going to happen. He suggests I get an apartment instead, or even buy a trailer in a pleasant mobile home park. The truth is, I suppose I could easily afford a nice trailer on a kitchen steward's salary. Troy knows I want the opportunity to make a life here with Sherri, even *with* all the bullshit.

"There are some things I would like to talk to you about, Eddie Dee, but not here. Let's meet after work at the Beach Club and have a beer or two," Troy whispers softly.

"Let's do that," I say, smiling, exhaling the drag from my cigarette.

"Upstairs the other day, I heard you singing 'Change Is Going to Come' by Sam Cooke. You have some strong pipes on you," he says, leaning back in his chair, taking a drag on his almost-gone cigarette.

"Thank you. Like I said, I like to kick ass and sing about it," I declare, standing up, feeling motivated and grateful all at the same time. I take a last, soothing puff of my cigarette, put it out in Troy's ashtray, and head toward the door.

"Now, if you have problems around here with any local Seaside assholes, you make sure you come get me," Troy says.

"Yes! I got it, big bro! Loud and clear!" I confirm, feeling, for the first time, somewhat unique now that I have some backup.

I use the stairs and arrive on the main floor minutes later, enter the kitchen, and there is Buddy, arms folded across his white, short-sleeve shirt, like he's the president of these Shilo Inn properties, chatting with chef Dennis. The kitchen is in complete disarray; all the gray plastic tubs in the waitress' station is overflowing with dirty dishes while the garbage and dish tanks are all badly backed up from a sudden push of large lunch orders, which is a good thing. Without hesitating or saying a word, I wade into the mess, hustling all the garbage cans outside to the dumpster, then return to the kitchen and notice the two dishwashers are somewhat slammed. I'm energized and give them a hand quickly, catching up the dishwashers that were piled with dishes, pots, pans, silverware, and a mountain of water glasses. The room service phone rings over in the waitress' station. Melinda, a gorgeous sweetheart of a waitress, answers it. "Hello, Shilo Inn. How may I help you? Sherri? Hi, yes, he's right here. Eddie? Telephone, dear," Melinda calls my name, knowing I am close by. I begin to worry that something is wrong, because Sherri never calls me at work just for the hell of it. I step over to the counter and pick up the old school room service receiver attached to the Bach-colored rotary phone.

"Hello, Honey, are you alright? Is everything okay?" I ask, not knowing what's going on.

"Yes, Honey, everything is okay. I found us a trailer to buy, Baby!" Sherri says joyfully.

"That is good news, Sweetheart. Where at?" I ask.

"Pine Cove Trailer Park, on Highway 101, right at the edge of town," she answers.

"How much is it?" I ask.

"Twenty-eight hundred dollars, but I'm going to see if they can take payments, Baby!" Sherri says excitedly. "Oh, and by the way, Honey, nobody has called us back about a house or apartment, so this is it, Sweetheart," she tactfully reminds me, as if I can forget the underlying, immoral circumstances of the dysfunctional hate permeating the area.

"Okay, I got to get back to work. I will talk to you later. Okay, sweetheart?" I say, rushing to get off the phone. I stroll over to the cook's line to see my friend, Jim Dunkin, or as I sometimes like to call him, JD.

"Where is this Pine Cove Trailer Park?" I ask, on the off chance that he just might be knowledgeable about the location of the mega-trailer park.

"It is right across the street from the Pizza Palace, just short of the city limits," he answers thoughtfully as he chows down on a piece of freshly cooked bacon.

"I am pretty sure, my brother from another mother, I will be purchasing a trailer in the Pine Cove Trailer Park," I explain, especially since Sherri and I had no other callbacks for housing or apartment rentals.

"However," Bro Jim says, "just think, we will practically be neighbors."

"Now, that's slap-dookey cool with me!" I respond, giving him a righteous high-five. "I will talk to you later, Jim."

I walk off the line to the dry storage for a little minor stocking of some new products that were just delivered. An hour and a half later, I rotate the wine boxes, replace an empty beer keg with a full one for the bar, and now it's time to punch out. Fortunately, the eight hours just flew right by. I'm grabbing my jacket from the break room, about to punch out on the black time clock next to the chef's office, when Dennis sticks his head out and asks me to come have a chat with him. I walk into his reasonably sized office with the safety posters on all the walls, and he asks me to close the door behind me as he takes a seat behind his desk. "Starting with number one, Eddie, I'm really glad I hired you. Nobody has to tell you what to do, and even if they do, you just take care of the situation at hand with no argument. Your work ethic is beyond my expectations, so let me say, thank you. Did Troy talk to you about the upcoming position?" he finally asks.

"Yes, he did. I know what the job entails, so let me talk to Sherri first, and I will get back to you on that," I tell him.

"Okay, you do that, Eddie." Then he whispers, "Number two, when you start tomorrow, take everything out of this office and give it a real going-over?"

"Sure, I can do that, not a problem. What time should I start, Dennis?" I ask, scanning the entire office.

"You can start at seven if you want to, Eddie. It's up to you. I know you are going to do a fantastic job," he replies, leaning back in his chair.

"I shall carefully convert this cave into a condo!" I respond, cheerfully boastful, while visualizing the entire office clean.

"That's all I have, Eddie," Dennis says confidently, standing up and extending his hand to shake mine. I walk out of his office, then out the employee entrance, past the dumpsters, happy as a kid in Chuck E. Cheese's, on down Ocean Way, crossing to the corner of Downing

Street walking on cloud nine, wondering exactly how much of a raise I will receive when I accept the position.

From out of nowhere comes that canary-yellow Chevy Nova with the tinted windows, barreling down on me in the middle of the street at full, wheel-spinning speed. *Who the Hell <u>are</u> these crazy-ass, ignorant dysfunctional fools*, I wonder, *and how do they know exactly when I get off work at the Shilo Inn?*

"You fucking Nigger! You best go back where the hell you came from, or else you be a <u>dead</u> nigger!" a piercing voice from the driver side of the Nova yells as I run for cover. I can hear the engine rumbling loud, tires screeching toward me as I run into the storefront openings across the street. "Nigger, you a dead man! You fucking porch monkey!" the irate passenger shouts, as they speed by so lightning-fast I still can't identify them. What the hell is going on? My heart is thumping like thunder in my chest after being nearly vehicular-slaughtered again. This is just way too strange. Somebody at the Shilo Inn has got to be in on this shit. But who? I wonder if they think I am that damn Joe guy. Or is it because I am with Sherri Lynn? I walk nervously up to the Beach Club, my arms skinned up from the concrete doorway I managed to scamper into. Then, as I walk a few more steps across the parking lot of the Beach Club, I notice Troy through the front window, sitting down, talking to somebody directly across from him. He hasn't seen me yet, so pissed-off attitude and all, I enter the Beach Club tavern. It's filled with a very nice crowd of people and I make a beeline straight up to the black, button tuck upholstery–trimmed bar.

"Hello, Rob. Could I have a Miller Draft, please?" I ask politely, taking a seat on an open barstool, trembling slightly as I retrieve a cigarette out of my shirt pocket. A million thoughts are racing through my mind while Otis Redding's "Mustang Sally" plays on the jukebox. The big, constitutionally therapeutic drag of nicotine helps bring my stress level down and starts to calm my stormy mental comfort zone. Right on time, Rob, the bartender, slides me my mug of beer, which I instantly pick up and, without taking a breath, drink halfway down like a desperate, disoriented alcoholic. Everything is a little bit enhanced now, as the ice-cold beer waterfalls down my throat, cooling, soothing, like instantaneous liquid aroma therapy.

And just like that, who decides to drop in to the Beach Club but that same drunken individual who thought I was Joe the last time he saw me. Well, blow me down! I can see that he's a tad bit tipsy as he enters the bar and I think, *Here we go again!* But I have a comforting hunch things are going to turn out quite differently this time since I have Troy as a backup witness.

"How the hell are you?" the stout, ill-informed Caucasian chap asks when he notices me at the bar. As he approaches me, he asks Troy, "Who is that individual right there? Isn't that Joe?"

Troy looks back at me and says, "That's not Joe Alexander, that's Eddie Dee Williams, from Portland, Oregon. Joe is from St. Louis, Missouri." Then Troy stands up courteously, ready to introduce him formally to yours truly. "Steve, this is Eddie Dee Williams. Eddie, this is Steve." I shake hands peacefully, face to face with Steve, who finally gets the message.

"Man, I apologize for thinking you were Joe," he says, swaying turtle-slowly. "Let me buy you a beer, at least," Steve says, humbly apologetic. I accept his request for forgiveness like a human being should, as well as accepting his offer of a beer. We shake hands and part ways. I sit down next to the small table by the window where Troy was sitting before the ignorant incident.

"Are you okay?" Troy asks, sensing something really wrong.

"We'll talk about it later," I tell him, somewhat irritated.

"Ain't nobody in here, is it?" Troy asks, looking around cautiously.

"Somebody keeps trying to vehicle-assault me with their hot rod of a car," I say, searching the interior of the peaceful tavern. Eddie Rabbit's "I Love a Rainy Night" is playing on the jukebox.

"When did this happen?" Troy asks, seemingly very interested as he swallows part of his drink.

"On my way down here from work. I was walking down here from the Shilo and this canary-yellow Nova with tinted windows starts speeding toward me, attempting to run me over. The driver's yelling, 'Nigger, go back home, or else be a dead, fucking porch monkey!' I had to jump out of the way and hide in the doorway of some business. This is the second time this shit's happened since I have arrived here,", I say to Troy, gently probing for some kind of advice.

"Well, Eddie. All I can tell you is be cautious of your surroundings at all times. I don't have any idea who would do something like that to you, but it comes with the turf," he says, pulling out his cigarettes. I hear the Beach Club telephone ring noisily. Rob turns around, picks up the receiver, listens for a second, and yells out, "Eddie, telephone!" It's for me? I look at him a little confused, but he gestures with the phone, indicating yes, it is for me. I take the phone from him, somewhat apprehensively. "Hello? Hi, Honey, what's going on? Okay, I will see you when you get here. Bye, Baby," I reply, surprised, handing the phone back to Rob.

"So, what did your young lady want?" Troy asks curiously, smoking his cigarette.

"Sherri is on her way over so we can go check out a trailer for sale at the Pine Cove Trailer Park," I say, grooving to the music. "So, would you happen to be acquainted with the Pine Cove Trailer Park, Troy?" I ask, holding my fresh mug of beer.

"I drove through there some time ago, but other than that, I know nothing about it," Troy replies, as he takes a last drag on his cigarette before putting it out in the black plastic ashtray. "Eddie, this seems like an excellent opportunity for you. You pay it off and all you have left to do is pay for the space rental. You take the kitchen steward position and you will have that trailer paid off in no time flat," Troy says, using his sales pitch to close the deal on me accepting the position of kitchen steward, which would make me the supervisor of the janitors and dishwashers.

"Yes, that would be a good thing," I reply, taking a drag off my cigarette. "So Troy, tell me. Where do you go and perform at?" I ask, trying to get an idea of what exactly the musical scene is down here in this neck of the woods.

"Well, actually I play an assortment of gigs—a wedding here, an anniversary celebration there. Mainly it's word-of-mouth advertising," he answers. "Plus, I DJ at the Shilo Inn Lounge all week long during Spring Break, and Wednesday through Saturday during the peak season." He suggests we get together and jam some time. It's great to have someone to talk to and who I can trust down here. By chance, we discover we were both born under the same sign of the zodiac, Libra, and that we were born one day apart, Troy being a few years my senior. "Here's a joke, Eddie!" Troy says, leaning forward on the table. "This here fine blonde lady brings this hung black man home from the club. She gets buck naked on the bed and says to the black man, 'Do what you do best to me, you black Mandingo man!' So he ties her up and steals her purse, jewelry, microwave, and television set!" We both start laughing loudly, which eases the tension I felt when I came in the bar, not so very long ago.

A few minutes later, Sherri enters the bar like she in a hurry, wearing a sweatshirt with a Seaside logo, blue jeans, and white sneakers. "Hi, Baby," she says, leaning over to give me a kiss on my full, chocolate lips. "Hello, Troy. How are you doing?"

"I'm doing just fine. And thank you for bringing a very nice brother man down to the coast, Sherri," Troy says, smiling and shaking her hand.

"You're welcome," she says, while rubbing her leg against mine, getting my undivided attention. "Honey, I told the man who is selling the trailer we would be there shortly," Sherri says, purposely rushing me to vacate the premises.

"Well, if I know what's best for me, I'd better drink up and go handle some housing business," I mutter, as Sherri stands next to me, impatiently swaying back and forth, waiting for me to guzzle my beer. I slam the empty mug down and stand at attention like I'm back in boot camp. "Okay, Troy. I am going to get out of here," I say as I shake his hand, feeling the start of a good buzz coming on. "So I will see you later. Thanks, Rob," I say respectfully, as Sherri and I walk to the door and exit the establishment. We hop in the black, two-door Cordoba, opening the unlocked car doors, which I still get a kick out of. You don't ever leave your car doors unlocked in Portland—that is, if you want to find your car where you left it. Sherri starts the car as I slide into the black leather passenger seat and shut the heavy door. I fill her in on the latest news, starting with the bad: about my recent, and second brush with the yellow Chevy Nova. She says, "I think it's a case of mistaken identity. Maybe they think you are someone else. Like the dude at the bar, or that wacked-out weirdo on the beach who called you Joe, as well." Then I change the subject to the good news regarding my possible promotion. "And what was your answer?" Sherri asks, quickly forgetting about the Nova, now wondering if I made a questionable decision without discussing the situation with her first.

"Covering my bases, I informed Dennis that I wouldn't give him an answer without discussing it with you first, Snooky. Once I talked to you about the promotion, then I would get back to him with a decision," I say, knowing better than to make an on-the-spot decision, right then and there.

"How much more does it pay?" Sherri asks smoothly.

"I believe a dollar. Which I will most certainly check out," I respond.

"Don't you have to be on call, or something like that?" she asks, visibly concerned as she makes a left onto the highway.

"I will be responsible for making sure both shifts are covered, but that doesn't necessarily mean I have to work them all," I say truthfully, looking out the window, surprised that I actually know our exact location, and which direction we are headed. She slows down to make a right onto a gravel road, directly across from the gray, castle-facade Pizza Palace Restaurant. We roll past the yellow Pine Cove Motel and travel down an inclined gravel drive, make a right turn down some raggedy road where trailers are lined up along the outer perimeter, and RVs in the center of this horseshoe-shaped trailer park. It is located very much rearward to the motel of the same name. This not-very-well-maintained raggedy road is punctuated with numerous, deep potholes and looks like it has never been paved, or covered with gravel, and Sherri bumps roughly down the incline. We pass a silver, prehistoric trailer that looks vacant, but is occupied, then continue right down the long, curving dirt road to where there are fifth-wheels in the center of the horseshoe and trailers surrounding the outer part. We circle the entire trailer park, and Sherri pulls over to a right-hand side space marked 29.

"Is this it?" I ask Sherri, instantly slapped with a shell-shocking Kodak moment, visibly surprised by this abandoned-looking, raggedy trashcan of a trailer. Its sheer list of trailer construction appears a few levels way beneath ghetto standards; the exterior is painted a faded, rusty maroon. There's a huge, flat piece of silver-colored metal patching the exterior wall of the trailer next to the front door. Judging from the hole and the appearance of that wall, the trailer appears to have been basically breeched by a blowtorch, like it was used in military field maneuvers, and they patched it up as cheaply as possible. There's no skirting covering the space underneath from the bottom of the trailer to the ground to keep the upper body of the trailer from freezing. This junkyard-appearing, ghetto-fabulous trailer is my only logical option? There's no step unit anywhere in sight for the front or back door, so I grab a handful of doorframe in each hand and pull myself up and inside the awful-smelling dwelling. Just to the left of the doorway, when you first saunter into this broken-down tragedy of a traumatized trailer, there is a three-by-twelve-inch wide hole in the floor. The paneling on the wall near the door is missing as well, and you can inspect the naked insulation at your leisure. The atmosphere inside sports quite an ancient, funky undercarriage stench, like the whole thing has not been aired out in far-too-many months.

"Snooky, Honey? Exactly how big is the trailer?" I ask, staring unbelievingly as I inspect the brown stove, then down at the filthy old tile covering the tiny kitchen floor.

"Ten by fifty-four feet. Three bedrooms, one bathroom, living room, and kitchen," Sherri says.

"Where is the refrigerator?" I ask, staring directly at it. I keep asking Snooky questions while constantly inspecting, but I'm getting no answers.

"This trailer is for sale as-is, Honey," Sherri finally states voluntarily, as she strolls down the narrow hallway, looking in every room and closet space. "Come here, Baby. And look before you judge," she says sternly.

We both go to the end of the trailer to inspect the master bedroom. There's a closet with drawers built into the trailer in very good condition.

"This isn't too bad, is it, Baby?" she asks, trying to be positive.

"No, Honey. As long as we have each other, we will be just fine," I add, trying to be optimistic. I have come to the realization that we don't have much of a choice, since racism has raised its ugly head. "The proprietor will be here in a minute, Honey. What should I tell him?" she asks, while inspecting the miniature bathroom again, in anticipation of an answer.

"Well, if he's going to allow us to make payments, I really don't see why not, Snooky. I would rather own a trailer, than rent one," I add hurriedly.

"Where will we get the money, though?" Sherri questions, now that she knows it's her turn.

"What about my promotion? If this is as good as it gets, I'll accept the position and we can afford to buy it. This entire trailer will require a lot of tender loving care," I say, as I'm inspecting the oven inside the filthy, prehistoric brown stove. "But more like a can of gasoline and a match," I say, being hilariously sarcastic, which Sherri didn't think was funny at all.

"Well, I suppose you should take the promotion," she finally admits, "I just don't want you to work the entire time, Baby," she adds, stepping out of the narrow kitchen into the living room.

"Look, Honey, I'm not going to corner the overtime market, or anything of that nature," I state, continuing the previous conversation. "My plan is to just spread the overtime all around with the rest of the crew. That way, we can still go on vacations, Snooky Nooky Poo Poo. So, when we need to take some time off, I can easily do that," I tell her, as we hug, then kiss. Then we hear a car on the noisy gravel drive pull up slowly outside the prehistoric trailer. Exiting a blue, late-model Buick in excellent condition is an older gentleman in his sixties, slender, five foot seven, receding white hair in a crew cut, wearing a powder-blue, short-sleeved shirt, light-gray slacks, and black loafers. A look of suspicion washes over his well-lined face once his eyes on my melanin-rich skin; a programmed red alert.

"Hello, my name is Don. Are you the folks interested in purchasing this here trailer?" he asks with one hand in his pocket; no handshake.

"Yes. My name is Sherri, and this is my significant other, Eddie," she says casually.

"Well, I'm asking a firm twenty-eight hundred dollars. I can't go any lower than that," Don says, facing the trailer. "I already lost money on this trailer, maybe you guys can do better. All somebody needs to do is give it some tender loving care, and it will be a nice home. For a small family, of course.

"How old is this trailer?" I ask, glancing at the condition of the trailer's roof.

Don thinks for a second. "I believe 1962," he answers, not sounding too sure.

"Well, we can't pay the full price all at once. However, we can make a down payment and pay it off in six weeks," I say respectfully, boldly, yet truthfully.

"Well, I will have to check with the wife," Don says, unsure of our situation. "Where did you say you guys work?" he asks, obviously suspicious.

"We both work for the Beachfront Shilo Inn, here in Seaside," Sherri says.

"What do you do at the Shilo Inn, Eddie?" Don asks, curious.

"Well, I started as the janitor, then dishwasher, and now I have just been promoted to supervisor," I say, smiling proudly.

"Is that right?" Don replies. "You must be a very hard worker to move up so quickly?"

"Well, it's very simply just hard work, mainly," I tell him boastfully. Without missing a beat, Don informs us he will get back to us after he talks with this wife. Part of me believes it's just another excuse for us not to find a place. Don excuses himself, gets in his car, and leaves the trailer park.

"Well, I think we have a very good chance of purchasing the trailer," Sherri says. "This is where we are going to wind up, and this is going to be our home."

We're still optimistic four days later, even though we have not heard from the owners of the trailer. Now, we have to find somewhere else to stay as peak season is upon us, commencing with Spring Break. We have no other alternative, not even going back to Portland. It's sunny outside, for a change. As I empty the garbage cans into the dumpster, I notice the seagulls soaring above me in the salty wind, the tourists on the sandy beach flying kites, desperately desirous of a tan—some swimming, others jogging along the coastline. One thing is for sure: it's springtime. Spring Break here lasts for the entirety of the next two weeks. Kids flock here from Portland, Seattle, Tacoma, Olympia, and from as far South as San Diego and Los Angeles. They come to Seaside from other areas in the Northwest as well, and they all have the same objective—to party like there's no tomorrow.

The first week is the Oregon University System's Spring Break, then the following week, it's Washington's turn, which also includes a lot of students from California. That same afternoon, Sherri finds me caught up on my work, sitting at the table in the break room, apartment hunting the classifieds in the Astorian Newspaper. "Baby, we can get the trailer, only if we can make a down payment of 650 dollars today, and then make payments of 650 dollars every two weeks," she tells me.

"Okay, then, let's do it. But the money is going to be tight. Here is my check," I say, pulling it out of the pocket of my light-blue, short-sleeved shirt.

"So, what time are you going to get off so we can sign the contract, Baby?" Sherri asks excitedly.

"I should be off at four, as long as nobody asks me to rack up some overtime," I say anxiously.

"Okay, Baby," Sherri replies, as she leans over to give me a goodbye kiss.

"Well, I better go inform Dennis that I will accept the position of kitchen steward," I tell her, which I had already hinted I was going to do. I sense that things are finally starting to look up for us.

I ask Jim and Spin, my cronies from work, to help me patch up the trailer. It's going to need a lot of work before we can call it our Pine Cove sweet home. "A righteous earned promotion and now you are buying a trailer. That calls for a celebration!" Spin says, as we all stand in the hallway outside the break room.

"Hey, Bro. Spin's right, but we should get everything done first, then have a party. Maybe they will let you have a bonfire in your space!" Jim says eagerly.

"You can really do that down here?" I ask Jim curiously.

"Some trailer parks let you have bonfires," Jim says, quickly slapping his hands together. "This is not quite like Portland, my brother," he says, smiling, wiping his hands with a damp rag before going back to work.

I go downstairs to the banquet level, down the hallway to Troy's office to inform Dennis I will most certainly accept the position. "Well, then, the job is yours," Dennis says smiling, shaking my hand as he smokes a cigarette, leaning back in his desk chair.

"Well, thank you very much. I just hit the daily double," I reply, smiling like I just hit a home run. "How much more will I be making, Dennis?" I ask, closing the promotion meeting.

"About a dollar an hour more," he tells me, as he puts out his cigarette. "Troy will show you how to do the scheduling for the janitors and dishwashers, Eddie. Right now, I'm heading back upstairs," he says, as he jumps up from his wooden chair and exits the office.

"Well, congratulations, little brother," Troy says, shaking my hand, smiling hard like he's the master and I'm the apprentice.

"Thank you very much, Troy. I wouldn't even have this opportunity if it wasn't for you, bro," I say appreciatively.

"You're welcome, little bro. Now, what do you have planned after work?" Troy asks politely, offering me one of his cigarettes.

"Sure. Thank you," I respond to the offer of one of Troy's cancer sticks. "I am going to sign the contract on the trailer today, and make a list of what I need to do before I even think about moving out of the cottage."

"Now, listen to me really good, Eddie. There are a lot of good people down here who will help you out. All you have to do is just stay away from all those other ill-minded assholes. Other than that, you should be all right," Troy says.

After he gives me a five-minute mini-class on scheduling the dishwashers and janitors based on the number of scheduled banquets, holidays, and the peak season, I leave his office on top of the world. Thank you, Lord! I scurry to the main floor looking for Sandy, another levelheaded, intelligent bar waitress, who is now going to be my future neighbor. I exit the elevator onto the main floor, past the dish tank to my left, the cook's line to my immediate right, and walk casually through the waitress' station. I go out the side door that leads to the main lounge and the restaurant area, which overlooks an exquisite view on any given day, with the statues of Lewis, Clark, and Sacajawea in the center of the turnaround, and the beautiful Pacific Ocean and gorgeous Tillamook Head visible through the huge, double-sided picture windows. I scan the room and see Sandy, with her namesake-colored curly hair; Caucasian, five foot four, slender, petite figure in a blue mini-skirt and white blouse walking toward a tableful of customers. I wait patiently until she comes back to the bar where I am standing.

"Hi, Sandy," I say.

"Hi, Eddie. What's up?" she asks, while filling some glasses with ice and water.

"I just bought a trailer in Pine Cove Trailer Park," I tell her, smiling.

"That is so cool!" she says excitedly.

"I may need some help fixing a couple of things before moving in there. So, do you know anybody in the trailer park that knows how or has the tools to work on a trailer?" I ask.

"Hold that thought. Let me get this table, Eddie, and I will be right back in a flash," she says, as she walks over to the table.

"Congratulations on your promotion, Eddie, my friend. Can I get you a Sprite?" Frank asks me, smiling.

"Thank you very much, Frank," I say proudly as we shake hands.

"Don't think for one minute you don't deserve it, Eddie," he tells me, fixing me a Sprite in a chimney glass and setting it on the bar in front of me. "Big guy, everybody around here knows if they have a predicament, they best get Eddie if they want that dilemma appropriately resolved," Frank adds, showing extreme approval. Frank is a smoothly cool soul, five foot eight, slender build, light-brown hair, and wears mood glasses; a real down to earth, ex-hippie who basically tells it just like it is.

Sandy walks back up to the bar next to me after seeing to her table. "So, we are going to be neighbors! My boyfriend, Arthur, is going to like that," she says, smiling. "He will help with your trailer, Eddie," Sandy adds happily. "Is it the rusty-red-colored trailer?" Sandy asks.

Since I am not embarrassed, I confirm that's the trailer we bought. "We had no other choice. We can barely afford to buy that trailer, and besides, nobody will rent to us," I explain briefly.

"Okay, neighbor! We will see ya!" Sandy says, as she heads back to her customers with a tray of drinks in hand. I head to the kitchen, now much less disturbed about our major decision. Marty, the busboy, approaches and informs me that Sherri is looking for me. I hurry out to the lobby, then down the hallway, to find Sherri standing there, talking to Don. It's obvious he didn't believe I worked at the Shilo Inn, or he wouldn't be sneaking around, asking people in management questions—alerting Andrew, Sherri's supervisor and the restaurant manager, as well, asking personal questions behind my back. Hell, I'd be willing to bet if I told him water's wet, he probably wouldn't believe that either.

"Hello, sir, how are you doing today?" I ask.

"I am doing just fine, thank you," Don replies, standing next to Sherri in the carpeted hallway. "The wife thought it best I come up here and verify your employment, Eddie," he says randomly.

I think, *Yeah. Right. Go right ahead, I just have STUPID written across my forehead!*

"The deal has been finalized," Sherri says. "Don wants us to make a down payment today, and payments exactly every two weeks until the trailer is paid off in full, no exceptions."

"Where do I sign, please?" I ask, standing there being cool, calm, collected, and civil. Don hands me a contract as a reminder that I am expected to live up to my end of the agreement. I read and comprehend the business contract quickly before signing it, and hand it to Sherri, who signs it as well. At the last minute, Don also informs me of my need to register the trailer with Mr. Baske, the trailer park landlord, as well as pay for the trailer rental space, which is 130 dollars in addition to the payments on the trailer itself.

"So, I will see you people two weeks from today," Don states, through his wall of resentment, uncertainty, and sabotage as he walks away. We both take a seat on a padded bench in the hallway. Does this man think I'm not going to pay? Or that I am going to skip town?

"I am so sorry you have to go through this racist, ignorant shit, Baby!" Sherri says, hugging me after Don has disappeared from view. "But, Baby, we have a home now," she whispers in my ear, gives me a subtle smooch, then looks at me with her hypnotic green eyes that smile, therapeutically soothing my soul to not give in to some evil, bamboozled, light-skinned, middle-aged human.

"I know, Baby," I say as we embrace, giving each other another kiss. "You just pay him, Sherri. I don't want to see that racially biased asshole-of-a-human again," I say dejectedly.

"Yes, Baby," she replies tenderly.

"You know Sandy? Who works in the bar? She lives in Pine Cove directly across the road from us in the RV section!" I say suddenly.

"No, I did not know that," Sherri says as we both rise to our feet and move away from the comfortable cushioned bench.

"Well, her man Arthur is going to help me secure the trailer so we can speed up our moving plans, since we agreed to be out of the cottage before Spring Break. however, that is not the case. So, Jim, my friend the cook, is going to help us with the trailer maintenance, as well," I explain.

There's a list of preparations and repairs that have to happen before Sherri, Jeremy, and I can move into the trailer park. It's probably going to take days to get everything online; the power, the stove, the heater, the water heater needs to be replaced, and the big hole in the living room floor desperately needs to be patched.

After work, Jim, Sherri, and I head out to the trailer park to take a look. The trailer park is possibly a little over a mile from the Beachfront Shilo Inn. We arrive at space number 29 and before we even get inside the trailer, Jim starts planning steps for the project ahead.

"We can cut some wooden planks to lay across the bricks to make steps for entering the trailer. That's really easy, bro. Wow! Why would somebody do that?" Jim asks, laughing as he's looking at the hole in the floor, then the four-by-eight-foot section of wall that's missing its paneling.

"I don't comprehend it, but I need to secure it. Jim, my friend, what is it going to take?" I ask, feeling a little shafted.

"Baby, we need another refrigerator," Sherri says sadly, closing the refrigerator door.

"Are you serious?" I ask.

"Calm down, Eddie. The power isn't on yet, and it's too late in the day now to get it turned on," Jim says as he flicks light switches on and off around the trailer. "Let's wait until tomorrow, since we got to get the electricity turned on for the power saw. Then we can patch the floor and build this wall."

Then there's a knock on the open trailer door; it's Sandy and her man Arthur. "Hello! Just hop on up here, you two! How are you doing?" I ask, smiling, excited to see them both, shaking Arthur's hand. The five of us go through the proper introductions, and then it's back to business. Arthur is six foot one, stocky, real muscular, with dark-brown hair and a lighter, bushy moustache.

"Eddie, it would be a good idea if first thing tomorrow morning you go see Mr. Baske, the slumlord, and put everything in your name," Arthur suggests.

"Where is his office at?" I ask urgently.

"His office is on Holiday Street," Arthur says as he puts his arm around Sandy.

"Tonight, we should just make a list of everything we need," Jim suggests, as he walks down the hallway, looking into the rooms.

"That water heater's been sitting for a quite a while. Might not be any good. I know somebody who is selling a stacked combo washer and dryer for almost nothing. And it will fit in your bathroom, Eddie," Arthur suggests, already being a good neighbor. Thank God! Finally, I have some nice folks around me! My friends are being very positive, which is helping me feel better about Sherri's and my new investment we've contracted ourselves into. "I can bring some scrap wood from work, if that will get things moving along," Arthur says, letting go of Sandy after eyeballing the hole in the floor of my living room, "Let me go and grab my tape measure."

"Well, Sherri? What do you think of your new place?" Jim asks, hands on hips, scanning the trailer.

"I really like it. Jeremy has his own room, and we are just down the road from my parents in Gearhart. And my sister Kelly lives right across the highway on the next block over," Sherri says happily.

"So, this works out really well for you now, doesn't it, Sherri?" Jim asks, rhetorically. "That's a well-put position, now that I think about it."

"So, you are from around here?" Sandy asks Sherri, showing a casual interest. "Yes, I grew up here, went to school here, Jeremy was born here, and Seaside Upholstery in Gearhart is my father's shop," Sherri says boastfully. I'm still in fix-it mode, trying to open the kitchen windows to let some air in and the odor out. Arthur returns with a tape measure to check what size patch is needed to fix up the hole in the floor.

"Well, Eddie, you guys can take me home. We will have more time to spend on this tomorrow," Jim says, still in his cook's uniform.

"Yeah, you're right," I agree with my friend. "Let me talk to Mr. Baske tomorrow about what I need to do to get everything situated, get the electricity turned on, and transfer everything in my name." This is my home, this time. Keeping my promise to myself, I am responsible for everything, and the only person that can kick me out is me.

I wake up the next morning thankful to the Creator. The early bird gets the worm and I'm amped up, ready to get started, ready to vacate this locality, urgently getting everything in order and online with the trailer. I escape from work, letting Dennis know that I am off to register the trailer under my own name with Mr. Baske, and take maybe a half-hour to get my utilities turned on. I ride up to Mr. Baske's office on my bicycle, and when I arrive, I am still somewhat baffled that I don't have to lock it up. It's going to be there when I return. This definitely isn't the city. I walk into this small building and up to the receptionist's mahogany desk.

"Good morning, my name is Eddie Dee Williams. I would like to register a trailer that I just purchased at the Pine Cove Trailer Park," I say graciously.

"Do you have an appointment with Mr. Baske?" she asks me.

"No, ma'am, I don't," I tell her.

She hands me a clipboard with a paper application and says, "Please fill out the application form front-to-back." Then she stands up from behind her mahogany desk and disappears into a back room. I take a seat in a nicely preserved antique chair and fill out the application. After I am done filling out the application, an elderly man smoking a cigar appears.

"I'm Don Baske. And who might you be?" he asks maliciously, while perusing my application.

"My name is Eddie Dee Williams," I say, standing to my feet.

"Well, Mr. Williams, you should have come and talked to me before purchasing a trailer in my trailer park!" he says angrily, raising his voice as if I had committed a crime against him. Mr. Baske; attorney, landlord, five-foot-eight, slender, salt-and-pepper hair, full beard, wearing black suspenders. A self-centered bully.

"I did not know that was the way it went, Mr. Baske. I just had to find a place, since everywhere we tried, the racist landlords refused to rent to me!" I say, getting even louder. "The man who sold me the damn trailer wasn't too happy about me, either. So, I apologize for doing the right damn thing, which no one informed me to do until last night, man!"

"Well, you have to put down a first and last deposit," Mr. Baske says, lowering his voice.

"Not a problem. How much time do I have to pay it, Mr. Baske?" I ask, lowering my own voice.

"I will need that by the first of next month," he says.

"I will make sure you get what's coming to you. Now, if you will excuse me, I have to get back to work making an honest living," I add, preaching. "Have a nice day, man." I leave the office highly disturbed, grab the door handle, flex it open with one powerful push, feeling frustrated and tired of being treated like a piece of discarded, dehydrated shit on the Pacific Northwest Coast. I mount my bike hurriedly, heatedly, and head back to work at the Shilo Inn, wondering how some people can believe they are so superior and can talk to people any way they so damn desire without any damn level of respect. I am so weary of these ignorant humans who assume, which only makes an ass of you and me.

Back at work, I fill Sherri in on my latest experience being prejudged by Mr. Baske, who assumed I was trying to dodge the trailer space deposit, when in fact, I was 100 percent minded on doing the right thing. But she still doesn't get it. "Honey, like you always tell me, there's going to be storms before the sunshine," Sherri says, then kisses me as she disappears into the restaurant.

After work a few hours later, Sherri, Jim and I head over to Pine Cove and start working on the ailing trailer. Jim immediately changes out of his white uniform into a brown shirt and jeans in our new bathroom. As we are outside working, I notice someone in the next trailer looking out their window at us. Our neighbors are an old lady and her full-grown son. I certainly hope they are friendly. Jim and I go inside the trailer and turn on the faucets in the kitchen; water immediately starts running. Yes! Then I flip the light switch to the on position; the kitchen light comes on. Yes! I walk through the living room, avoiding the hole in the floor, switching on the bedroom, hallway, and bathroom lights, and turning on the faucets in the bathroom; they all work. Yes! I'm so excited, I temporarily forget about the hole in the floor, until the second I fall stupidly into it. The only thing I can do is stand there until Jim gives me his hand and pulls me up out of the floor.

"Honey, are you okay?" Sherri asks, while trying not to laugh.

"Does a snake have armpits?" I ask Sherri, once I'm finally standing on the floor of the trailer. "Hell to the damn NO! I'm not okay!" I say, highly embarrassed. "I just fell into a hole in my own house! How many people do that?" I look up just in time to see my good friend Jim's face go bright red, trying hard not to laugh. "Go ahead! Let it out, bro," I say, trying to get over my embarrassment.

Jim starts slow, then revs up his animated, addictive laugh to the point where I have to laugh too, which sets Sherri off, as well.

Our next task at hand will be fixing the hole in the living room floor, which we all had no problem agreeing on. Jim takes his measurements and he and I head out to the yard and cut some boards to make a patch with. Jim has a very good eye; the boards slide snugly into place and he nails them down. I have a whole floor, imagine that! No more hole. Yes!

Back outside, it's suddenly turned into a gorgeously sunny day, and I'm standing on the ground at the front door of the ghetto-fabulous trailer, stacking a dozen gray cinderblocks I purchased with the help of my neighbor Arthur and his blue Chevy truck. We are building a three-step stair entrance to the front door, and Jim and I are diligently trimming wood planks to-size using a picnic table from the RV section of the park as a sawbuck. Jim finishes zipping through a plank with the power saw he brought from home, then turns to me and whispers confidentially, "Eddie, don't look now, but your landlord is coming over here."

"Hello!" Mr. Baske calls out as he walks up to me. He is wearing overalls, hands in both pockets. He halts and says, "Mr. Williams, I want to apologize for tearing into you like that. I was very wrong for that. If there is anything, within reason of course, that you want, I will see what I can do."

Maybe this guy isn't so bad after all, I say to myself.

"But I'm not lowering your space rent!" Mr. Baske says boldly, gesturing instantly to redefine his initial statement.

"Ask him for a fire pit!" Jim whispers to me, nudging me in the side with his elbow.

"What?" I ask Jim silently, as I rub my ribcage where he 'nudged' me.

"Ask him if can you have a fire pit!" Jim says a little louder, nudging me gently this time, now more minding his strength. Not even sure what Jim's talking about, I decide to try my luck. It couldn't hurt. The landlord's admitted he was wrong and apologized. Now, I'm not so sure he is such a bad person, after all.

"Mr. Baske, I know what I would like to ask of you," I say.

"And what is that, Mr. Williams?" he asks, glancing curiously at the progress we have already made on our trailer project.

"I would like permission to have a fire pit in my yard," I announce.

He ponders my request for a long second, then finally says, "Well, okay. But just pay your rent on time and you and I will be just fine." Mr. Baske then starts walking over to the other side of the trailer park.

"I don't believe it, Eddie!" Jim says in disbelief, stopping his measurement of the plank he was about to cut, "What happened to make him apologize like that to you?"

I give Jim the update about Mr. Baske yelling at me like I was the plague, when I was actually trying to do the right thing. "See, Jim. All people are good, it's just that most of them didn't get the memo," and Jim laughs at my comedic antics. Just then, a blue pickup truck comes down the potholed horseshoe of a dirt road and parks directly across from my trailer. The truck door opens and out steps Arthur, who has more building materials in the truck bed. Arthur, Jim, Sherri, and I continue to work on the trailer into the late evening. We had to replace the water heater, which cost us more money that we didn't even have. However, things seemed to work themselves out. Somehow.

11

· ·

Pine Cove Trailer Park

Three days later, we have the ghetto trailer habitable enough so that Sherri, Jeremy, and I could finally vacate the cottage. I give Joe and his wife, Debbie appreciative hugs of thanks, and we proceed to move into the trailer on the other side of town. I'm very excited to start my life with Sherri in our single-wide, ghetto-fabulous trailer home.

Sherri's elder only sister Kelly is our first official guest. Kelly arrives with Jeremy, her son, Jason and her daughter, Stephanie. Jeremy is so excited; he doesn't even stop to hug us and just runs into the bandaged trailer to his new room, which is furnished with built-in bunk beds. Kelly introduces me to her two beautiful children, who actually speak to me respectfully, like I am an actual human being.

Kelly, who also works at the Shilo Inn as a dinner waitress, looks somewhat like her younger sister. She is intelligent, sexy, pleasantly thick in all the right places, and wearing a sweatshirt and jeans. "So Eddie, how does it feel to own a trailer?" she asks, while we stand outside next to her brown station wagon, looking at the antique-colored trailer that still needs lots of work.

"Well, Kelly, it's nothing like moving into an apartment or a house," I reply, contentedly smoking a cigarette.

"Hey, Sherri, I have the stove working!" Arthur states, standing in the doorway of the trailer.

"Yes!" I say excitedly, balling up my fist victoriously. "Now I don't have to buy an oil-burning stove."

"What if I still needed one? Would you buy it for me, Baby?" Sherri asks, walking toward me very sensually.

"Yes, Honey. If my gigantic old bankroll is large enough and you want it, sure. Why not," I mention, being sarcastic.

"You know why you should want to do that, Eddie?" Kelly murmurs, leaning in close, keeping it just between us. "Because God is a white woman."

I just burst out laughing. Mainly because I can't believe she said that, but also that she must realize Jesus is a fair-skinned brown Nazarene with hair of wool-like dreadlocks and melanin-tanned feet of brass. Saying Kelly's pronouncement gave me a good laugh is the ultimate understatement of the century. As tears flow down my face like an unstoppable waterfall, I'm bent over at the waist from stomach pains, courtesy of my continuous, cramp-inducing spasms of laughter. Jim also begins laughing, making it doubly difficult for me to stop, because he agrees that Kelly is quite a funny character. Humor is good for the heart and soul.

Meanwhile, I notice a gray, late-model car pulling up to our trailer. Sherri's parents emerge from the car, and Jeremy, along with Kelly's kids, run out to greet them with open arms. I am still somewhat tickled, hunched over, holding my stomach, laughing. Ron and Donna, Sherri's parents, approach us from their well-maintained Buick, and, after greeting their grandkids, wonder aloud what's going on. "Hello, everybody, what's wrong with Eddie?" Donna asks, smiling curiously.

"I just told Eddie that God is a white woman, Mom," Kelly is serious, but grinning. unable to keep a straight face. I start laughing again, even louder than before, this time limping around in circles, trying to walk it off. The children and Jim join the laugh fest.

"Well. *He*, is really white, you know that, Eddie?" Donna asks, kicking my spasms of laughter into high-gear. I'm laughing even harder than before, with my hands over my kidneys, breathing sporadically, trying to hold them together so they don't burst, as the frantic inertia of this unstoppable giggle fest lasts a good half-hour or so.

Later on that night, long after the sun has vanished, everybody's departed and Sherri is in the majestic trailer putting Jeremy to bed. I decide to stroll around this dysfunctional, World War II-era, abandoned, run-down, disregarded, trailer-trash, hobo-looking trailer/RV park. As I stroll, I notice some outdoor lavatories with showers and laundry facilities, complete with washers and dryers, in a quaint little tan building in the middle of the horseshoe, where RVs are parked alongside the fifth wheels. Walking carefully to avoid the huge, shallow-to-deep mud puddles and potholes in the raggedy road, I casually smoke a cigarette, listening to my inner voice wondering, *How are the rest of my newfound neighbors going to react to yours truly?* There are a lot of weather-beaten double-wide and single-wide trailers, all outfitted with adequate skirting, some real old, some kind of fairly-new, some out-of-this-world pink, some dirty white, some swanky-appearing, manure-green salty trailers looking like straight-up unattractive sugar shacks. I come to the conclusion that I now reside amongst the genuine people; that my magnificent, newfound family no longer lives a half-block from the beach (I'm missing the cottage already) and has been reduced to living in the ghetto-fabulous Pine Cove Trailer Park at the edge of the city limits in a biracial relationship, just this side of the town of Gearhart Oregon.

Weeks pass as we settle into our own sugar shack trailer, making friends with most of the people in the park, with the ironic exceptions of the neighbors on either side of our trailer, who are racist, and in all probability have a problem with Sherri and I being consumed with our *Jungle Fever* relationship. On a positive note, we finally finishing paying off the balance owed on the trailer, making the last payment today on time. I'm feeling that right about now the ex-owner is stereotypically thinking, Imagine that. *A chocolate human paying off his trailer!*

I'm standing outside the now non-leaking trailer, smoking a cigarette and talking to my neighbor Mike, who is Justin's dad, and lives a little way around the park's horseshoe from us. He stands a short five foot six but is quite stout, has blond hair, blue eyes, and is a real weird, darkly humorous kind of a guy. He's chuckling as he warns me in a low voice, like I am in some kind of trouble, "Somebody's pulling up, Eddie, to collect on some bill you owe The Man!"

I notice a blue Buick pulling up to my trailer, as expected. Surprise! It's Mr. I-Can't-Believe-He-Made-All-the-Payments-On-Time, former-owner of my-piece-of-the-rock trailer. Sherri and I are so satisfied to see him, just so I can pay him, finalize the contract between us, and enjoy the sense of freedom derived from all of his ill-mannered, unethical insults.

"Good morning, everybody," Don says, grinning, one hand in the pocket of his gray, fitted slacks as he approaches us. He pulls his hand out and extends it toward me as he walks up, saying, "I recognize, Eddie. You two have the rest of the money. But let me just say that since you were on time and lived up to your part of the bargain, we want to knock off about two hundred dollars." That's certainly good news, considering the extra expenses Sherri and I didn't figure into the budget. Nevertheless, something just doesn't seem right. Looking me straight in the face, Don dispels this illusion. "You are a good colored man and you kept your word," he actually says out loud, sticking his foot in his mouth. "I don't think I will live long enough to see a colored president, but I hope you get to, Eddie." Finally, shaking my hand, "You Colored people really get a bad deal in life."

Sherri hands him the money, in return he hands her a receipt, and respectfully hands the title to me. I've already forgiven him for passionately calling me *colored* and accepted it as no insult. Obviously his racist mentality could not critically fathom an African American president. Maybe now he has a different outlook on life. Just maybe. Excellent brainwashing example of W-H-I-T-E, weird humans ignorant to equality.

My next payday is something of a treat. The sun is out, seagulls are flying over the ocean and the Shilo Inn, and there's nothing but blue sky as far as I can see. I ride my bike home after a somewhat long, physical day, which keeps my fat-free physique in shape. As I pull up to the trailer, Justin and Jeremy are playing in the dirt with their Tonka trucks. I park my bike by the steps Jim and Arthur built for us, which are among all their other repair work, including replacing the water heater.

On this particular sunny day, the Almighty has made, I dismiss from work early since it's a boring, turtle-slow shift in the restaurant.

And, it being payday, I decide to ride my bike to the local Thriftway grocery store on Holiday Street, next to the Seaside Police Station, and cash my Shilo Inn paycheck. I'm so proud, blessed, and quite excited that this check won't be totally consumed by bills or another trailer payment—just my child support payments, which are super-spectacular, quite alright with me.

I park my bike near the entrance and the automatic doors instantly open for me. There aren't many people in the store today because it's a sunny weekday afternoon. I take a place at the end of the checkout line and wait for an elderly couple to finish their purchase ahead of me. Once it's my turn, I remove my check from the pocket of my light-blue short-sleeved shirt. "Hello, madam," I say, graciously acknowledging the cashier. The lady stares at me saying nil, just standing there with her arms folded across her chest, as if I am a nonentity. "Ma'am? I would like to cash my Shilo Inn payroll check, please?" I ask courteously. The outlandishly grumpy woman then puts her hands on her hips, flabbergasted about something. Somehow, I sense this isn't going to be a trouble-free transaction.

"I require four pieces of picture identification" comes abruptly, harshly out of her mouth.

"Excuse me? Nobody, by any stretch of the imagination, walks around these United States of America carrying four pieces of picture identification, why you are doing this to me, lady?" I say, distressed, with my open hands outstretched at waist level, palms exposed.

"I have the right to refuse service to anyone," the xenophobic cashier says, turning her body facing away, but still staring at me with her arms folded like I was an extraterrestrial who had shoplifted something off of her.

"May I speak to the manager?" I ask the cantankerous, no-makeup-wearing, fluffy-figured lady. The short, elderly, bigoted Caucasian couple directly behind me in line is looking at me like I have an awful lot of Almighty gall and no business questioning the cashier's authority.

"I AM THE MANAGER," she bellows outrageously, "and I have the right to refuse you service! So. If you don't have four pieces of picture identification, it is not going to happen. Now, if you will excuse me, I have paying customers to attend to." Miss Racially Prejudiced Cashier, rolling her hateful eyes, unfolding her arms and putting her hands on her hips, gives a little start toward me as if to provoke me into reacting with malice at her defiance of my rights as a citizen of these United States. She finally looks disdainfully away from me and on to the next customers in line, as if she has somehow successfully reduced the sum of my human-ness to a slave. After all the racial discrimination I've sustained in the five short months I've been here, the thought of the lowest of the lowly filing a grievance with the department of law enforcement next door does not strike me as an appropriate solution.

Upon ultra-short deliberation, I remove myself from the confines of the grocery store, emerging disenfranchised, with a knot of nauseous pain in my stomach, not from laughing but from the humiliation and the heightened level of disrespectful hate I undergo. I voluntarily served my country honorably in the United States Army and I categorically refuse to be treated like a second-class citizen. I am furious as I pedal the bike up to my trailer, punch the kickstand down with my heel as I dismount, and, still fuming, stride through the open door of our trailer.

"Honey, those damn ignorant-ass people at the Thriftway store would not cash my damn check!" I announce, pissed off to the maximum.

Sherri, barefooted on the couch, and wearing a T-shirt and baggy gray sweatpants, instantly ceases folding the laundry, slips on her shoes from under our small, but decent dark-brown coffee table. "What store was it, Baby?" she calmly asks, now facing me, extending her hand patiently for the payroll check.

"The Thriftway store. On Holiday," I state, fuming as I hand her the payroll check.

"Watch Jeremy, please. He's playing outside somewhere with Justin," she says, grabbing her car keys off the built-in wooden shelves dividing the kitchen and living room.

Fifteen minutes later, I see her pull up and park the Cordoba. She quickly enters the trailer with her hands full of cash and hands it to me. "You cashed my check without my Oregon identification card, Social Security card, credit card, birth certificate, or any picture identification of me?" I inquire, in shock.

Sherri, unfazed, does not respond to my request, and simply goes back to folding clothes over on the couch. I walk leisurely out of the trailer, down the steps, light a cigarette in disgust, and prepare to take a soothing walk to calm my decapitated comfort zone way down. What part of this equation don't I comprehend? I actually don't think it is mentally/emotionally feasible for me to identify with this reality. Welcome to the privileged, supreme superficiality of so-called white civilization.

A few days later, I schedule myself for a little overtime to make some good money with the dinner shift and allow the night dishwashers to close. I am certainly looking forward to be finally heading home. Satisfied with the operation, I clock out, put my time card back in the proper slot, and head out the employee exit. Before I set out for my abode, however, I decide to stop by the Beach Club to have an ice-cold mug of beer and watch the rest of the Portland Trailblazers game. I am a do-or-die Blazer fan, to the point I will never ever root for another NBA team. That's how authentically dedicated a fan I am. I swing the black door to the tavern open and there are only a couple people in the establishment, but no one I quite recognize. I make my way to the four empty stools, pop a squat at the bar, probe for my lighter to light the cigarette stuck between my earth-toned lips.

"Hey, Eddie!" Rob the bartender says, beating me to the punch as he hands me a book of matches.

"Hey, Rob. How's it hanging? Could I get a cold mug of beer, please?"

"You sure can. Ed. And it's hanging," Rob replies, filling a beer mug for me. He slides the polar bear-cold mug of brew on the counter and I hand him two one-dollar bills in return. There's nothing quite like the first sip of an ice-cold beer after an eventful day of overtime work.

"Ed, would you watch the cash register for me for a second while I go change the keg?" Rob asks me politely as he dries his hands.

"Sure, bro. Go for it. I got this, my good friend," I utter congenially, looking up at the bar's overhead TV. I am fired up as I watch the Trailblazers aggressively playing the Los Angeles Lakers in the Memorial Coliseum in Portland. The Blazers are winning a 128 to 86 in the fourth quarter with only three minutes to go. I'm on the edge of my stool, excited by the extreme thrashing of the game, simultaneously with one eye on the cash register.

My attention being split between the game and register, I almost don't notice this nasty looking Caucasian guy approaching from the far pool table, who strangely stands next to me with a cue in his hand. I swivel on the bar stool with the glass mug in hand, facing toward the central area of the tavern, not wanting to be caught off guard, thinking to myself, *Better safe than sorry.*

The unfamiliar human being speaks, greeting me with, "Hello, man. Can I ask you a question, if that is okay with you, dude?" His voice is mildly friendly, and he's dressed in an old Oregon Ducks T-shirt and worn, holey jeans.

"Yes, you can ask me a question," I reply calmly, wondering what will be the next thing to come out of this stranger's mouth, other than the strong stench of alcoholic beverages.

"Well, me and my friend over there playing pool were just wondering, is niggers' dicks bigger than white people's cocks?" he asks loudly, making like his five-foot-ten, slender friend staggering around the pool table, who's no threat, dared him to come ask me.

"Excuse me? What was the hell was the question again?" I ask, feigning shock, wanting to hear it just one more time, while also gaining time to position myself to block that cue stick, if need be.

"I asked you, are niggers' dicks bigger than white people's cocks?" he says once again, even louder this time, either seeking my humiliation or to accelerate my anger to rage—take your pick. "Well, man. Would you please pull your black cock out so we can see if it's true, man?" the tipsy outsider rudely requests chuckling, smirking to his comrade who is still shooting pool on the far table. He's glaring down at the zipper of my jeans as if I were his property once, making this obscenely weird circumstance even more uncomfortable for me. Rob returns just in time to hear the ignorant customer's request, instantly yells at the lame lunatic men, commanding them to rapidly vacate the bar, otherwise he will call the police force. "You don't talk to him like that! You best drink up and get the hell out! Right now!" he announces again to the two men, astonished by Rob's drill sergeant tone. Pouting, they remove themselves from the Beach Club, breathing out the foul nicotine-breath of uncertainty. Once they are gone, Rob turns to me and says, "Sorry about that, man. That was entirely not cool! Let me please buy you a beer, Eddie."

I guzzle down the beer to quiet my slight attack of nerves, trying to forget the whole, humiliating incident that just took place. I am relieved at the seemingly positive outcome of this situation. "Are you okay, Eddie?" Rob asks concerned, leaning over slightly with his hands on the bar as I turn around to face him.

"I'm all right, my friend. I am just glad it didn't get physical. I hate it when that happens," I reply, relieved, downing the rest of the penguin-cold beer from my half-empty mug, then quickly lightning up another cigarette.

"You got that right," Rob says, wiping down the length of the narrow bar with a damp, off-white bar towel. I glance up at the television, exhaling a calm-inducing nicotine cloud. Finally, The Trailblazers have beaten the Los Angeles Lakers like they stole something, 130 to 88, and that's good enough for me.

I decide that the dysfunctional riffraff have long vanished on their way, and its time for me to head home. It might have been a mythical, so-called supremacist holiday that I was not aware of, but there was just too much excitement for me today. "See you later, Rob," I say, throwing a wave in the air as I exit the civil establishment. I walk cautiously out the front door and unlock the bike from the rack just to the side of the club's main entrance, swing my leg over, and mount the dry black seat that was designed for a woman, not a man. Ouch, goes the framework of my natured jewels.

I pedal just a few blocks until I become aware of these sirens and flashing lights approaching closely from behind me. Are you kidding me? This can't be happening. There has got to be a logical explanation. Those bright blue and white police lights can't be for me! I cannot fathom that I am getting pulled over on a bike at ten o'clock in the evening right by the Convention Center, not at all that far from the Beach Club tavern. What crime have I just committed now?

The officer gets out of the patrol car and quickly blinds me with his standard-issue black Magna-light. "Where are you going?" the thin but tall navy-blue uniformed officer asks, being unlawfully nosy, obviously not looking for a suspect in any crime.

"I am going home, officer," I reply civilly, in disbelief at the situation.

"Where is home?" he continues.

"Right here in Seaside at the Pine Cove Trailer Park, space number 29, officer," I respond carefully, courteously.

"Let me see some identification, young man," he orders. "Are you employed?"

"Yes, I work at the Shilo Inn," I whisper as I hand him my Oregon identification card.

"I will be right back," Mr. Clean-Shaven officer utters before he walks back to his patrol car, definitely intent on running the usual, by-the-book check on me to see if I have any warrants. *Here we go again,* I reflect silently.

Seconds later, much more quickly than any of the other times before, the officer returns to where I am, still sitting motionless on my bike. "Well, you are clear. However, while you live here in Seaside, just you keep your nose out of trouble," he says to me as he hands me back my plastic-coated Oregon identification card.

I start to pedal my bike toward home, flustered and fatigued from this instance of ethnic harassment, when someone behind me calls out, "Brother Ed!" It's John, alerting me to his presence. "What the Hell Seaside Bitchin' Police fuckin' with you again for? I saw the whole damn, stupid incident, dude!" John says hurriedly. He's got on a yellow T-shirt and jeans, spitting chew on the road, shaking his head. I dismount and we leisurely walk together for about a half-mile. Then John veers left, heading home, and I get back on my bike and quickly pedal cross Highway 101. Though mentally scarred, I unconsciously convert my rage into isolated numbness.

I arrive at the trailer, park the bike in front of the steps, and open the door, I see Jeremy watching one of my all-time favorite movies, *Bill and Ted's Excellent Adventure.* Jeremy and I just love to watch dim-witted comedies, over and over. Sherri's in the diminutive living room, stretched out on the cushions of the wide, green couch, leaning back against the arm in a white nightgown, reading a novel. Somewhat somberly, I say hello to my loving family and immediately go directly to our bedroom and straightaway crash onto our bed.

What can I possibly be doing that actually provokes these awkwardly disturbing racist encounters and ceaseless unethical harassment? my inner voice asks me, scanning my cranium for logical answers. Then Sherri trails inquisitively along the hallway into the room, wondering to herself what happened. But since my back is turned to her, she assumes I am sleeping or just want to be left alone.

Later on that evening, aware of the fact that I have endured more than my share of racism and that it seems to track me down like a runaway slave, Sherri, sensitive to my rage, suggests going to Portland for the day. I have been so explosively frustrated and tired of explaining every racist ordeal I am exposed to; I spend a bundle of quality home time restricted to the trailer park or occasionally visit Jim Dunkin at his house one mile down Highway 101 in the town of Gearhart. We watch the Trailblazers in the playoffs, play ping pong, or throw darts. Otherwise, I just stay at home watching a lot of stupid, crazy comedies with Jeremy, like *Short Circuit, Back to the Future, Bill and Ted's Excellent Adventure, Beetlejuice,* and *Police Academy.* Which is how I perfected various animated voices and many impersonations I perform without even thinking about it, like Beetlejuice, Richard Pryor, James Brown, Bill Cosby, Bobcat Goldthwait, Eddie Murphy, James Earl Jones, Louis Armstrong, Cheech and Chong, Tony Montana, The Godfather, and many more. I play board games like Jenga and Scrabble with Sherri, Arthur, and Sandy, or go fishing with Jeremy, Justin, and Mike in the Nehalem River, which is in walking distance. At the very back of the trailer park, there is a huge, vacant, grassy field of Baske's land next to the Seaside Airport, which is a less than hundred yards from my trailer's back door, where happy campers go to drive their golf balls.

This particular Friday eve, Jeremy is across the highway at his Aunt Kelly's house on Oregon Street. Sherri's reading a novel while taking a bath, and I am watching MTV videos with Bobby McFerrin's "Don't Worry, Be Happy" on the television screen, now that we have cable. I'm thinking about the phone we will have this coming Monday, when there's a knock at the front door. As I open it, I am certainly not expecting to see my first cousin, Ray Purifoy from Portland, who drove for about an hour to visit with me. I open the door wide as he stands there, smiling handsomely from ear-to-ear, utterly amused. "Hi! Surprise! What going on, cousin?" he laughs.

"Come on in here!" I say, happily surprised to see him and his white '76 Cutlass Supreme with its blue top parked in front of our rusty-red trailer. Ray is five-ten, 189 pounds of extreme, hulk-muscled physique, fair-skinned complexion, a clean-shaven ladies' man, and the youngest son of my Aunt Sally Mae and Uncle ZJ. "How did you find the trailer?" I ask as he steps inside. Ray is dressed to impress in a white, short-sleeved Polo shirt and dark corduroy pants.

"Where are Jeremy and Sherri?" he asks, grinning, checking out the ghetto-fabulous trailer.

"Jeremy is across the highway over at his Aunt Kelly's, and Sherri is in the bathtub reading a Raul novel," I say.

"Well, that's fine, Eddie, because I'm not staying long. I just wanted to see you and where you were staying, and I just felt like taking a drive up here, that's all. You know, cousin, just get out of the city, get on the highway and drive," Ray confesses, scanning the silver, nineteen-inch color television in the corner. "Went up to the Shilo Inn, told them that I am your first cousin, and they gave me directions to the trailer park. It was easy," he says, sitting down on the couch. We visit for another twenty-five minutes or so, then we're outside and Ray and I are saying our goodbyes. He gives me a hug and takes off in his clean Cutlass Supreme, stating he will stay a lot longer next time, which will be sooner than I anticipate.

Sherri and I always spend our weekends now working at the Shilo Inn, since we are in the hot, sunny, peak summer season. The merry month of May showcases conventions at the demandingly elite Convention Center on First Avenue. Each week, Sherri makes exceedingly decent gratuities, as well as yours truly getting some much-needed overtime from the busloads of tourists who flock here from all over the world to sightsee the fabulous Pacific Northwest Coastline. When the sun is brilliant, the beach is crowded, and this has an unfailing effect on my dishwashing employees, who have a tendency to be captivated by the warm weather conditions and take unscheduled sunny holiday days off on the stunningly seductive sandy beaches. This kind of weather makes keeping your mind on your work incredibly complicated, especially when you have amazing-looking women bouncing around all over the place looking like goddesses having fun in the dazzling sun.

Any given Sunday after the seafood brunch finishes at the Shilo inn, we fellow male employees—Jim, Marty, Spin, Stevo, John, Gary, and myself—would take up a collection for a case of beer from the Beach Club Tavern, where you can get cases of beer to go. Then we would congregate around an adult-sized, tubular steel, four-person swing set in front of the Seahorse Motel next to the Shilo Inn and enjoy the view; beautiful women from all over the world in gorgeously tiny bikinis sunbathing and playing volleyball on the sparkling sandy beach. Mondays and Tuesdays are, more or less, Sherri's and my days off, since I am currently the supervisor of the dishwashers and janitors and schedule the weekly labor shifts. My brand new promotion is not a very complicated position to grasp, since it's more or less picking up the slack in every facet of the functions of the backside of the inn; maintaining the kitchens, restaurant, and banquet rooms as a smoothly running operation. Among the dozen Mexicans under me, Benjamin, a five-foot-ten, black-haired, hefty, café-skinned Latino from Mexico, is the most productive dishwasher, and very reliable. I have a great professional relationship with my crew, and Benjamin and I get along so well. He taught me the Spanish alphabet, which made about forty words easy to learn in a very short time. Learning Spanish was a lot easier than German, which I had to learn to speak in the army when I lived off-base in an apartment with my son and deceitful wife in Giessen, Germany, making my livelihood with the Germans in the town of Krofdoff Kleinberg.

Some employees are systemically traumatized by the fact that I am a chocolate American supervisor at the Seaside Shilo Inn, especially certain Caucasian males whose dysfunction can't grasp a mocha-chocolate supervisor directing their work-related duties. Not all of them, just a chosen few, mind you. I hire people on the spot if I feel they are motivated. However, a few of my subordinates like Buddy—a good person with a strange disposition—and I suppose a couple of the other dishwashers are not able to stomach having a mocha-chocolate supervisor. They seem to dislike taking orders from yours truly, even though I supervise fairly; I ask politely and professionally in situations that need to be addressed and don't boss people around like I'm on some kind of abusive power trip. Most human beings have common sense, and in addition are opposed to having somebody in a position over them who treats them like they cannot produce anything without a whip to their backside. I take pleasure in pulling my own weight. It keeps me in muscle-toned shape. My expectations of an employee are not elaborate or complicated; use your common sense to facilitate doing your job without needing a supervisor breathing down your neck, which scenario seems to work out just fine.

It's pouring rain a few days after the Cinco de Mayo weekend and I decide not to take my bike to work, so I catch a ride with Sherri because of the storm. However, I forget to retrieve the bike from the trunk of the Cordoba, and space out the fact Sherri gets off earlier than me. Luckily, the storm has passed by the time my shift is over, and I am walking down Ocean Way toward home when shockingly, after all this time, that canary-yellow Nova finds me once again. They're on my ass like a fly stuck on manure, like they have an electronic locating device.

"Nigger, it's your coon ass when I catch ya!" the raging racist shouts out of the open driver's window. The roar of the beefed-up, fast-moving, high horse-powered machine scares the shit out of me, to say nothing of the unanticipated presence of these ignorant, racist punks again, bully-screaming, "Nigger, you fucking best go home!" A half-empty can of beer catapulting at me from the passenger side of the Nova misses me by an easy mile. With my excessively fast-thumping heart trying to beat its way out of my chest once again, plus nervously having to urinate, I waste no time running quickly to the Beach Club, fling the door open, and head straight for the lavatory, successfully avoiding pissing myself from the sheer terror of the recurring attempted vehicular homicide.

Holding my breath to prevent myself from gagging in the urine-smelling men's room as I relieve myself, I somehow manage to gather sufficient wits about me to make a pledge to myself: I will, on no account, ever put myself in this freakishly hazardous position again!

Now that our phone has finally been turned on in the trailer, I call Sherri from the Beach Club and explain what happened. "Better just come and get me. I am not in any shape to walk anywhere, for any reason," I tell her, paranoid. She arrives quickly and we head for home before I am racially besieged again.

The very next weekend turns out to be the absolute opposite. Sherri and I accept an invitation to a get together at Carolyn's, another waitress who is a very nice individual and lives in Astoria or someplace close to it. Larry, the very thin cook—black hair, and somewhat of a cool guy—and my friend George, the prep cook, both want to tag along and party with Sherri and me at Carolyn's, so they ride along with us in the black Cordoba.

After a busy day at work, we make our way up to Astoria with Sherri driving, naturally, to an area off Lewis and Clark Road that I wasn't quite familiar with. We arrive at Carolyn's magnificent, warm home and the dinner party is casually cool—no racist idiots to muddle things up—delicious food, tons of wine, conversation that's not out of the norm except for a few of Carolyn's somewhat flirtatious innuendos, frequently suggesting that Sherri and I spend the night for what I presumed would be a probably pleasurable one. Sherri puts the nail in the coffin when she suggests we go have some private, weekend Mother's Day holiday fun.

Well, after dark, the four of us—Sherri, George, Larry, and I—leave the get-together in the Cordoba, feeling somewhat buzzed and carefree. George and Larry are in the backseat with Larry sitting directly behind me and Sherri driving. Seconds after we hit the road Sherri, on an impulse, takes off like a greyhound and unintentionally runs a stop sign. As bad luck would have it, there's an officer of the law parked across the street in a shaded area, who pursues the Cordoba immediately, flashing bubblegum-machine revolving lights. *Damn! So much for a calm evening!* I think.

Sherri hastily pulls the Cordoba over as the officer drives up behind us. The lady in the Clatsop County Officer's uniform emerges from her brown-and-white patrol car and walks up to the driver's side door. Sherri presses a button, lowering the electric window. "Excuse me, ma'am, but didn't you see that stop sign?" the lady officer asks very politely.

"I did not," Sherri replies, quaintly stylish.

"May I see your driver's license, registration, and proof of insurance, please?" the Lady Officer asks, just as politely as before.

"I don't have any of the above," Sherri replies truthfully. Then, from way out of the blue, Larry, sitting in the backseat, psychotically sucker punches George in the jaw with his right fist, who responds by yelling angrily and retaliates by reaching under his two-toned, hooded sweater, and coming up with a can of mace that he sprays in Larry's mug, part of which hits me in the face as well. Larry instinctively covers his face with his hands as the burning chemicals take their painful affect rapidly. My own eyes are now ablaze, having been insanely caught off guard.

The situation is now way out-of-hand, and the Lady Officer, remaining strategically aloof, but concerned, calls for backup. The chemicals' physical potency intensifies the burning in my dripping eyes, and snotty mucous has started running out of my nose like a wide-open faucet. I'm having no little difficulty breathing and my eyes are screaming for me to rub them, at which time two backup patrol cars abruptly arrive from different directions, skidding to a simultaneous stop in the gravel on the side of the road. I get my car door open and tumble out of the black Cordoba, a legally blind, assaulted casualty, coughing my lungs out from the strong concentration of mace. I struggle to keep from falling, try to calm down, breathe, not throw up, and frequently have to bend over at the waist from the dizzying effects of the mace.

As the two backup officers approach the scene, I hear the Clatsop Lady Officer clearly attempt to explain to the backup officers what exactly happened. "Hey, the black man had nothing at all to do with it!" she informs the other officers, crystal clear. Nonetheless, as everybody exits the ghastly, chemical substance-contaminated vehicle, one repugnant officer doesn't see things quite the same way as the Lady Officer of the Law.

All of a sudden, this one ill-bred lawman is in my face shouting thunderously at the top of his raspy, seasoned-with-a-Southern-drawl lungs. Despite my sense of smell being currently outraged, his exhortations have the strong odor of deregulated, funky-ass death breath! "What's your name, boy?" he shouts, as he tries to make me aware that, with a badge and a gun, he's superior. I really need medical attention, like yesterday, so I'm attempting not to gag from the combination of the mace and his bad-ass, unrushed-teeth, no-Listerine-thank-you breath that's boiling all the way up from his intestines, but he's more concerned with treating me like I am a so-called black nonentity.

"He hasn't done anything!" Lady Officer announces in an authoritative voice. "That black man did not do anything at all!"

"Whose side are you on, anyway?" the racist officer responds, which makes me gag that he's trying to induce fear in me, while the other backup officer does absolutely nothing about anybody else involved in this loony state of affairs. I know is turning back toward me because the cloud of his nose-insulting, odor-of-ass breath is starting to offend my olfactory sense once again. "What's your name, boy? Tell me your name, boy!" he continues, spewing his hateful breath. I slowly shuffle myself to the front of the car and bend over, resting on the cool hood. Tears are still streaming down my face and mucus willfully flows out of my nostrils. I'm blinded, not only by the mace, but by the intensely bright lights of the patrol vehicles. "Boy! What you hiding from me, boy?! You got a warrant?" Mr. Racist Officer shouts at the top of his voice "I bet he's got a warrant! That's why the boy won't answer me!" he states loudly to everyone that can hear.

"Honey, why don't you just tell him your name?" Sherri commands loudly, as if *I* have broken the law! I am so pissed off; I can't believe Sherri is this delusional! She doesn't understand citizens' rights, my complete innocence according to the Lady Officer, or this racist officer's total lack of concern for my health or well-being! I can't get any damn-ass respect whatsoever! She doesn't understand that he is constantly trying to humiliate me by repeatedly yelling, "Boy! What's your name, boy? You are hiding something, boy!" She also doesn't understand that it is interpreted as what you might call psychological, emotional, verbal, and mental abuse.

"My name is Eddie D. Williams," I respond, walking away slowly, nose running, hard to focus my burning eyes, still can't quite see, very hazy, clouded vision, intensely frustrated, and highly disturbed at this here obstructionist "Officer of the Law."

"What, boy? What's your name? Eddie Dee Williams? Boy, you really want me to believe your name is Eddie Dee Williams, boy? Let me see some identification, boy! You could be telling me any damn name!" he yells loudly, enjoying the power behind his legal badge. With my blurred vision, I reach slowly, like I am Toby from *Roots*, for my wallet in my gray slacks, slowly and cautiously hand him my Oregon identification card like a runaway slave would with freedom documents who doesn't want to be 'accidentally' shot. Mr. Racist Officer snatches the identification card out of my open hand, reads it, then strides purposely to his patrol car to see if I alone—selectively, absolutely no one else—will have a warrant check run, even though my fellow passengers have collectively committed assault and run a stop sign.

"Why didn't you answer the police officer when he wanted you to?" Sherri, in all her revolting, Caucasian-privileged, selective audacity asks me.

"Don't talk to me," I manage to rasp out to her. Minutes later, Mr. Racist Officer Returns from his patrol vehicle with my identification card, tosses it to me, and verbally warns me to stay out of trouble. Nobody warns anybody else. The four of us get back in the car where the fumes from the mace linger motionlessly in the passenger compartment of the Cordoba.

"Why didn't you just tell him your name when the officer asked you?" Sherri asks once again, still brainwashed ignorant of my rights having just been raped.

"I *know* you didn't just ask me that dumb-ass question again!" I answer, irritated by the uninformed question's ignorance. "Initially and logically, the Lady Officer informed both of the backup officers that the so-called black man didn't do anything. Not once did she say it, but twice, and the other officer heeded the statement she made regarding me," I explain to her.

"Why didn't you just answer the man?" Sherri insists ignorantly yet again, demanding a response to an absolutely dysfunctional question.

"So therefore it's okay for you to run a stop sign in front of a Clatsop County Sheriff? And it's okay for Larry, wearing a T-shirt and jeans, to assault George in front of the same officer? And it's okay for George to retaliate with mace from his multicolored, hooded, knit sweater pocket, to defend himself against a blind-side assault in the car? Because you guys are all so-called white," I say angrily. "NOTHING fucking happened to any of you! BUT! Since I am so-called black, I get to be harassed by an asshole whose breathe smells like manure, AND I DIDN'T DO SHIT! I didn't commit one damn infraction! Since I am perceived as a BOY, I'm supposed to answer him while you law-breaking, privileged, so-called white idiots stroll away with *no* ticket for running the stop sign, *no* disorderly conduct charge, and *no* violation of any kind. *No* criminal check run on any of you light-skinned, bamboozled, brainwashed idiots absolutely is freaking ANYTHING!"

"Sorry," George says immediately.

"Hey, brother," Larry starts, but I am not hearing that shit!

"Save it, Larry! I am not the' one!" I add at full volume, wishing this pain would cease. "My eyes are still burning! Let me out of here, I need to get some air!" I say. "I can't believe you said that shit! I thought you were better than that, Sherri Lynn," I say loudly, still slightly bent over. Sherri, obviously pissed as well as insulted, immediately slams on the brakes and pulls the car over, allowing me out into the fresh air of the countryside, still somewhere in Astoria. I get out of the car and slam the door, antagonized, racially stressed out, and with the mace still in my eyes. As I take a couple of steps down the road away from the car, Sherri takes off, spinning the tires in the gravel, leaving me in the total darkness of a shoulder-less road. But the vicious circle hasn't completely closed just yet. She's pulled over again, but this time by detestable Mr. Racist Officer who was so diligently harassing me. He pulls up behind her in his patrol car, and in a moment I see the ill-mannered officer standing there, leaning down and having a short, civil chat with Sherri through the open driver's window of the Cordoba. She takes off abruptly down the clear road, her taillights disappearing into the night, leaving me here, far away from our homestead, in the middle of nowhere.

Under these extreme circumstances, I make a calculated decision to walk heading South on the left side of the no-shoulder road, hoping it will lead me back to Seaside. Seconds later, approaching as if in a high-speed pursuit, nauseating Nazi Officer of the Law drives up, skids his patrol car to a stop just yards in front of me, exits the car, marches over to me, and grabs me by the collar of my black jacket. "I'm taking you in, boy! You are under arrest!" he yells at the top of his voice as he slams me face-down on the hood of his patrol car. I don't resist as he grabs my hands behind my back, snapping the cuffs on so forcefully they bite into the skin of my wrists, cutting into the joints, sending aggravating waves of pain along the nerve pathway. I can't believe this is happening.

Wait a minute. Yes, I can.

I'm getting arrested for walking down the street and being assaulted with mace while breathing, by a so-called white American who thinks he is some kind of modern-day bounty hunter, and I am a fugitive slave. Once Mr. Racist Officer finishes handcuffing me, he grabs the back of my jacket collar. "Get up, boy!" he says loudly, jerking me to a standing position like I am resisting, his foul breath still smelling worse than rotting chitterlings. Then he stuffs me roughly in the backseat of the patrol vehicle head first, like a ballooned throw pillow. I ask myself, Is hillbilly sheriff going to take me to jail, or is it just killing-time and then dump my anatomy who-knows-where? Only time will tell. I struggle to sit up as Mr. Racist Officer drives off, trying to get as comfortable as I can, what with the handcuffs biting me and my burning, blurred vision.

Now, if I'm going to jail, I should be charged with something, my inner voice says to me. So, I ask, "Officer, would you be kind enough to let me know what I'm being charged with?"

"You are being charged with disorderly conduct and interfering with police business," the alleged officer arrogantly answers. At this particular moment in time, I've been incapacitated for the last hour. I ran no stop signs. I sucker-punched no human being in the face. I didn't provoke the Sheriff to call for backup. I did not assault anyone with mace. However, I'm the one going to jail with no probable cause for the third time this year. This isn't even an exceptional example, yet it clearly illustrates why American Africans are viewed as committing more crimes—a disadvantage of sorts—than so-called whites. Privileged, so-called Caucasians often ignorantly and habitually get away with their illegal infractions just like clockwork, twenty-four seven. For example, on the news cycle, charges are dropped constantly when the alleged violator is Caucasian. African Americans are discriminated by any means necessary. I contemplated this revelation about the criminal justice system, being well aware of this unfortunate, dysfunctional fact for the entire three-day weekend I was in jail until I was sick to my stomach.

Sherri drives up to Astoria early Tuesday morning to pick me up from the county jail. I jump, practically insanely, into the passenger seat of the vehicle before she can come close to bringing the Cordoba to a complete stop. "Hi, Baby!" Sherri says, dressed casually in a gray sweatshirt and jeans.

"Hello, Honey!" I reply, as I give her a kiss while closing the car door effortlessly. "I'm so sorry for questioning you like that," she admits, appearing sexy and apologetic simultaneously, explaining that her father has set her mind straight. "Dad says that they were enormously in the wrong for what they did, and that you should file a complaint and sue them for false imprisonment." Sherri's speaking as fast as usual.

"What did the officer say when he pulled you over, Honey?" I asked, still wearing the same black shirt and gray slacks, frantically needing soap and a hot shower, which explains Snooky curiously sniffing me.

"The racist redheaded officer only pulled me over to ask me where that black guy went," Sherri says politely. "I told him you were walking down the street getting some air because the mace was still burning your face. Then he gives me a direct order not to let you back in the car or he'll arrest me!" Sherri says miserably.

"The officer lied and told me he arrested me for disorderly conduct, and of course, the unlawful mishap on my part, presumed black and not answering him fast enough," I say.

"Honey, did he try to hurt you?" she asks, appearing frightfully gloomy.

"He just slammed on his brakes over and over, trying very hard to alarm the diarrhea out of me," I tell her. "Where is Jeremy?" I ask, changing the subject.

"He's over at Kelly's with the kids," she says.

"Did you tell Dennis what happened to me?" I ask eagerly.

"Yes, I told him. He said it's too bad you have to go through all of this racial harassment and discrimination." She continues passionately, "But you are not to worry. They understand that this was none of your fault, Baby." I assume she is as weary of this ongoing, selective, in-your-face treatment as I am.

It's exhilarating being outside in the elements again, seeing beautiful, partially blue skies mixed with fluffy, grayish-white clouds, smelling the salty air, and hearing the sweet sound of the Pacific Ocean. The next day I am summoned by my new probation officer for an informal meeting at her office on Duane Street, in Astoria. Of course, Sherri drives me up to the department of corrections where I had been imprisoned. My new probation officer turns out to be five foot five, medium build with big hair, and wearing a probation officer uniform. The meeting lasts no more than about five minutes. Right after exchanging greetings, she immediately gets to the point and asks me about the incident last weekend. By the time I explain what transpired at length, she's appalled by the fact that the officer was a racist, and that I am of a mind to sue. In view of the fact that she had no corroboration of my violating my probation, she informed me that I could report to her monthly by mail and that I was free to go. I was in and out of that Department of Corrections Probation Office and back in the Cordoba with Snooky Nooky Poo Poo faster than a greyhound chasing Rusty the Rabbit at the dog track.

Early on a Sunday morning a few weeks later, armed with red roses, a card, and a balloon that announces *Happy Birthday*, I sing, "Happy birthday to you, happy birthday to you, happy birthday, dear Snooky Nooky Poo Poo. Happy birthday, twenty-two," waking her up softly, pleasantly, after I've prepared to go to work for my Sunday Brunch labors. Sherri has prearranged to take the day off for her own special day, since Mother's Day weekend went selectively bonkers, and which I unofficially spent in the Clatsop County Jail for over three days, one day for each charge: two counts of disorderly conduct, and one charge of interfering with police business while under the involuntary influence of mace. Meanwhile, I'm attempting to grab any overtime I can scarf up to make up for my lost wages, thanks to official police brutality.

12

· · · · · · · · · · · · · · · · · · · ·

Seaside Finest

A mini-update of first-rate news now that summer has arrived: the old gray-haired lady and her eccentric son moved their double-wide trailer, vacating Pine Cove Trailer Park, which provides more playground area for Jeremy, his pal Justin, Sandy's children, Levi, Sara, and her Jeremy, and well as the other neighborhood goonies kids. Sherri and I are fortunate enough to enjoy the comforts of a gigantic, oversized lot now that our neighbors have moved, as it also gives us more than adequate room for picnic tables.

On our next shared day off, we're blessed with a brilliantly gorgeous, sunny summer day, and Sherri and I have decided in advance to have a few friends over to our neck of the woods as an alternative to going somewhere else and, logically, it seems safer that way. I invite my coworkers Jim, and his lady friend, Darlene, and her daughter Tiffany, John, Marty, Kenny, and Terry, as well as my neighbors Arthur and Sandy, and her three children, and blonde-haired Mike, Justin's father, who is a hospitable single parent. We're all rather keyed-up for this little celebration as it will be our initial picnic complete with a blazing fire pit to kick off the season in Pine Cove Trailer Park. We intend to squeeze every ounce of gratification we can out of this opportunity while it lasts, and good ridden to our other racist neighbors, on the opposite side, of my trailer. They never spoke, always just stared, and

I experienced a heartfelt, thrilling relief watching them drive off, irritated, in their vomit-green Volkswagen Van.

Once they are gone, John, Marty, Terry, Kenny, and yours truly walk over toward the public bathrooms where we see a couple of gray picnic tables we can scavenge up for the barbecue, which will provide ample, comfortable seating for the entire company. They're old and weather-beaten from the environmental elements, but in good shape and still sturdy enough, so the five of us hoist them up under our own steam over to our extended trailer space. Earlier in the day, Sherri and I purchased a nice, inexpensive barbecue grill for the occasion. I also picked up some steaks, hamburger meat, chicken, hot dogs, chips and dip, condiments, some whiskey, and a couple cases of beer and soda in two large white Styrofoam coolers.

Jim—casually dressed in jeans and a gray, pullover shirt—brings some elk meat and is unanimously voted Barbeque Grill master, while I'm elected supervisor of music. I hurriedly arrange our small, black, plastic, six-inch-high detachable speakers in the window of the trailer, along with the mini-stereo AM/FM radio/cassette player. Sherri's making potato salad while chatting with Darlene and Sandy, when I realize turning the silver tuning knob to the local radio station 1370 KAST-AM out of Astoria would be appropriate, since these new acquaintances are country-western fans.

With the music rolling out of the speakers, everything is going just fine. We're alternately driving some golf balls out into the wide green field behind the trailer park's tree line by means of this number 1 wood Spalding golf club that we discovered in my modest six-by-six storeroom shed with the floppy hanging rusty-red front door. It's actually a stationary, multicolored trailer at the rear of the park and resembles an outdated reddish outhouse. Jeremy, Levi, and Justin are playing joyously with John and Marty, tossing the football around. It's not really summertime-warm out yet, but it's a nice, peaceful, relaxed, clear blue-skied, sun-drenched day.

Hours later toward sunset that evening, our other glowering neighbors return in their dark-green off-white trimmed Volkswagen van. The historically antisocial foursome speedily scatters out of the van, returning to their trailer as the six-foot-two-inch father of the gang just stares disturbingly our way, and then enters his trailer.

"Your neighbor really sucks, brother Ed," Marty, wearing a too-tight gray T-shirt and blue jeans, states brashly as he stops playing catch football. The unfriendly neighbors swiftly enter their white single-wide trailer with its white-painted wooden crucifix attached firmly to the crown of the trailer, just above the front door to their abode.

"Now, don't they suck big-time, Eddie Dee?" John mentions shyly, as I toss him the ball and put my hands on my hips.

"John, nevertheless, all people are good people. Unfortunately some of them did not get the memo," I assert, while reaching for the cigarettes in my navy-blue T-shirt pocket. It's getting dark and chilly outdoors and John, Marty, and Terry have formed a Hacky Sack triangle when the automatic overhead trailer park lights come on. And that means it's officially time to ignite my first fire the old-fashioned, authorized-by-law way.

I toddle gallantly up to the fire pit, get down on one knee, and set the dry kindling on fire with the blue lighter from the front pocket of my charcoal-colored jeans.

"Hey, brother Ed. Smile. We can't see you!" Marty jokes, as the others crack up laughing, beers in hand, and then he walks over to stand on the stone border encircling the firepit. As the intense flames continue to consume the correct oxygen/fuel mixture, they light up the fine-looking night.

"Honey, that fire is not going to burn that tree, is it?" Sherri asks as she walks up behind me, not hiding the fact that she's somewhat apprehensive.

"Snooky, after computing the risk a while ago, I strategically dug the hole for the fire here, where it would not burn down this, the only living tree we have in our robust yard," I methodically elaborate to Sherri. However, I will, for the sake of protection and from a safe-fire science approach, hustle over to turn the water on. There is a long green water hose hanging conveniently coiled on a wooden contraption over the old-school faucet ten feet away from the fire itself, just in case. Sherri backtracks to the trailer as I head over to the faucet and fill a tan, two-gallon bucket with water. Everybody eventually congregates around the fire pit as the flames subside enough for the overly excited kids to be able to easily and safely roast the marshmallows Sherri has just brought out of the trailer. Jeremy and I collect long, leafless twiggy sticks while Spin, Jim, Darlene and her blonde-haired daughter Tiffany, along with Justin, are sitting down at the paper-covered, weatherworn picnic table, attempting to eat these enormous paper plates of potato salad, baked beans, chips and dip, hot dogs loaded with condiments, and barbecued chicken and elk

"If you don't believe me, ask Eddie!" Terry declares, then chugs down the rest of his beer.

"Eddie, is it true that society is brainwashed to hate you and never trust your entire race?" Marty asks, appearing highly interested as he smokes a cigarette.

"Yes, that is correct," I confirm promptly.

"I told you so!" Terry says, gesturing with his free arm in celebration, as if he just won some remedial contest.

Then Marty asks, "Can I put my hand on your head?"

"Why?" I ask in return.

"Because there is a racial joke I am curious about," he admits truthfully, his grin breezy with freckles.

"What's the joke, Marty?" I request, wanting to hear the dehumanizing joke.

"Why do blacks always have sex on the brain?" Marty asks, his control switch stuck on goofy.

"I don't know. Why, Marty?" I respond, carefree.

"Because they have pubic hair on their heads!" Marty alleges, laughing, stepping backward gradually as he rubs my head.

"Wait! Hold up! I got one!" Terry announces, noticeably tipsy as he tosses a twig in the bonfire. "What did President Lincoln say after a three-day bender?" Terry pauses. "I set *who* free?" Terry blares comically, as everyone laughs and waits patiently for their turn to tell a joke. Jeremy, busy-boy-dirty from head to toe, along with his excited mob of young acquaintances, are content roasting marshmallows, then he sits down at the picnic table with his loving mother.

"Don't you know, Marty, it was once against the law for a dark, brown-skinned African man to speak his native tongue? That he was raped, stripped of his own language, prohibited to gain knowledge of, study, or write any language?" I murmur progressively.

"No, I was not aware of that," Marty replies, looking very surprised while drinking beer and chewing his tobacco.

"It's a superlative example: slave master commands the son slave of the mother slave to have forceful intercourse with his own biological mother, in front of his own biological father, thereby destroying any trust inside the family. Master then labels the slave a motherfucker, or the other everyday expression, son of a bitch. God created light so you can appreciate how beautiful dark is," I announce arrogantly, as well as logically.

"Did you guys know that the abundant resources of alcohol, crack, crank, heroin, and readily available guns in their neighborhoods are part of a master plan designed to sabotage Eddie's persuasion into spiral extermination?" Terry adds eagerly and takes a swallow of his beer, the overload from his mouth dripping down on his brown, muscle T-shirt.

"Now, here is the kicker," I say to Marty, although everyone in hearing distance is listening. "Being as there are so many persuasions in the whole wide world, why are there only two ethnic races in the absolute world that are described by a color?" I ask logically, and not receiving an answer.

"That's a good question," Jim responds from the grill, since he's listening in.

"Kris Cringle is society's selective brainwashing phenomenon at work, bamboozling your own parents to be the first adult humans on the entire planet to boldly lie successfully to their very own offspring, consistently year after year, that there is a Santa Claus, enabling entitlement. Maybe it's psychologically satisfying to verbally apply a so-called white lie. Another example: Why do they call black ice, black?" I ask, unable to come up with a logical answer. "That is so linguistically ignorant. It doesn't make any sense to me. At all!" I add, perplexed. "Ice is not black. This makes not a drop of physical, scientific sense whatsoever!"

"Did you know that a black man was once considered part human and part animal?" Terry mentions rhetorically.

"Also, black people eat watermelon, fried chicken, and drink strawberry soda!" my neighbor Mike interjects loudly, buzzed and smiling, staggering under the influence, head-butting himself into the conversation, smoking the last half of a Marlboro.

"That is a brainless-ass stereotype. I don't eat watermelon, or any kind of melon," I say with conviction, sipping my beer.

"What? Are you serious, Eddie?" Marty asks, seemingly genuinely surprised.

"You have never seen me eat that crap of fruit at work, have you?" I ask as I leisurely light a cigarette.

"No, now that I think about it, I have never seen you in the middle of a watermelon," Marty admits, cracking open a can of Miller High Life.

"I never seen Eddie eat watermelon, and he's my neighbor," Sandy says, smoking a cigarette and drinking a beer as she stands next to me.

"It's all a bunch of bullshit," Arthur interjects calmly. "You're either a good-quality person or just another asshole in this world."

"It makes me gag. Plus I'm pretty sure I am allergic to it," I mention, taking a drag of my cigarette.

"What are three things you cannot give a nigger?" Mike utters, dribbling beer down his white T-shirt and onto his jeans, stumbling, almost falling. "A black eye, a fat lip, and an education!" Mike says, laughing, eyes barely open. Choking, I almost spew my beer on everyone at hearing the word *nigger* while I'm swallowing at the same time.

"Hey, brother Ed. You think there will ever be a chocolate president?" John asks me as he raises his beer up to his mouth, one of his tan boots resting on the stone surrounding the fire pit.

"Of course. I consider it as being obvious in the future, that there will be a chocolate president of the United States. I currently pray I live to see it. It's just that this present racist generation is going to have to pass away first," I forewarn John Trent, then take a sip of my drink out of its Styrofoam cup.

"Eddie, don't take this personal. I like you because you are a terrific human being. But there is never going to be a black president. Ever. My white race is too damn prejudiced to let some shit like that happen," Mike announces, stumbling tipsily close to the fire pit with a lit cigarette in one hand and a drink of whiskey in a Styrofoam cup in the other.

"Yes, Eddie my friend Mike's right. There are way too many racists," Terry interjects effortlessly. "Jesse Jackson by no means had a snowball's chance in hell of winning the presidential general election. First and foremost, Ku Klux Klan leader David Duke would have had Jessie Jackson assassinated," Terry mentions boldly, putting on his worn brown flannel shirt and reaching into the Styrofoam cooler for another bottle of beer. "You know why black voters declined voting Jesse Jackson for President?" Terry asks glibly, standing erect.

"No, I don't have the slightest," I respond pessimistically.

"He promised to create jobs for them if elected."

Laughter immediately engulfs the fire pit-lit yard.

"Brother Ed, I really like you. However, there's probably never going to be a black president in America. Ever," Marty adds seriously, patting me on the back. "See, there are a lot of racist-ass people on the planet, especially around this here township, and state," Marty mentions strategically, nodding his head, spitting chew in his Styrofoam cup.

"Yeah, Eddie. He's got a point. There's a lot of racists in this world," Jim adds, as he's covering up the food with aluminum foil to keep out the bugs.

"Uh-oh, brother Ed, we got the bad-company bastards!" John announces as he sees the Seaside Police patrol car cruise into the trailer park. "And I bet you your neighbor called the police force on you, Eddie Dee!" he adds, belching hard and tossing his empty beer can in the bucket.

"What time is it?" I ask diligently, as the black-and-white patrol vehicle comes to a dead stop in front of our trailer. The two dark navy-blue uniformed, black-booted, pistol side armed, officially attired Seaside Police Officers emerge from their patrol car—the driver tall, medium-build; the other five ten or so, with sandy-blond hair. "Good evening. Who's the owner of this trailer?" the tall officer asks.

"I am the registered owner of the trailer, officer," I state, as Sherri walks gracefully up next to me and holds my hand, making the situation even more potentially explosive.

"What's your name?" he asks me sternly as he approaches.

"Eddie Dee Williams, officer," I respond, while remaining respectfully cool and profoundly calm.

"We have received a complaint from one of your neighbors that you are being way too loud. And by the way, who gave you permission to have a fire pit in your yard, Mr. Williams?" the sandy-haired officer demands, seemingly eager to cite me for some criminal infraction.

"Mr. Baske, the landlord of this trailer park, gave me face-to-face permission to have a fire pit," I state straightforwardly, standing my ground.

"That's true!" Jim announces, stepping forward in the direction of the officer, holding his blonde, blue-eyed daughter Tiffany, who loves my Donald Duck impression. "I was present as well, when Mr. Baske unmistakably said that Eddie could have a fire pit," he mentions, attempting to confirm the specifics of the agreement, because the brainwashed police have no intention of taking my word for its legitimacy.

"Let me see some identification!" the ill-advised officer commands me. Just *my* identification, no one else's. Since I have no desire to wake up tomorrow and read in the Astorian that I am deceased, I reach slowly and carefully into my back pocket to retrieve my wallet, just in case these ignorant, trigger-happy peace officers stereotypically color me black and develop the notion that I am going for a gun. I nervously, fearfully, but nevertheless gently hand over my State of Oregon identification card as the officer requested. He then takes out his multipurpose black flashlight and inspects my ID card, making sure my picture on it is legitimate, not fake, and that I am giving them the correct information. They believe nothing I say.

"Mr. Williams, do you have any warrants?" the officer asks in a commanding voice, yet sounding a little uncertain. He hands my ID to the other officer who returns to the black-and-white unit to run a criminal check to see if I'm a fugitive from justice.

"No, I do not have a warrant, officer," I answer courteously, knowing it's not going to make a bit of difference. This is just the usual racist tactic of criminalizing my character and trying to embarrass me in front of my Caucasian friends, coworkers, my lady, and my neighbors, and designed to prevent me from interacting with this company in the first place, which may be against Celestial Law.

The officer attempts to strike up a conversation of discovery regarding my background. "Where are you employed, Mr. Williams?" he asks, standing there, keeping me under surveillance, like a hawk on a mouse. All my friends can do is look on in dismay. For most of them, this is their first opportunity to not only observe racism in action, but also at its greatest depth of immorality. I can tell by their expressions that their virgin eyes have never witnessed this dilemma before; it's so obviously plastered all over their faces.

Jeremy playfully runs up and catapults himself into Sherri's arms, asking, "What are the police doing?" as he looks at the officer watching me in case I decide to scamper, since they've already assumed I have a warrant based solely on the earth-tone shade of my skin.

"I am employed at the Seaside Beachfront Shilo Inn," I tell the officer.

"What exactly is your job description there, Mr. Williams?" the astonished-eyed rookie officer continues to drill me with additional questions, probing, anticipating a negative within my response.

"I am the supervisor in charge of the dishwashers and janitors," I state proudly, and not from a boastful position, still keeping still, not making any unnecessary movements, not accidentally putting my hands in my trouser pockets.

"How did you ever get a job like that?" Mr. Seaside Officer questions in an impudent tone.

"Honest hard work, officer. That's all. Just hard work," I reply intelligently, respectfully.

"You just stay put, Mr. Williams! I will be right back!" Mr. Officer of the Law commands yours truly, at the same time pointing his index finger at me, daring me to budge from where I am standing as he heads to the patrol car to discuss me with his partner.

"I told you guys it was true!" Terry says, pointing his finger at the peace officers' patrol car, making his position crystal clear.

"Brother Ed, what the hell, man?" John asks, traumatized at seeing me in a racist altercation for the fifth time and not knowing what the hell to think. "I can't believe Five-O didn't accept the truth from you, bro, about a damn freaking fire pit, which is not against the law down here!" Jim announces, honestly disturbed to see me go through this racial provocation.

"What the fuck, Eddie?" Spin garbles, tipsy as all get out, desperately trying to stand up from the picnic table but failing miserably.

Jeremy asks his mom, "Why are the police here?" Sherri responds by asking him to just be quiet; she will explain later. Moments later, both officers emerge simultaneously from the patrol car and walk back toward us, appearing somewhat dissatisfied they couldn't come up with a warrant one me. Without any preliminaries, the tall one hands me back my ID card and says, "Mr. Williams, it is now ten minutes after ten o'clock, so I would recommend you bring the noise level way down to minus zero and disperse these festivities immediately. Since your friend here says that he witnessed Baske giving you permission to have a fire pit, we are going to let that go for now. But. If we have to come back out here tonight, or any other night for that matter, we are going to arrest you. Do you understand, Mr. Williams?"

Then, Mr. Other Officer chimes in and basically repeats what the tall one said, only more stridently, threatening and belittling me in an authoritative manner as if I had disrespected them somehow. "You are already on probation, so I really wouldn't push it if I were you," shorter officer says loudly and harshly, pointing his finger and humiliating me in front of my lady Sherri, treating me like I am less than a human being. It's like they are piggybacking off each other, like Tweedledee and Tweedledum.

"You all have a nice evening," the tall one says, and they both about-face, return to their patrol car, start up the gravel drive, veer to the left, and disappear into the nighttime darkness. As I watch their taillights fade from sight, I am acutely reminded that each day holds the substantial probability of encountering individuals who have been infected with the virus of racism.

"Eddie? Is this like, standard operating procedure, for them to exasperate you like that?" Marty asks, highly concerned and not really believing what he just witnessed with his very own eyes. Abnormal in the State of Oregon? Oh, hell no! Yes, there seems to have been an enormous surge of racism since *I* arrived on the Pacific Northwest Coast.

I head over to the trailer and turn the chirping stereo that you can scarcely hear even if you are not talking completely off in lieu of another unexpected helping of unlawful, unnecessary verbal threats, courtesy of the notorious "protect and serve" Seaside Police Department. "I had been speculating to myself exactly when the neighbors were going to take some selective, bigoted action toward Sherri and me," I mention to Kenny, who's sitting at the picnic table, drunk as a worm in a bottle of tequila, finally eating some food.

"Hey, bro. Darlene, Tiffany, and I are going to head for home," Jim says, holding his precious, exhausted daughter over his shoulder.

"Thanks for coming, my brother, and for grilling the meat for me. It was excellent! And I am so glad you were here as a witness to let the cops know I had permission from Baske to have a bonfire. Since they would never have believed brown earth-toned human me," I whisper dejectedly, feeling awkwardly numbed and dehumanized.

"They are only doing this to you because of the shade of your skin, Eddie. They don't want to recognize the real you," Jim articulates genuinely, giving me some much-needed human encouragement.

"All right, neighbor. Will see you later," Arthur announces and finishes his can of beer. Sandy waves to everybody and follows Arthur over to their fifth wheel just across the yard.

"Thank you, Eddie, for having us over. We had a nice time," Darlene says, and gives me a hug goodbye. "Sorry you have to be treated like shit," she adds sincerely.

"See you guys at work!" I shout, heading for the door of the trailer as John, Marty, and Terry take off on their ten-speed bikes.

"I love you, Eddie, my chocolate bro. Please don't leave town just because of a few assholes! Stay here, bro! Please? Okay?" somberly intoxicated Spin pleads, standing there swaying in his barbecue sauce-stained, light-tan T-shirt and white jeans. As he stumbles drunkenly aboard his gold ten-speed Schwinn bike, I tell him, "I'm not going anywhere! I will see you tomorrow at work!" He finally gains his balance and control of the bike and pedals off into the night.

Oregonians know from experience that summer rain storms never really go away. The beach is empty of tourists due to high winds and blowing sand, which hinders visibility as I look out the lounge windows of the Shilo Inn, but I am still able to marvel at the sight of the huge, dancing ocean waves rolling in from the Pacific as they crash into the sheer stone face of Tillamook Head. This outlandishly seesawing weather is not good for business. "Things are molasses-slow at work today," Gary, the breakfast cook says, as he sidles up next to me to enjoy the view. "What time you getting off work, brother Ed?" he asks. Gary resembles the actor, John Carradine, and is a cool individual.

"I don't know, Gary. Why? What's up?" I ask inquisitively. "You should come on over to my place and drink some beer and check out my music collection," he states, folding his arms across his chest.

"Sounds like a plan, my friend," I say, and we shake hands soulfully in agreement. "About what time are you getting off work?" I ask, looking around the almost empty restaurant and lounge, which reflects the status of the beach that is devoid of tourists.

"I am pretty much done," he says, and heads to the kitchen with me following him. Inside the kitchen area, I see John just standing there, looking at the time clock.

"It is as dead as a corpse up in here, Eddie Dee. There have only been a few customers, but closer to no customers," John says.

"You are coming over to my house today, aren't you John?" Gary asks, high-fiving John casually.

"Yeah! Of course!" John says excitedly.

"Well, I am going to head out now and venture by the store to pick up some things along the way," Gary says as he punches his time card to leave.

"Are you going to ride your bike in this crappy weather?" I ask Gary curiously as I head to the break room.

"Yeah, I suppose. If it gets too windy, I can always carry my bike home," Gary chuckles as he puts on his scarf and jacket. "By the way, John. You know where I live. Why you don't show Eddie? Then I will meet you guys at my place in, say, half an hour?" Gary tosses over his shoulder, headed for the employee exit.

Half an hour later, it's still storming out. I grab my coat from the break room and say out loud, "I don't think I'm going to take my bike."

"Hells bells, Eddie Dee, let's just hoof it over there. It's not that far, a little less than a quarter of a mile," John says, putting on his coat. We head for the employee exit, not really knowing what Mother Nature has in store for us. Sure, we know it's windy outside, but the elements can be deceptive. We try the employee door but it's momentarily being held shut by the powerful mixture of wind and rain. Using our combined strength, one forceful push swings the door open, and John and I slowly fight our way along the sidewalk through the pressure of the strong, wind-driven rain, which is coming down in sheets. We make our way toward Gary's, heads down and walking slightly hunched over the whole time until we finally arrive at a complex of really broken down powder-blue cottages, which look similar in construction to the Flying Dutchman place where Sherri and I first stayed when we moved to Seaside. We make it through the screen door onto the patio, which is stacked with lawn furniture turned upside-down. We ring the bell, and as far as we're concerned, Gary can't answer the door fast enough. John and I are so soaked, we're dripping.

"Well, come on in, you guys. You look a little wet!" Gary says sarcastically. We step into Gary's small, clean, and tidy hippy haven apartment; there's the usual black shag furniture in the living room, but the walls are covered with shelves full of music CDs. Another man comes out of the bathroom while Gary goes into the kitchen to kidnap some beer. "My name is Bob Redding," he says, politely cool. He's six feet tall, black hair, wearing a T-shirt and jeans, and is as skinny as yours truly. Gary walks in with beers for us and introduces us to his roommate.

"My name is Eddie Dee Williams. Nice to meet you. I say my name like that so you won't get me confused with this other chocolate guy named Joe," I explain. "Some folks can't tell us apart because they think we look alike, even though I have not met him yet," I add.

"My name is John," John introduces himself as Bob shakes his extended his hand.

"Eddie, you are from Portland?" Bob asks me as John and I sit down on the groovy, black blanket-covered couch. Bob and Gary sit on the floor after passing the bottles of beer around.

"Yes, I am from Portland," I reply. "I got tired of the city. I met my lady, Sherri, who was raised here, and I always wanted to live at the beach. So, here I am." I can't help but notice all the CDs in Gary's huge collection.

"Hey, Gary, you have got quite the excellent CD collection, dude!" John says, sipping his beer and taking a chew of tobacco.

"Eddie, you love music. I know because I always hear you singing at work. What would you like to hear that you think I don't have?" Gary asks me, standing to his feet.

"How about some Parliament Funkadelic or Bootsy Collins?" I request honestly, with no real expectation that Gary possesses The Funk. I soon discover that being sucked into believing stereotypes cuts both ways.

"Ah, yes. I got it right here," Gary says. "You *are* a Funkateer, aren't you, Eddie?" he asks, and I nod my head yes. Then he tells me that he has exactly what I want to hear. He scans the shelves of CDs on the right-hand wall, scrolls down, picks one out, walks over to the CD player, slides it into the slot, puts the machine on track select, and then pushes a button. Out of the wall-mounted speakers comes Parliament's "Get Up for the Down Stroke." *Get up for the down stroke, everybody get up, everybody get up, everybody get up, everybody get up—* jamming out The Funk and bringing back fond memories.

"If you like funk, then you just might like this, Eddie," Gary says over his shoulder as he walks out of the living room. I hear him shuffling in the bedroom, searching for an unknown. He finally comes out with this Rastafarian-style crocheted hat in his hand that's made from yarn the colors of the Ethiopian flag—forest-green, mustard-yellow, and burnt-orange. "You can have it if you want it, Eddie. It's yours. Nobody else will wear it," he declares as he hands it to me. And here I thought he was going to hand me the eight-inch, green-colored bong he had in his other hand. Oh well. I inspect the hat just to make sure it doesn't have lice crawling all over it, then put it on my head.

It actually makes a good hat, considering the weather we are having today.

"Hey, Eddie, are you the one to talk to about a job as a dishwasher or janitor?" Bob asks straightforwardly.

"Yes, I am. Why don't you come up to the Shilo Inn and fill out an application?" I answer, while adjusting the hat to fit my head tightly.

"Are you doing any hiring right now?" he probes.

"No, my friend. Not right now," I say, then finish my beer. "But that does not mean I won't be hiring. All kinds of things happen; you just never know. That's why you still ought to put in your application."

"He's right, Bob," John says. "Weird people just up and quit for all kinds of reasons in this sand hole of a city."

"You want another beer there, you guys?" Gary belches, as he takes the empty bottles with him to the kitchen.

"Sure, I will have another one, Gary," I say casually, as Bob hands me the bong and a lighter.

"Make that two beers," John says, then guzzles the last of his, lets out this atomic belch, and I reply by coughing out a cloud of cannabis smoke.

The four of us hang out until it gets gloomy late, then John and I decide to head back to the Shilo so I can retrieve my transportation. The storm has finally abated somewhat when I pick up my bike and John and I go our separate ways when we reach Holiday Avenue, since his house is in the opposite direction. I'm pedaling away just a few yards after crossing Highway 101 to the trailer park when the carnival lights of the Seaside Police Department's finest patrol car flash behind me. I dismount onto the sidewalk right in front of the Pine Cove Motel, far to the rear of which, is the trailer park. I put the bike on its kickstand just as the cop in the parked, idling patrol car hits me with his spotlight, blinding me like I'm number one in America's Top Ten Most Wanted fugitives being sought for triple capital crime. The slightly sprinkling weather is no deterrent to the Seaside Police Officer—clad from head to toe in rain gear, complete with elastic-banded clear plastic Smokey the Bear hat protector—emerging from his patrol car to commence the interrogation, which triggers another windblown cloudburst guaranteed to make this next unnecessary line of selective law enforcement treatment that much more enjoyable.

"Where exactly are you headed tonight?" the six foot tall, imperious officer asks commandingly from-the-hip, checking out the bike, then the multicolored Rasta hat on my dry, covered head.

"I am going home," I reply, waiting patiently for the continuation of this latest, numberless upheaval.

"And where is home?" he commands steadfastly.

"I reside at the Pine Cove Trailer Park. My name is Eddie Dee Williams. I own my own trailer, space twenty-nine," I recite in a low monotone.

"Let me see some identification. You know the drill!" he demands, aiming his black, multipurpose cop flashlight down at me from hat brim height. I turtle-slowly reach for my wallet while simultaneously attempting to dodge the rain, even though my face is already dripping wet. I don't make any sudden, unusual moves which would cause this "officer of the law" to violently shoot me dead, just because he can. I slowly and carefully hand him my identification somewhat nervously, somewhat petrified. "So. You live here in Seaside. Where do you work at?" Mr. Medium-build Police Officer insists as the rain continues pouring down, obscuring my twenty-twenty vision.

"Shilo Inn on the Promenade," I mutter, drained from being racially harassed for the umpteenth time.

"Really. Is that so?" he says. "Yeah, right," he whispers. "What exactly do you do there, Mr. Williams?" he requests, standing close in front of me as cars zip past north and south along Highway 101.

"I am the kitchen steward in the restaurant," I inform him.

"What is that?" he asks, staring closer at me and looking somewhat dismayed.

"I am the supervisor of the dishwashers and janitors," I answer politely, obviously steaming in my intellect, clothes completely saturated, waiting impatiently to be legally dismissed.

"You have any warrants, drugs, or weapons on your person, Mr. Williams?" he continues, regardless.

"No, I do not, officer," I reply, not looking him in the face, grateful I have this warm, insulated hat on my head, though.

"Don't lie to me, Mr. Williams!" he warns me, looking me dead in the eyes.

"I don't have any of the above, Mr. Officer," I reply, returning his gaze.

"All right, Mr. Williams. We'll see. You stand right there and don't you move!" he orders, then walks back to his patrol car. About five—but more in the direction of ten minutes pass as I stand there, watching the colored flags on top of the gray Pizza Palace directly across Highway 101 whizzing like kites in the wind. By the time the fully weatherproofed officer finally emerges from his patrol car and saunters casually back to me, I am completely drenched.

"Okay, Mr. Williams. The reason why I pulled you over is because I noticed you have no lights or signaling devices on your bike," the officer alleges, clearly still not satisfied. "So, why don't you put your hands on your head, turn around, and allow me to frisk your person for drugs and weapons? Once that is complete, you are free to go, Mr. Williams."

Without a murmur, I respectfully place my hands on top of my head, interlock my fingers, and turn around real, extra slowly, like a captured absconding slave who doesn't have the right to even breathe. This bigoted Seaside Police Officer of the secret congregation begins to pat me down, searching for whatever illegal article he can come up with so he can arrest me. He finally stops pressing, patting, and probing because he can't find anything. "Well, you are clean. This time," he mentions stereotypically, and seemingly a little disappointed. Then, from way out of the superior supremacist countryside blue, he has the following instructions for me. "Mr. Williams, this is what I want you to do," he says as I turn around slowly to face him—very attentive, wet, yet psychologically and emotionally worn out. "Look-a here," pointing his index finger in my chocolate face. "My sister has a son who needs a job. I want you to hire him!" he commands me, like I were his very own bought-and-paid-for personal property. This privileged "request" is so mind-blowing, I can't actually believe he said that shit to me! I take a short, mental time-out to answer him, just to make certain it wasn't the cannabis causing me to hallucinate.

"No, I am not hiring at this particular point in time. However, he can fill out an application at the front desk of the Shilo Inn Restaurant," I manage to gurgle out.

"Well, Mr. Williams, you are free to go. And have a nice evening. Take care!" Mr. Seaside Police Officer says over his shoulder, as he returns to his warm, weatherized patrol car. He makes a U-turn onto Highway 101 and heads south into the stormy night.

Standing there in the rain, foolishly glaring down at my weather-beaten bike, I light a cigarette, take a couple of puffs, wipe off the wet, black seat, and swing aboard. With a cigarette in one hand and the other on the handlebars, I cruise sorely, slowly down the raggedy gravel incline, not even bothering to dodge the potholes, which by this time are nothing but sodden dirt buckets full of mud so yellow it surpasses the motel's paint job. I reach my trailer space drenched, not caring about shit, and park the bike on its kickstand next to the warm, ghetto trailer, entertaining myself privately as I finish my cancer stick. I am no longer concerned with the precipitation as I puff modestly, slowly on my not-quite-so-wet cigarette, trying unsuccessfully to calm my anger, unable to ignore the towering, red-hot, close-to-overflowing rage that's barely pent up inside my anatomy.

Inside the trailer, Sherri picks up on the tobacco aroma and opens the blinds to see me standing outside in the rain, next to the trailer, looking like I've been anesthetized. She opens the door and steps out in her silky white nightie onto the soaked wooden steps, barefooted with her unpainted toenails, hair loose and down on her shoulders, looking apprehensive about my not having come inside. "What's wrong, Honey?" she asks caringly, spying. Silence. I have no interest in conversation. She can't possibly fathom what I am going through.

Then, finally, speaking dully as through the fog of a dozen tranquilizers, "I was pulled over by the Seaside Police Department. Once again. This time he said I didn't have turn signals or sufficient lights on this bike," I whisper, frustrated. "After that, he had the privileged, hypnotic nerve to compel me to give his nephew employment at the Shilo Inn."

"No! He did not," she responds, both hands on her hips in a state of astonishment.

"No one could make this shit up, honey," I say blankly, as I grind out my cigarette under the sole of my saturated shoe, then step inside the warm, dry ghetto trailer. Sherri gets chilled and follows, quickly stepping back into the trailer.

With all the drama going on around here, I feel that it's necessary for me to take my mind off the constant stream of ignorant local events. On the morning of August first, Sherri and I depart to go salmon fishing with her dad, leaving Jeremy over at Kelly's house. I have never been fishing in the Pacific Ocean and I'm extremely excited, even though it's just six o'clock in the morning. The local newscast says today's going to be a calm, warm, sunny mid-seventy-degree day, although colder at the coast, so we make sure to pack lots of warm gear for our day out on the water. "I am not concerned about what I am wearing," I tell Sherri. "I'm going to catch a gigantic fish, so I don't want any hard feelings afterwards."

"So, you think you're going to catch something, baby?" she asks as she's getting dressed.

"Think? Honey, remember I said this: I will not only catch the biggest fish, but the very first fish! I have a good feeling about this!" I announce, putting on my thick coat, doing a quick two-step. Then dawn breaks wide open and we are blessed with a beautiful sunny day. Ron pulls up to a stop in his late model, clay-brown Chevy truck with a gray, thirty-two-foot boat on a trailer hitched to it. He gets out, smoking a cigarette, and checks the boat and trailer out to make sure everything is still in order.

"Honey, your dad is here!" I yell to her inside the trailer. "Let's go, sweetheart!" I say, excited. I grab the bag of food for the trip and open the trailer door wide. "Well, good morning, Ron! Isn't this a nice day for me to catch the big one?" I ask, standing on the steps, looking up at the sky, smiling from ear to ear.

"Well, good morning, Eddie. I don't quite know, but it looks like it's going to be a good day to try!" Ron replies, smiling. Sherri comes out with another bag, looking quite comfortable in jeans and sneakers. "We have to stop in Hammond to get our fishing licenses and bait, first," Ron says. "So, Eddie, this is your first time ever fishing in the Pacific Ocean?" Ron asks, as we're driving down 101 Northbound.

"Yes, this is the first time I've ever fished in any ocean," I say jokingly, but true.

"Do you know exactly what you are doing when we get out there?" Ron asks curiously.

"No, I don't," I say quickly, "which is why I believe I am going to catch that big fish I mentioned earlier!"

"So, you believe in beginner's luck?" Ron questions me teasingly.

"Nope. Actually, I just believe in being in the right place at the right time, which I refer to as right on schedule," I add excitedly.

"Sherri, he just might catch the big one. The way he's all hyped up, he's probably got a rabbit's foot in his pocket!" Ron says, winking as he pulls into the bait shop parking lot. A short while later, we arrive at Retirement Beach, and it looks just like a postcard—tranquil, sandy, and blue-skied. I am truly blessed to witness this natural beauty. Ron wheels around forward, puts his rig in reverse, backs the tailored boat into the water, and stops. Sherri and I exit the truck and walk alongside the boat, guiding it off the trailer as it slides out into the water, leaving the anchor ashore so the boat doesn't drift away. Ron, ramrodding the operation, grabs the anchor and throws it in the water so Sherri and I can get in and start getting our sea legs. Then Ron parks the truck, gets aboard and retrieves the anchor, stowing it out of the way. We start drifting out into deeper water, farther and farther into the river as the view of the beach is getting smaller.

"Oh, Eddie? Can you swim, by any chance?" Ron asks, smiling as he starts the boat's motor.

"Yes, I can swim very well. My father once worked at the YMCA, and my siblings and I had swimming lessons," I reply. Farther out in the water, we see around two-and-a-half dozen other fishing boats as Ron slows the boat down to a quiet slide as we enter the mouth of the Columbia River, heading for the Pacific Ocean. "What's the story on that huge ship over there?" I ask Ron curiously.

"That is a charter boat that you pay to fish off. They provide the poles and bait, and they usually catch fish," Ron says, "but that's not always the case."

After about an hour or so, that humongous charter boat is getting somewhat closer. It's about seventy-five yards away when I cast my line right in front of it. About that same time, a six foot, heavy-set man on the charter boat with a fishing pole is reeling in what appears to be a huge Chinook Salmon. However, halfway up the side to the weather deck of the charter boat, the over-twenty-pound salmon falls down into the blue Pacific Ocean, hitting the baited hooks on my line and quickly sinking. Suddenly, the line is spinning at high-speed out of my reel, causing my pole to bend almost completely double, almost snatching me out of the rocking boat and into the sun-sparkled salt water. The crowd of people on the charter boat are yelling obscenities, heckling me.

"Don't you pay them people any mind, reel that damn fish in, Eddie!" Ron commands loudly, as the rest of the small-boat fishermen around us are rooting loudly for me. I reel the nice-sized fish up to the boat while Sherri gets the net under the fish, which is not going to be giving up quietly. Once we have him on board, I quickly drop my rod and grab the fish in a headlock, when Sherri tells me to use the heavy, wooden club behind me. Holding the fish down with my knees, I smack the salmon in the head seven times, until I successfully knock him unconscious. At this point, I can still hear the distraught man on the charter boat continuing to whine, cursing loudly about the fish he could not keep on his line.

"I told you I would be the first to catch a fish, didn't I?", I brag to Sherri, as well as Ron. "Didn't I tell you? I told you I would catch a big fish!"

After a couple more hours, we decide to call it a day, but I have no complaints, since I caught a large Chinook Salmon and spent some quality time with my lady and her father. I shall never forget my day on the Pacific Ocean for the rest of my life.

Days later, I'm cruising home on my bike after a good shift at work, daydreaming about a cold beer and watching this new television show, *In Living Color*, that I recorded on the VCR. I pedal across 101 into the trailer park, down the gravel to the second right, into my yard, and behold! We no longer have all the comforts of a playground-sized lot! What we now have are new next-door neighbors; a green-and-white, single very-wide trailer, already hooked up with water and electricity. I park my bike by the wooden steps and enter our somewhat decent trailer, which doesn't have a whole lot of furniture. We do, however, have company: a long-haired blonde, slender female around Sherri's age, wearing blue jeans, a white blouse, and big round prescription eyeglasses.

"Honey? Good news!" Sherri says, walking toward me, her brown hair combed sexy, in jeans and a gray sweatshirt that says *Seaside* in large, faded blue letters. Sherri graciously introduces me to our new, non-ignorant neighbor as she rises up from the couch. "This is Dinah. We grew up together here in Seaside, honey."

"Hi, Eddie, nice to meet you," Dinah says, then sits back down on the couch. "And this is my Daughter, Katie, and my son, Robbie," Dinah says proudly.

The second we realize we are both Libras and our birthdays are at the end of this month, we instantaneously got along famously.

13

. . . .

Thoroughfare to Nowhere

Roughly a month afterward, it's Thanksgiving Day and it is difficult to digest the enormously bright star in the sky at this time of year, absent the normally anticipated two-toned, gray clouds. Business is booming today, which makes the daylight fly by fast. Marty Nelson, John Trent, and I decide to head over to Dave and Melinda's house after our shift for some happy hour cocktails. We amble out through the double glass doors of the main entrance to the Shilo Inn, heading down Ocean Way when John Trent announces, "Oh my stars! Marty missed it."

"What did I miss, John?" I ask, curiously nosy.

"There was this bleach-blonde brick house in the lounge. Five foot nine, white silk mini see-through dress, no freaking underwear, and a shaved camel toe!" John says, giggling, bragging.

"I told you I saw her in the bar, you dummy," Marty replies, glaring into John's mug as we walk along.

Unexpectedly and unnoticed, that damn perverse canary-yellow Chevy Nova bulldozing road demon bigot appears out of nowhere on Ocean Way, just short of the Beach Club's gravel parking lot, accelerating at high-speed, heading right for us. The bully speed demon maliciously continues to floor it, speeding up to batter me, causing my heart to pump blood so furiously it sounds like thunder in my ears. Someone yells out of the driver's side of the racing yellow Nova, "You're a dead nigger!" Even with my reflexes caught somewhat unprepared for this situation, I instinctively dart to the left side of the car, dodging the vehicular weapon, desperately trying to get a first-class look at this racist who's trying to put the fear of death in me, but they're just going too damn fast to identify.

Marty and John Trent jackrabbit to the right side of Ocean Way, getting successfully out of harm's way. "You nigger lovers!" the psychotic driver yells at the top of his lungs as he speeds away, discharging a hefty cloud of funky, gray exhaust.

"Are you guys all right?" I ask, concerned for both of them.

"Eddie, I will, by no means, ever again doubt nothing you say for the entire rest of my life," Marty promises as he slowly straightens up, gasping for breath, trembling hard.

"Who the hell was that?" John asks, flabbergasted, as he unbends as well.

"You *are* asking Marty, right, John?" I ask sarcastically, annoyed.

"Well, no one in particular, Eddie Dee," John says, still a little shaken as he pulls a smoke out of his pocket. We walk slowly up the street, meandering to the front of the Beach Club where Troy's '55 mustard-yellow short-bed GMC truck is parked.

"Both you guys were born here, and you don't have any idea who the hell that was?" I ask, walking unhurriedly alongside them, my hands balled up into fists, still shaken and pissed off at the same time.

"They were going so damn freaking fast! Hell, you couldn't see who the hell they were!" Marty says, at the same time shaking out a cigarette from his pack, trying to calm his distressed nerves.

"Dude, I am so clueless who the hell that was, Eddie Dee," John says while rubbing his head.

"Are we still headed over to David Duke's or what?" Marty asks. We go inside the Beach Club, pick up a case of beer, and then make our way over to David and soon to be Melinda Duke's house.

Two weeks later, knowing I'm stressed out and needing a breather, Sherri, being sympathetic to my unexpected run-ins, sets me up with transportation to Portland on a mail truck, given that the Cordoba is malfunctioning somewhat.

It's a very chilly Friday. The mail truck winds its way to Astoria, then heads for Portland by way of Highway 30. Mike, who's driving the mail truck, lives by himself across from us in the trailer park. He's five eleven, slender and sandy-haired; a nice guy, a veteran like me, and his favorite football team just happens to be the Dallas Cowboys. I'm riding shotgun and I've brought along my prized vacuum-packed frozen Chinook Salmon roll as he loads up cargo at different stops. We discuss different topics all the way up to North Portland where my loving parents live.

"Thank you very much, Mike. This really helps me out a lot," I declare genuinely.

"You're welcome, Eddie," he replies. "If you need a ride back to Seaside, just be in the back of the post office Sunday afternoon at two o'clock." He turns the truck around and takes off toward the main post office downtown. I walk up the steps to front door of the house I grew up in, and before I can even knock my mother, wearing tan slacks and an apron over her white blouse, is opening the door.

"There's my son," she says, smiling and giving me an affectionate hug. It's good to be seen.

"Hello, Mother. This is the fish I caught," I say playfully, as I attempt to hand it to her like a trophy. However, it's quite heavy.

"What kind of fish do you catch, son?" she asks.

"It's a 23-pound Chinook Salmon. I caught it on the first day of the season," I reply, closing the door."

"Yeah, right. You caught that fish?" my slender, five-foot-seven, Hershey's chocolate sister Denise—who we call Nuffy—says as she comes out the bedroom dressed like a model in a black dress. Right on her heels is my fourteen-year-old sister, Nicole. "You need to come to Hollywood instead of trying to catch fish over there in KKK-crazy land!" Nuffy says.

"You just mad your man can't catch the great trawl in the Pacific Ocean," I brag jokingly, "'Sides, Hollywood is not ready for Eddie Dee Williams yet, sis." I remind her of my ultimate plan.

I happily toddle down the hallway to put my trophy salmon in the deep freezer, set down my luggage, take off my long coat, and deposit my things in the TV room next door to the bathroom. I can clearly hear Pops approaching from the kitchen. "Hey, look what the KKK blew in from the Pacific Coast!" Popeye rants, grinning, sitting down at the table, setting down a paper bag with an unopened brown bottle of liquor in front of him.

"Hey, son, give me some love, now. Unless you are too good to give your old stepdad a hug," Pops says, as he relaxes in his army fatigue shirt and brown corduroy pants. He sets his keys on the dining table as well as I walk casually over and give him a hug and a handshake. "Now that's what I am talking about," Pops says, tearful.

I foot it over to the stereo, turn on some music, then turn back to the table, lean across to Bub—and shake his hand. I can tell he's inebriated because he has his hands held closely together like he's praying. At least he's not crying yet. However, it's early and the night is young. Just you wait. "Good to see you again! Alive," we express to each other simultaneously, as "Southern Girl" by Maze flows out of the stereo speakers.

"What's going on there, Eddie? You all right up there in Whitey-Land Seaside?" Popeye asks, grinning jokingly.

"Yes, I am all right, Popeye," I reply honestly, unemotionally.

"Well, then, tell me just one thing, Eddie," Popeye says as he goes, drink in hand, to take a seat on the couch, and pauses for another second. "How's your head? Is your head okay?" Popeye busts out laughing.

"Nuffy, what's wrong with your brother?" Bub asks, laughing as Nuffy scurries up on us.

"My brother has this thing for crazy-ass, psychotic women," Nuffy announces, thereby making it official, as she stands next to me.

"I am not paying my younger sister no mind at all," I say, merrily gesturing her into invisibility with a simple wave of my hand. "Pops, I need to stock up on Shamelah and Deon's impressive gifts for Christmas. You think I could utilize the truck?" I ask.

"Yeah, sure, do what you got to do, son. See about your kids. One day, they will see about you," Pops says. With a shot glass in his other hand, he uses the empty one to hand me his ring of keys off the table. "I am just glad to have you home, and that you are all right," Pops says genuinely.

It's good to be home, I think as I look at my beautiful, close-knit family. Then, there's a knock at the front door, so I walk over and open it, and it's my Aunt Marie and Uncle Walt. "Hey, boy! When did you get here?" Uncle Walt asks cheerfully as they step into the warm house.

"Not very long ago," I reply as I close the front door, hugging and kissing my Aunt Marie, then helping them out of their long, woolen coats.

"How are you doing down there, Nephew? Really," Uncle Walt asks me. "Lie to me. Tell Mama the truth."

Pops finally turns on some good music, playing "Superman Lover" by Johnny "Guitar" Watson.

"I'm doing all right, Uncle Walt. Really," I say, reassuring him.

"You know how some crazy-ass white folks can be, don't you, Nephew?" he asks me.

"Yes, Uncle, I know how SOME Caucasians can be," I reply strategically.

Then, there's a knock at the back door. "Somebody open the door for Slim!" Pops says, while looking for another record. When no one volunteers, he tells my little sister Nicole, who he calls Mama, to get the door for Slim. My mother follows instinctively. "How are you doing, Miss Georgia?" Slim asks politely, entering the kitchen door.

"Oh, I'm doing all right, Slim. How are you?" Mom inquires.

"I'm thirsty, Miss Georgia," Slim says fashionably. She hands him a glass with ice in it. I'm pretty sure he knows what to fill it with as there's quite an assortment of alcohol on the counter. "Eddie, how do you do it? Live way out there at the beach?" Slim asks, walking elderly-slow into the living room, shaking his head for all to see.

"It's because these kids weren't raised in the South," Popeye says tactfully. "These offspring that were raised up here for a few generations are not scared to live in an all-white, racist-ass town."

"Eddie, is you the only black person that lives down there?" Slim asks worriedly, while Pops pours a shot of whiskey into his glass.

"No, I am not the only chocolate one, Slim," I volunteer, smiling as I face him.

"Yes, but you are the only black one working at the Beachfront Shilo Inn in a supervisory job," my mother diplomatically interjects her objection.

"Nephew, what your mother is trying to tell you is that you are just doing too much in Seaside, Oregon!" Aunt Marie says, somewhat fearfully.

"You're a supervisor. You're with a *white* woman. And, you *own* a trailer!" Uncle Walt enumerates, astounded. "None of that is going to sit well with some of them ignorant-ass white people, young man. You remember that, Nephew."

"Just be careful. That's all we are saying to you. Just be careful," Pops says, rising to his feet.

"How many times have the police harassed you there in Seaside, Eddie?" Bub asks, sitting at the dining table across from old man Slim.

"Close to a dozen incidents. They have been at my trailer park I would say at least ten times because of the so-called racist Christian neighbors on my right side, who don't believe in interracial relationships," I confess gingerly. "However, since my new neighbors Dinah and Bob moved into the trailer space on the other side of me, they are getting all of the police visits and complaints now."

"But you are still being harassed, aren't you, Eddie?" my mom asks vigorously.

"Yes, Mother. Okay, let's change the subject," I say, cheerfully hospitable.

"Aren't you going to see your kids?" my mother asks after venting her court case.

"Why, yes I am."

It's the perfect time to leave. I stride across the manicured lawn toward the black-and-white truck with the matching canopy that's parked on the side of the street. I start it up and allow the hibernated engine to warm itself, well-aware that defrosting the windows may just take a little while. I light up a cigarette and grudgingly wait for the motor. Once I'm finally on the road, it takes no time at all before I'm approaching the Janzen Beach Mall on I-5, just yards away from the Evergreen State of Washington. I make a stop at Toys "R" Us, then head over to Angela's house, my ex, to see my Nubian princess daughter, Shamelah. Angela and I were together for the first eight years after my military service ended. I visit for a short while with my daughter, who is nine next months, and make my way to Lisa's house—which is only five minutes away—to see my son, Deon.

Lisa tells me little Eddie moved to San Diego with his cousin David, who is in the military and stationed there. My kids really can't wait to visit the sandy beach. Shamelah and Deon, who are a year apart in age and look practically identical, make me promise to bring them to the beach this summer. However, I am going to surprise them by "kidnapping" them for the entire week of Spring Break. I truly can't wait for them to come down and visit; I've missed them and I love them so very much.

A whole December has gone by. It's New Year's Eve week on the Oregon coast, and time for the official whale watching season. I arrive to work my shift at the Shilo and am looking forward to getting off early enough to celebrate with my newlywed neighbors. I stride through the employee door in an excellent mood, ready to punch the time clock for the last time this year. I see the cooks manufacturing food for the early-hours breakfast rush. "What is going on, Spin, my brother?" I ask, tasting the toothpaste that replaced the nicotine in my mouth a short while ago.

"Well, Ed, my brother, I am feeling pretty hung, dude. My hog is hanging low today, primarily to the left," Spin replies proudly, giggling.

"Say, Spin, do you have time to fix my favorite breakfast, please?" I ask, swiftly animated.

"You mean your pancake with an over easy egg on top?" he asks.

"Yes, that one, kind sir. Please," I add, as I head to the employee break room.

"Not a problem, my friend. I will get that right up for you, Eddie Dee," he replies.

I make my way over to the waitress' station to make myself a cup of coffee before I head to the break room. I drop three authentic sugars in my coffee and stir in some cream; it's my usual routine. Then I head for the break room, only to find profoundly attractive Janelle, five foot nine, trim framework, long dishwater-blonde spiral perm, wearing a white blouse and short, blue jean skirt, plus a lovely smile, sitting at a table smoking a cigarette and drinking a cup of coffee. "Hi, Eddie," she says as she stubs out her cigarette, and gets up to go back to work.

"Good morning, Janelle. How's my pal doing today?" I ask as she passes by me.

"Fine, Eddie," she says, leaving the break room.

I sit down in one of the metal chairs, and as I wait patiently for my breakfast, I examine the Daily Astorian, searching for an automobile since I will be receiving my right-to-drive reinstatement shortly. Just as I start hearing my stomach rumble, Spin strolls into the break room with my usual, exceptional breakfast. "Hey, Eddie Dee, are you are going to Dave and Melinda's wedding reception?" Spin asks, lighting up a cigarette.

"That depends on when I get out of here," I reply, in the middle of my search for the bottle of buttermilk syrup.

"Well, I am not going to the wedding," he broadcasts, while blowing smoke rings into the air.

"Why is that, Bro?" I ask, as I surgically slice up my pancakes with knife and fork.

"Because, Brother Ed, weddings suck! That is just a freaking fact of life," Spin smirks, one hand against the tan-colored wall. "Damn, dude, I thought we were going to party down, brother, and bring in the New Year together!"

"Whenever I get out of here, my Brother Spin, is all I can say right now, Holmes," I reply, jigsaw puzzled. "Dennis mentioned that the whole time he has worked here, somebody always calls in sick on New Year's Eve. So, I might have to stick around tonight," I add.

"Hey, Ed, I got a couple of orders to start. I will talk to you later, bro," he announces, them walks back to the kitchen line to sterilize his hands before he returns to work.

Just then the break room phone rings, which is a rarity. I hurriedly reach over my breakfast to answer the outdated black rotary phone on the long metal table. "Good morning, Shilo Inn, Eddie Dee Williams speaking. How I may direct your call?" I respond professionally.

"Eddie?" a raspy, accented voice says.

"Yes, this is Eddie," I reply, having some difficulty identifying who exactly it is on the other end of this touchtone phone message line.

"Eddie, this Julio. I cannot work today because I am sick," he says very faintly into the phone.

"Okay, Julio, thanks for calling me. Take care. Bye," I whisper, polite but still irritated. I have misplaced my appetite. I shove the plate of food away from me, and with distress being my only recourse, I light up the cigarette I fish out of my shirt pocket. Well, I shouldn't be surprised. However, I *am* thoroughly dissatisfied. Plus, I know Sherri is not going to be a happy beach bunny kind-of-camper and, if truth be told, I one thousand percent don't want to hear her mouth, regardless of the situation.

Spin returns to the deafening silence of the break room, gets a look at my face and asks, "What's wrong, Ed? Did you get the dreaded call already, dude?" then he rescues a butt from the ashtray, straightens it out, and lights up.

"Right on damn schedule, just like Dennis predicted! Every year, it never fails!" I blurt out, staring sadly at the tan wall.

"Well, dude, tonight's going to suck big time if you are not there, brother Ed," Spin says, as he puts out his cigarette and leaves the break room.

"Do not worry, and have no fear, we are going to party like it's a brand New Year!" I call out after him, not really believing I'm going to be off work in time. I butt out my own cigarette in the ashtray just as Sherri enters the break room. I can tell by the way she comes in she's quite excited.

"I am getting off early, maybe early enough for me to go to the wedding!" she says, all happy-faced.

"That's nice," I reply in a crumbly monotone.

"Honey, what is wrong?" she asks.

"Julio, my closing dishwasher, just called in sick and I cannot leave until I find a replacement!" I confess, agitated.

"But you don't have to stay here tonight," Sherri says politely, as she sits down next to me, dressed in her full waitress uniform.

"You don't know that. I am responsible for the night *and* day shift dishwashers, remember," I say matter-of-factly.

"Yes, I remember," she says, holding my hand to her face. "But, baby, that also means you can delegate authority and call somebody else in." Then she takes my hand and using it to caress her stocking-clad thigh. She is not taking no for an answer. And, while Sherri has a good point, I still don't see myself getting off early enough to celebrate the New Year with her or anybody else.

"Okay, sweetheart, I will see you later," I say, then present her with a goodbye kiss. Sherri lightly kisses me back, gets up hurriedly, and returns to her work station.

I make a checklist of everything that needs to be done, both upstairs and down, before I can even think about escaping from this establishment. Then I head to the chef's office where I see the door is slightly ajar, as Dennis has just arrived in his bright white uniform.

"You were so right, Dennis!" I proclaim as I slide into his dirt-free office. "Someone called in already," I tell him, as he's standing there behind his desk, knowingly nodding his head. Even he seems a little surprised that it happened so early.

"You have to be here or get someone else to cover for you, Eddie," he tells me.

"I have no problem with that. It is part of my responsibility as kitchen steward," I reply sociably.

"Well, at least it won't be that busy tonight," he adds, in an effort to somehow lessen the blow. I leave the office relieved and go up to the front of the kitchen where the waitress' station is and have a word with Sherri.

"Hey, what time do you get off, baby?" she asks as she writes up an order ticket.

"Dennis says I should be able to leave if I find a replacement for the dinner shift," I say.

"And if you don't find someone? Then what, honey?" she asks, with an undisguised look of displeasure on her face, "Baby, I don't want to be the only woman there without her man on the last day of the year *and* the first day of the year, especially at a wedding reception!" she confesses, with a melodramatic face right off the cover of *Vogue*.

"Okay, honey! Just stop it, please? I will find somebody! All right, Sherri Lynn?" I toss off in a convincingly authoritative tone over my shoulder, as I blissfully head out for the numerous work stations that are calling my name.

My plan of action is to go back to Dennis's office and get the phone numbers of all the dishwashers. Then I hustle back to the break room and start dialing. First, I call my most excellent dishwasher, Benjamin. The phone rings continuously, and just when I get ready to hang up, a man answers clearly, "Hello?"

"This is Eddie at the Shilo Inn. Who am I speaking to, please?" I ask politely.

"It's Benjamin, Eddie. What's up my, brother?" he asks, upbeat.

"I need somebody to work for me tonight. Do you know anybody who wants to work?" I ask, not really expecting Benjamin to work tonight.

"I cannot do it, Eddie, because I have to work at my other job tonight," Benjamin says, "but I will find you somebody, Eddie. You always look out for us Mexicans, so I will look out for you."

"Well, thank you, Benjamin. I will talk to you soon," I tell him, not mentioning the fact that I'm scarcely hopeful that he'll come through.

"I will find somebody for you, Eddie. Later, man," he says, then hangs up the phone.

Sherri strolls into the break room, sits down to finalize her books, punches out like she wanted, and looks at me. "I am finished with work, sweetheart. What time are you done?" she asks critically, badgering me for an unambiguous answer.

"I don't know yet, honey. Benjamin is looking for somebody to work as a big favor to me," I tell her reassuringly, hoping Sherri will remain contentedly mellowed out.

"Janelle is going to drive me home so I can change. Furthermore, we are going to Janelle's house, and then over to Dave and Melinda's. So call over there and somebody will come and get you, baby," she says, while untying and removing her murky blue apron.

Then Marty walks into the break room, bragging. "I am done! How about you, Eddie?" he asks, excitedly motivated. "Is your chocolate ass ready to party?"

Sherri, slightly upset, unfolds her arms, abruptly rises, and says "Goodbye," as she exits the break room.

"I can't leave yet. Julio called in sick, so I can't leave until I find a replacement," I tell him.

Spin sticks his head around the break room doorway. "Hey, bro, I am out of here. I will catch you guys later at the reception," he says as he and Marty head out the employee exit door.

Hours later, Marty returns in jeans, flannel shirt, and cowboy hat to retrieve his cousin John, then on to the reception. "What the hell does your chocolate ass mean, you can't go until you find a replacement for Julio?" Marty bellows, thunderstruck. "That's some bullshit! It's New Year's Eve! Aren't *you* in charge?"

"Yes, Marty. That's why I have to stay. It's my responsibility, bro," I say as evenly as I can.

"Well, it certainly sucks to be you, right about now!" John Trent throws in, hilariously sarcastic.

"Well, John and I are going to head over to Dave and Melinda's and get started on the keg. So you bring your chocolate ass as pronto as possible!" Marty commands as he takes the last drag on his cigarette.

"Like you guys are really going to drink up two kegs by yourself," I announce smoothly, standing rapidly to my feet.

"Two kegs? Eddie, are you serious?" John asks, eyes very wide open.

"I am as serious as octopus's shit!" I state, and we all three start laughing collectively.

"Well, we'll see you there my good friend, so hurry the damn hell up, Eddie Dee!" John announces loudly as he walks out the employee exit door. The Shilo Inn's day shift employees are all vanished, and I am left with the evening skeleton crew: three line cooks, the dinner chef, Joe, four waitresses, one dishwasher, and me.

The hours pass by turtle-slow and I still haven't received a return call from Benjamin. I have definitely missed the wedding by this time, and it appears I may fail to make the reception, as well. As we all prepare for the dinner rush, I am thinking, *I ought to have been out of here by now!* I am vaguely frustrated in my attempts to somehow find an upside to this atypical situation. I hear the Shilo room service house phone ringing clearly, but I don't want to have to listen to Sherri's verbal volcanic eruption, so I don't bother answering it. Instead, I reposition the two empty trash cans so they flank the waitress' station. Sally, the joyful bar maid, gives me a look filled with all seriousness as she holds out the phone's receiver in my direction. I just signal by shaking my head no.

"It's not Sherri, it's Jesus, silly!" she says, smirking, and hands me the phone diligently.

"Hello, this is Eddie speaking. How may I help you?" I ask hopefully.

"This is Jesus. I want to work tonight," the voice on the other end says in broken English.

"Who is this?" I ask, because I can hardly comprehend him.

"Yes. It is Jesus. And I need to work, yes?" he says repeatedly.

"Well, yes. Come right on in, amigo! Right now would be good, mucho gracias!" I say as calmly as I can, trying desperately to not let him hear me doing my own little dance of victory while I'm still on the phone, although I can't help it. "Yes! I am out of here!" I yell loudly, celebrating after I hang up the phone and terminate my call with my miraculously wonderful dishwasher, Jesus. I immediately call over to Melinda and Dave's house to let Sherri know I am coming after all. "Hello, Melinda? This is Eddie. Congratulations! And I'm sorry I was not there for the wedding," I say apologetically to her.

"We know you had to work, but we will have somebody come and get you. Okay, sweets?" Melinda says joyously.

After I hang up the phone, I do a little reprise of my victory dance. *No more labor this year*, I say to myself. A few minutes later the dinner chef, with his perfectly trimmed beard, walks by the break room and reaches in to grab some ceremonial dinner items. He notices me sitting there and then stops. "Eddie, are you still here? Go ahead and go! We will take care of this. We were all dishwashers and janitors once," he says, standing there in his clean white uniform, long, sandy ponytail braided down his back.

"Yes, but I'm just waiting for Jesus to get here, that's all," I answer, looking up at the break room clock.

"Go and have a happy new year!" Chef Joe orders me. "You've been here all day, right? since about eight this morning?" he reminds me. "Eddie, you go on. We will take care of this, no problem." And at that same moment, Jesus walks through the back door and it's finally time to go. I punch out on the time clock, emotionally at ease now about keeping my promise, then eagerly grab my black jacket.

Moments later, Janelle drives up to the front double doors of the Shilo Inn in a maroon Camaro. We take a speedy shortcut down the back roads behind the high school and over the highway to the Pine Cove Trailer Park. "Thanks for picking me up," I tell Janelle graciously.

"No problem. Were you busy today?" she asks, obviously comfortable driving fast.

"No, it was somewhat slow. But it's over now and time to bring in the New Year," I say, as she pulls up in front of the trailer and I run inside. It's time to party!

I quickly hop into the shower, lather up, shave, rinse, and dry off in record time. I did a good job considering I'd been at work for over ten hours today and smelled like the dish washing tank and probably unsolicited fetid compost. That's the way it goes when you're the supervisor; you're supposed to kick ass. I go to my closet in the bedroom and get out a pair of shiny gray slacks. I also grab a black shirt and a black-and-white sweater. Lastly, on the top shelf of the closet, I spot the Rasta hat that our gay friend, Gary the breakfast cook, gave me that no one else would wear. I decide to wear that as well. Once I have everything together, I set it on the bed and get dressed, then I head out the trailer door. I jump into the car with Janelle, she starts it up, and quick like a bunny, we're off to the wedding reception.

In just a matter of a minutes, we arrive at 1101 Broadway Street, a three-bedroom home on the east side of Highway 101, just opposite the beach. "Janelle, I want you to know how much I really appreciate this," I tell her, as sincerely as I know how.

"You are welcome, Eddie. I'm just glad that I can help out. That's what friends are for, right?" she says, smiling as she parks the Camaro. She's dressed in casual jeans and a sweater, and looks as gorgeous as ever. We exit the car and walk down a long narrow cement walkway to a screened-in, covered patio, the door of which is already open. I walk in through the next door to the living room and see five-foot-six, black-haired David Duke, one of the night waiters at the Shilo Inn, with his kids and his Grandmother.

"Eddie, you made it," he says casually, while holding his daughter, a beautiful blonde, blue-eyed toddler named Samantha.

"Congratulations, Dave! Sorry I couldn't make it to the wedding, but you know how that goes," I say, as I shake his free hand.

"But you are here now, brother. So, come and meet my grandmother," he says. "Grandma, this is my good friend, Eddie."

"Hello, Grandma, very nice to make your acquaintance," I say respectfully.

"Nice to meet you, Eddie," five-foot-four Grandma replies as she takes Samantha out of Dave's arms.

"Where is the bride?" I ask.

"She's in the kitchen with your lady," Dave replies, holding Samantha with both hands. I venture into the kitchen directly ahead while wondering where the rest of the gang is at. Melinda, Sherri, Janelle, and Lori are all in the kitchen, chatting.

"Congratulations, broom jumper!" I say, giving Melinda a huge, loving embrace.

"Thank you, Eddie, very much. I am so glad you made it," she replies, happily hugging me in her white blouse and jeans.

"Hi, honey! How is my favorite lady in the whole, wide world?" I ask Sherri, giving her a quick smooch. "Did I do well, or what, Snooky Nooky Poo Poo? I told you I would locate somebody to cover for me."

"Yes, you did, baby. You did very well," she replies, while putting her arms around me and I admire her white pants outfit. "What made you put *that* hat on?" Sherri asks, staring at me, flabbergasted.

"I don't know, I just thought it would be fun to wear," I answer, modestly amusing. "Well, if you'll excuse me, I'm going to catch up with the guys." I glide my skinny chocolate anatomy leisurely down the short hallway and outdoors into the ordinary garage. I begin singing my rendition of Lionel Ritchie's "All Night Long" with both my hands in the air. *Well, my friends, the time has come, to raise the roof, and have some fun. Go away, no more work to be done this year. Let the music play on.*

This six foot, dark curly-headed, stocky dude with a weird disposition looks at me alien-crazy, standing all by his antisocial lonesome personality self, downing a beer.

"Hey, brother Ed, that's Joe Nicolazzi, Lori's old man," John says, before I can even ask him.

"It's about time your chocolate ass showed up, brother!" Marty says, holding a Styrofoam cup of beer and dressed in cowboy attire as he walks up and gives me a handshake and a brisk hug. "I told you, bro. You are the hardest working brother from another mother and you should not have to work tonight!" he says, smiling and slurring his words. "And what the fuck is that on your damn head?" he shouts intoxicated at full volume.

"Gary, the breakfast cook, gave it to me to me because nobody else had balls enough to wear it. I decided, what the hell," I tell him, smiling while grabbing a Styrofoam cup and getting some beer out of the tap.

The New Year's Eve reception party is in lukewarm full-swing, the music is rocking, "Highway to Hell" by ACDC pouring loudly out of the speakers, while we all anticipate bringing in the New Year and celebrating David and Melinda Duke's recent state of matrimonial bliss. All of sudden there is a loud pounding at the door. I recall the front door being unlocked without thinking twice about it, and that it wasn't that long ago.

A big group of people that I have never seen before come walking in through the door as I am entertaining the children with my simplistic Donald Duck impression. David Duke's friends are wearing biker attire; jeans, leather vests, steel-toed boots, and long, silver wallet chains, but no colors. There are seven of them; five enormous men, and two somewhat tall women. The tallest guy with long, frizzy gray hair, who must have been close to 240 pounds or more, looks directly at me in an unbelieving sort of way as I'm entertaining the children by rescuing them from all this massive adult boredom. He seems to be the leader of this unsophisticated group. However, I could be wrong. He presents David Duke with an odd, yet mystic, wedding present: a cellophane sandwich baggy containing a considerably chunky-looking amount of an off-white powdery substance, which appears to be meth. He's also carrying an unopened half-gallon of Jack Daniels.

"This is my wedding day, man. I promised my wife that I would not do any drugs today," David tells the enormous, Goliath-looking leader of this particular clan, who's apparently afflicted with a stern, but unsure face. "Please man, I cannot do this. It's my wedding day," David pleads, his hands in a supplicating gesture.

The stern gray-haired leader is now wearing a noticeably disapproving look, almost as if he's interpreting David's response as a personal rejection of him in public, as five-foot-four-inch Grandma protectively holds onto her beautiful blonde-haired, blue-eyed granddaughter, Samantha.

After the huge jeans-attired, corn-fed gentleman's offering is turned down in deference to the wedding reception, he strides off in the direction of the house with the rest of the gang following close behind him, and I continue my Donald Duck impression for the kids. The seven newly arrived "guests" disappear through the doorway that leads to the lavatory. The New Year's Eve celebration is in the process of getting higher and higher, as the only limit is the sky. I stroll leisurely, happily down the hallway to get some more beer from the keg out in the old-school garage, where everyone is standing around, or staggering around. I chatter for about a minute or so with my beer-fueled friends John, Spin, and Marty, who are all pretty intoxicated—especially Kenny, who's wearing a Bach-brown cap and a white pullover sweatshirt, and keeps putting his arm around me drunkenly and stating laughingly how much his hog loves my sensuously full, chocolate lips. "Brother Ed, if I was gay, the hog would just love your lips!" he says, laughing ecstatically as I smoke my cigarette and laugh amusedly along with him.

"Hey, brother E! Drink up, dammit!" Marty shouts, and pulls a cigarette out of his flannel shirt pocket while brother John yells comically, almost drooling on his white T-shirt and blue jeans from the chew in his mouth, "Nice fucking hat! I didn't really think you were going to wear that multicolor Jamaican hat!" He's holding two Styrofoam cups; one for drinking, and one for catching his chew juice, which turns my susceptible gag reflex inside out.

Everyone is getting high and having a most excellent, festive time at this New Year's Eve wedding reception on the beautiful Pacific Northwest Coast. Earth minutes later, I toddle out to the living room where the kids, David Duke, and Grandma are, when the biker contingent exits the lavatory one by one. They march into the living room where David and his delightful grandmother are watching as I return to entertaining the kids, since Rayann and Samantha had requested an encore of my Donald Duck impression before I made my beer run to the garage. As "Welcome to the Jungle" by Guns N' Roses plays in the background, Mr. Enormous Biker-Person-in-Charge emerges from the bathroom, and for some known-only-to-him reason, grabs one of his male counterparts by the shirt collar and seat of his jeans, and tosses same through the combination screen-and-glass front door of the sun porch. The glass shatters bleakly into a zillion sharp little pieces in all directions, the sound of which instantly, terrifyingly startles Grandma and the young children. *That guy must have done something dreadful to piss that man off like that,* I think, which I also recognize as a possible indication that it's only going to get worse.

"Please leave. I don't want any problems on my wedding day," David Duke says to the leader, raising his hands in a peaceful gesture of "let's chill out." Then, lovely blonde, newlywed bride Melinda's voice floats into my ears, and I discern something reminiscent of a commando-style means of verbal communication. "Eddie, please come here." She immediately grabs my right hand and latches onto my arm, holding on tightly for dear life, and escorts me all the way to the kitchen, as if I am provoking danger and she is detaining me. "I would like to talk to you about something serious, Eddie," she says to me, visibly nervous. We're now in the middle of the somewhat small yellow kitchen.

"What the hell is going on?" I ask her, wondering to myself for a split-second, *Where is Sherri?*

"Eddie, I think something really bad is going to happen to you!" she announces frightfully, still holding on to me, an unhealthy, worried expression written all over her attractive, newlywed face.

"What are you talking about?" I ask her, focusing my full powers of concentration on her unexpectedly breathtaking words of caution.

"They have been calling you a nigger, Eddie, and they want to kill you!" Melinda adds, terrified, as well as cute, scary, and sad all at the same time.

"How do you know all of this, Mel?" I ask her in a friendly tone of voice, knowing she cares as deeply about me as I do her. Then, all of a sudden, I hear a loud, echoing thump, followed by another crash and

Grandma and the children alternately screaming, more glass flying through the air, the rapid trotting of women's and kids' footsteps on the wooden floor, and loud, frantic screaming. Apprehensive, frightened, and shocked, Melinda and I move over to a corner of the kitchen where we can still see into the adjoining room. While I'm waiting to hear an answer to my question, I can see my friend Kenny fighting with Mr. Enormous, getting beaten pretty well senseless, then violently choked by the bully as well. The screaming continues and Melinda is now holding onto me for dear life. "Eddie, do not get into it! They are going to kill you, Eddie!" she keeps saying as I watch her coworker Lori's fiancé, Joe Nicolazzi, who's also the best man, getting his skull and spine stomped very hard into the wooden floor by two huge, drugged and drunken biker-looking guys wearing steel-toed boots. Pretty soon, there's no movement from him whatsoever as Joe lies there, still as death. He is obviously unconscious, not far distant from death's door, lying on the floor, bruised, broken, and spattered with his own blood. Then, one of the bully bikers rotates the rings on his fingers and starts clawing and stabbing Joe's head and face at will. Joe's daughter, Rayann, is screaming insanely loud as the blood splashes up into the atmosphere as she watches the vicious assault on her powerless, lifeless father. Mr. Enormous still has his hands locked around Kenny's throat, continuing to choke him as he lifts him off the wooden floor and pins him up against the wall. Another biker is fighting with Marty like he slept with his wife, while another jerk, who looks very familiar, is thrashing John like he caught him picking his pocket. Melinda refuses to let go of me, and now we are trapped in the tiny kitchen against the sink with nowhere to go. She's holding on to me so tightly, it's like if she lets go, she's never going to see me alive again. "Eddie, sweetie, please don't get into it! Please, I'm begging you! Please!" she shrieks in my ear.

Joe and Lori's little four-year-old girl, Rayann, wearing a maroon plaid party dress, is terrified and screaming loudly, "Daddy! Daddy!"

"Hey! Watch out for the little girl!" I yell loudly, concerned for Rayann's safety.

"Eddie, please stay the hell out of it! They want to kill you!" Melinda repeats urgently. Message received! My mind instantly jumps from chill alert level status to madly flashing code red! Why I am just now finding this out?

The drugged-out, ill-bred bullies finally decide to stop thumping on everybody else and are looking straight at yours truly, while Melinda's petite anatomy continues holding onto me forcefully. "Nigger, you are next. We are going to kill you!" Mr. Enormous, bullying bigot predicts loudly as he points his index finger, which wears a knife ring on it, at me. Amped up on crank and soaring high, plus drunk from straight Jack Daniel's, he's now ready to commit a premeditated, aggravated, racist hate crime of a murder. He reaches behind his back, pulls out an enormous hunting knife, and starts toward me, moving in for the lynch mob-minded butchery of my anatomy. The piercing code red alarm bell call to battle stations explodes instinctively in my head. It's official! This punk-ass racist bully is going to try and massacre me. I silently shout a microsecond-long heartfelt prayer to heaven as I scan the entire kitchen for a weapon of defense—a black skillet, perhaps. As the gigantic racist bully gets closer, I glance over my right shoulder and there on the counter, just out of reach, lies a wooden-handled straight-claw hammer.

I think, this is how Emmett Till must have felt. He was a black teenager who was brutally beaten and murdered in Mississippi back in 1955 for supposedly just whistling at a Caucasian woman. He was castrated, his body mutilated, and finally shot, allegedly to put him out of his misery. I hope my fate isn't the same tonight; however, the odds are all against me right now. My loving, intelligent family back in Portland said this was going to happen to me if I stayed down here. Now it appears I am going to be dramatically lynched. That's all there is to it. I am caught like a deer in the headlights. Adrenaline and fear are pumping through me like diarrhea as I prepare to live, and not die on the last day of *this* calendar year.

The highly insane, bamboozled, brainwashed bully is racing toward me at maximum speed like some enraged slave master. Melinda will not let go of my left arm and is still holding on for dear life. The intoxicated, amped-up-on-crank, massive, bigoted bastard is going to execute me in five-four-three-two-one! Time's up!

At the very last micro-tick of a second, shifting into transformed military mode, I shove Melinda against the refrigerator door out of my way, grab the hammer off the counter, stand very tall, almost to the point of being on my tippy toes, and swing the hammer in a high arc as hard and fast and direct as I can without ever taking my eyes off the racist-ass bully's forehead. I connect.

Bam!

Striking the hoodwinked, bulldozing bully super hard, the peen of the hammer penetrates deeply into his forehead, just above his eyes. I instantly retract the hammer from his cranium and he nosedives lifelessly, crashing down onto the floor, the sound of his skull cracking even more from the impact echoing off the kitchen ceiling. I realize he is deceased because he's just lying there, still as the proverbial corpse, a substantial amount of blood oozing gradually out of the racist bully's head. I stand over him with the adrenaline rush that sent me soaring to a superhuman plane higher than the Incredible Hulk's, finally easing down to a manageable level. I am not to be bully-fucked with right about now! The ballots are in, the decision has been made, and I am not going to depart this life today! Therefore, let it be known that this so-called bigoted bad-ass bully syndrome will no longer be tolerated, for the simple fact that I have already endured more than enough ethnic bullying and it stops now!

That LL Cool J song plays raucously in my subconscious military mind—*I'm gonna knock you out*—sending me into extreme Eddie Monster, don't-take-no-shit-off-nobody monster mode. I maintain my adrenalin surge to keep my monster 747 soaring at an attitude/altitude of thirty-three-thousand feet above sea level. I calculate there are only four more ignorant, bulldozing, racist-ass bullies to go.

"Let him go!" I yell vociferously, using my enormous voice of power as I cautiously approach the bully who has Spin up against the wall, both of his hands clamped around his throat, choking the life out of him. Spin's feet are dancing in midair, bouncing off the hallway wall as he tries desperately to breathe. His face is a puffy, pale-purple mask, and he looks like he's headed for a one-way meeting with the Angel of Death. "Let him go!" I repeat, louder this time, brandishing the hammer in my hand so the idiot bully can't miss seeing it. He releases his stranglehold from Spin's neck, whose fall is reminiscent of a lifeless sack of potatoes, crashing to the wooden floor, where he massages his throat with both hands, gasping for air, trying frantically to catch his breath. The cowardly racist-ass bully exits the house running. There is one other bully fighting Marty, and I chase him out the other door, keeping the hammer cocked and ready to blast some more craniums if need be. I'm not taking any chances at this particular junction because they had the audacity and the outright gall to try and exterminate yours truly, just because of the shade of my skin.

"What did you do that for?" the tall, slender, ignorant blonde biker chick shrieks at me as she kneels on the ground, attempting to retrieve the knife that's being held hostage under the lifeless bully's body that I nailed with the claw hammer. I can hear the rest of the bulldozing, racist-ass, bullying punks' high-pitched howling screams outside the house, going completely, insanely berserk, while one of Mr. Enormous chauvinistic, racist-ass bully friends chants repeatedly, crying, "The damn nigger killed Bubba! Get a gun! That nigger killed Bubba! Get a gun! That damn nigger killed Bubba! Get a fucking gun!"

With the exception of the tall, blonde biker girl, they have all exited the house. I realize I have more pressing problems on the horizon, as I hear the faint sound of police sirens approaching from several different directions. Standing my ground and geared up for whatever comes my way, *not dying tonight* becomes a mantra in my head that forges a breath-snatching, dead-silent calm inside me.

"Are you guys all right?" I ask everyone, while still firmly grasping the claw hammer like it was a revolver. My black dress shoes are somewhat spotted with blood and there is a huge puddle of it in the middle of the kitchen floor, courtesy of the lifeless body's recently damaged circulatory system.

"Eddie! Get the hell out of here! We are fine, please go!" Melinda pleads, rising turtle-slow from the kitchen floor, as she stares at the corpse.

"Eddie, run! Get the hell out of here! Please, Eddie, get the fuck out of here! Go! Right now!" Marty shouts at the top of his voice as he gets up from the living room floor.

"Eddie, please run. We will be fine. Get out of here, bro," Spin rasps out as he continues massaging his throat, drained and moving slowly, still sitting awkwardly on the floor, leaning against the wall, I retire the hammer carefully to the wooden floor, having survived David Duke's wedding reception death ambush, which I shall in no way ever stop thinking about.

14

● ● ● ● ● ● ● ● ● ● ● ● ● ● ● ● ● ●

Dodging Death?

It's dark as a bat cave in the grassy, uncut yard so I decide to take off my white-and-black sweater, along with my multicolored Rasta hat. There's a stereotype that you can't see so called black people in the dark, therefore I'm going to use this to my advantage to transmit myself to safety, instantaneously hiding in the brushes like a scared fugitive because one of the xenophobic bullies is coming directly this way.

I crouch down quickly by the green untrimmed shrubs outside the door, my heart thumping feverously as the bully ass racists keep travelling by. I dart out, reality setting in: I have, of my own accord, murdered a man in self-defense.

Heavily perspiring, heart pulsating, I instinctively run across the street, posting myself at the Seaside fire station. I can see as well as hear the police sirens getting closer on Highway 101 north. Frantically scuffing up enough courage, I dash across Highway 101 towards the west Pacific Ocean side of the highway, when a Seaside patrol vehicle speeds with loud sirens, flashing blue and white lights from the south on Highway 101 turns left onto the street in pursuit of yours truly, so fast that they don't see me when I run by them, shooting across the Highway 101.

My heart is pounding like a cement hammer pulsating in my chicken-built chest. Even harder as another Seaside police car comes, but again they didn't see me at all. Quickly ducking under a green fir tree, planning in my cranium, I rapidly decide to sprint to the beachfront Shilo Inn and have Frank the bartender call big brother Troy to inform him of my unexpected urgent situation, and that I have murdered a male bully in self-defense with a hammer. I make a decision to take off down the alley like a racing greyhound as I dash across Holiday Street, behind the bank, towards Avenue A, then to a bridge with just five blocks to go to get to the beachfront Shilo Inn. I dash my skinny earth-tone ass like an erratic gazelle along the backside streets, staying in the dark shadows, hearing sirens farther and farther in the opposite direction, giving me a little comfort. I am almost there, as I hear the applauding soundwaves of the Pacific Ocean.

As I toddle up to the double lounge door of the Shilo, I penetrate the Shilo Inn Lounge and I stop for a second, hesitant to my whereabouts, scanning the establishment, looking for anything out of the ordinary reminiscent of the Seaside police department. I spot Frank at the bar—plaid white short-sleeved shirt, Bach slacks—just standing there.

"Hey, big guy. What're you doing here? I thought you were at the wedding reception," Frank asked politely, wiping down the bar with a damp rag.

"I was. However, a fight broke out from some kind of racially prejudiced bully biker group with us Shilo employees," I admit, breathing hard, sweating from running as I lean over the bar to talk softly so only Frank and nobody else can hear me. Frank leans over too. "I'm pretty sure I killed someone tonight Frank," I add, being extra cautious. "Some ill-minded bully biker assholes crashed the party, assaulting everyone in the dwelling. Then they attempted to maliciously slaughter me," I add, still somewhat traumatized from attempted death on my existence.

"What do you want me to do, Eddie?" Frank asks, throwing down the damped bar towel rapidly onto the bar, ready to facilitate. I ask Frank to call Troy please, and let him know what exactly has happened. I am getting anxious all over again knowingly beyond a shadow of a doubt, that I am a thirty-two–year-old African American army veteran felon, now murderer. Even though this incidence is self-defense, I'm praying that the racist isn't dead. "No problem. You got it," Frank replies while walking towards the rotary phone. Next, Frank talks for about a minute with Troy and immediately hangs up. Troy is on his way to come get me.

"I bet you need a drink about right now, Eddie," Frank says as he puts ice in a glass, then grabs the Yukon Jack.

"Thank you, Frank. How much do I owe you?" I ask, nerves at a standstill—shattered.

"Nothing," Frank says. "Eddie, I have known you for almost a year, there is nothing I can't find in your aura that says you did anything wrong tonight, so you got my one hundred percent support buddy." Frank reaches over the bar to shake my hand.

"Thank you, Frank. I needed to hear that," I say gratefully as Troy enters the lounge, walking fast to the bar.

"What happened?" he asks, pumped up.

"Some bigot bully so-called bikers crashed the wedding reception and proceeded to stomp the hell out of Joe Nicolazzi—fought John Trent, Marty Nelson, attempted to choke the life out of Kenny I tell Troy and Frank the whole story, how the leader of the bully bikers ran at me viciously, because all I said was watch out for the little small girl, Rayann. Then after the biker dotted me, he yelled straightforward, 'Nigger, you are next. We are going to kill you,' while they had Melinda and I entirely trapped in the petite kitchen. The ignorant humongous bully comes running at me full-speed, drunk off Jack Daniel's, super amped off of the sadistic speed up drug crank. He reached behind for his knife and in a horrific panic, me searching all around the entire petite kitchen, I spotted a hammer sitting on the end of the kitchen counter. Traumatized red alert, I picked it up at the very last second and knocked the hell out of him directly in his forehead with it," I added, pissed off all over again.

Frank and Troy are staring at me in shock, with their mouths wide open. "Okay, little bro. Finish your drink and let's bail the hell out of here," Troy says, patting me on the shoulder, then waving to Frank farewell. "The police will be here any minute." Troy starts towards the double glass doors.

"Take care, Eddie. We are with you," Frank says.

"Thank you, Frank, I really appreciate everything you've done," I say, slamming my double shot of Yukon Jack urgently down my esophagus.

We leave the Shilo Inn and step into Troy's silver Ford Thunderbird. Troy drives us causally back to his apartment on Wahana Road, a few blocks away from David Duke's abode. When we exit the vehicle his wife, Carmen is waiting for us. She opens the door.

Carmen, Troy's wife, concierge at the Shilo Inn restaurant—five foot five, blonde hair, gorgeous lady inside and out—looks out for me, similar to an elder sister. Entering from the back door, Troy and I walk into his and Carmen's apartment. Delightful, spotless, fresh-smelling kitchen. Little living room, couch, coffee table with an Easy Boy chair, plants, pictures, and whatnots carefully and artistically tucked away, presenting a French sway look.

"Are you okay, Eddie?" Carmen asks, highly concerned.

"No, I am not okay, sis. I would be lying if I said different, standing feverously beside myself," I respond.

"Have a seat, Eddie, and just breathe," Carmen insists as Troy sits down in his recliner. I sit on the relatively soft couch and begin to explain again what happened tonight.

"Where's Sherri?" Carmen asks, concerned.

"Oh my goodness, Troy, I got to go back up there and make sure they don't take it out on my baby, please?" I say, jump to my feet, standing up, freaking out, just thinking only about me and me small mindedly. Sherri slipped my mind through all the pandemonium, and I don't have any logical idea where exactly she is.

Troy rises up and flares into the back room, only to return with a 357 magnum. "Are you ready to go?" he says. Carmen brings me a gray sweatshirt, since I have on just a black long-sleeved cotton shirt, under my white sweater I had on that was necessary to ditch, in order to avoid the police in my retreat.

We hop in the late model Thunderbird around the corner towards the scene. We park strategically across the street on the right hand side, under the shadow of a big maple tree right in front of Seaside elementary school, cattycorner across from Dave and Melinda Duke's house. I observe Sherri's father's Chevy truck easily, along with a cluster of police cars, fire department, and ambulance.

"There's Sherri right there, little bro," Troy says, pointing his index finger at the windshield of the Thunderbird. I feel instantly relieved. I can see her getting in her dad's truck. I'm so glad she's safe and I feel much better now. "Let's go back to the house so he can unload the hardware and have a nice stiff drink, and figure out your next move, okay?" Troy suggests strategically. Troy drives the car quickly, making a U-turn with his headlights off in spite of all the police cars and emergency vehicles, just fifty-five yards away.

Back at his apartment, Troy goes to the bedroom as I sit on the couch, on pins and needles. Troy quietly scurries from the bedroom, then the hallway and mentions that Carmen is now asleep as he reaches down, opens the door on the lower part of the coffee table, and pulls out a fifth of whiskey. He sets it on top of the coffee table, closes the compartment door, then posts his anatomy carefully in his recliner. "Eddie, I'm not trying to be a lawyer of sorts, but there is such thing as self-defense in the state of Oregon, little brother, and I just don't want to see you toss in the towel in just yet, you follow me?" Troy asks me as he pours two shots of whiskey in two glasses.

"You do have a point, Troy," I mention logically, slightly bent over, not relaxed. "However I must also realize, we are in Seaside Oregon, a brainwashed bamboozled hoodwinked racist ass city." We sat in silence for a while and I realize its New Year's Eve and a good time to make a resolution. "Now I would like to toast to a better year," I say confidently, while holding up my shot of whiskey trying very hard to be positive.

"To a better year to you too," Troy awesomely replies as we both raise our glasses, clanking them together. "Ready to drink another shot of whiskey with me?" Troy asks, smiling big at the positives.

"Yes, let's have one more, then if you would be so kind as to take me to Sherri's parents' house. I know she's worried sick about me."

We earth-toned Libra men take our shots of whiskey and emerge into the night, once again into the Ford Thunderbird.

"Now, Eddie, let me make a suggestion. You don't know if this man you walloped in the head is deceased for sure, now, do you?" Troy cross-examines me freely, placing the key in the ignition.

"No, I don't know that for certain," I whisper leisurely slow.

"So, therefore, the district attorney does not know what to charge you with yet. Do you follow me, little brother?"

"Yes, I got it, Troy. I should wait for them to officially arraign me with a crime before I turn myself in," I say. However, I'm not convinced.

Troy, taking Wahana Road, in next to no time arrives at Ghearhart Oregon, where Sherri's parents reside. I respectfully request Troy to please pull over on Highway 101 and let me walk from here. "I will keep in touch with only you, until they have formally charged me, okay," I promise.

"You must be careful, and whatever move you make, let me know," Troy says while shaking my hand.

"Oh, and by the way, Troy. Happy New Years," I conclude, realizing that it's finally midnight. Troy drives away and disappears into the dark. I walk through the large empty lot behind Seaside Upholstery, then head towards the rear to Sherri's parents' house. I knock hard on the door two times. Sherri opens the doors, surprised, embracing me and weeping like I had just returned from hand-to-hand combat war. "I thought they found you and killed you dead, baby," Sherri sighs belligerently, embracing me tightly. I smell her silky long hair.

"Honey, you can't get rid of me that easy," I reply, grinning while giving her a kiss on her luscious chicken lips.

"You guys might want to come into the house since they are looking for you-know-who," Ron says subjectively from the living room.

"Eddie, are you okay?" Donna asks, motherly concerned.

"I'm a little shaken. I was worried those evil people would to take it out on her," I say, standing inside the house. "I was up there when Ron came and rescued you. I was in the company of Troy across the street in his Ford Thunderbird." I let them recognize that I plan on turning myself in; Sherri thinks it's an appalling idea.

"Well, I don't think it's a good idea for Eddie to stay around here. The police will be here sooner or later," Ron mentions, standing in the kitchen, closing the refrigerator. Sherri's parents let us stay in their fifth wheel trailer parked in the back incognito. Tomorrow, I will have to hide somewhere else. Sherri candidly opens the door to the fifth wheel, steps up, enters the mini trailer as I intuitively follow Snooky Nooky's lead. She turns on the light and immediately gets unclothed; so do I. We kiss and embrace each other as I wipe Sherri's tears from her face, nervously sincerely wishing a happier new year's, not knowing what lies ahead for the two of us. Then we compose endless lovemaking for hours, and pass out extraordinarily drained from a brutal, traumatic episode that has occurred on the final day of the year 1990.

Early the very next year, I am exceptionally thankful to see another day, waking up to Sherri already showered, dressed, and making some coffee then bringing it into the fifth wheel in Styrofoam cups. "Happy New Year's Day, Snooky Nooky Poo Poo," I say meaningfully.

"Good morning, baby. Happy New Year," she says, wiping the sleep from my unfocused eyes. "Mom said we could reside at the Gearhart by the Sea condominium she cleans. It is vacant, and we are more than welcome to stay until we find out exactly what's going on," Sherri adds nonchalantly, stirring her coffee with a wooden stir.

"Fine, I won't turn my fugitive self in just yet. However, I will have to eventually surrender. Agreed?" I say, getting dressed. I'm not trying to upset Sherri. However, it is what it is.

"I don't want to talk about that right now all I want is for you to get dressed so we can go over to the condominium baby, then get undressed while you do all the things you want me to," Sherri says sensually, approaching me with coffee and a kiss. I jump up out of the bed to get dressed, as I realize more details about the events that occurred last night, somebody definitely undisputedly wanted me deceased. In addition, I don't even know his name. David Duke comes to mind as I step down out of the mini trailer and light a cigarette— the last one I have, but that's the least of my worries.

Sherri steps out of the trailer with me handing me a cup of coffee as we stroll through the grass, like we were walking to the ball. "Ron's been listening to the CB and the police are searching everywhere for Eddie, so we should get going. Pronto," Donna says, walking towards us, strategically concerned.

"C'mon, honey, let's go. I don't want to get nobody into trouble because they helped me," I say.

Quickly scurrying, I get in the backseat of Donna's gray Buick, immediately lying on the floor. Donna gets in the driver seat and Sherri resourcefully hops in the front seat, and we head out Highway 101. As we are drive on, we see the Ghearhart police heading the opposite way. Nevertheless, we successfully make it to the condos on the beachfront without dilemma.

"Eddie, stay down until we get the door open, then we will come back and get you," Donna suggests, speaking softly. Once the door is open, Sherri comes back to the parking lot.

"Baby, we have to walk fast so nobody sees you," Sherri says. Inside is a very nice bright white condo with a Pacific Ocean view, queen-sized bed along with all the amenities.

"Thank you, Donna, for everything you are doing," I say sincerely, hugging her.

"You are welcome, Eddie. Well, Sherri, come on if you are going with me," Donna says, urgently ready to depart.

"Honey, I am going to leave as well as collect some clothes at our trailer, then pick up some groceries. I will be back in a little while, baby. You should call your mother, and call Troy," Sherri suggests. We tightly embrace, kissing, as it may be a while before we have the chance again.

Daydreaming laying on my backside on the fresh bed of linen, I decide to contact my friend Troy. "Hello, my brother, what is the word for today?" I utter, priming positivity.

"The word for today is he didn't stay dead," Troy said urgently, gladly.

"Well, thank God," I sincerely replied, relieved, into the white phone receiver.

"The meth snatched him back into existence in the ambulance, as I understand it. He was in major shock, desperately fighting the ambulance personnel who were trying to assist his medical needs."

"Thanks again for helping out last night, Troy," I whisper sincerely.

"Have you relocated?"

"Yes. That is why I am calling you," I say. "My word is my bond. Every move I make, I'm going to inform you. Who was the guy, anyway?"

"His name is Robert Hayes, nicknamed Bubba. He is Seaside Oregon's number one prevailing troublemaker, or now the ex-biggest maltreatment troublemaker," Troy says, comically. "I had a run in with him before. And I whipped his ass. See, if I had been there, this shit would not have happened," Troy preaches, factually regretful.

"It's not your fault, since Bubba his friends and his drugs were not invited," I say, truthfully subtle. "He strictly, undoubtedly took it upon himself to start pounding on everybody, plus kill just anybody," I utter, getting steamed all over again.

"Well, little brother, the DA says as long as you don't leave town, stay in touch with me, he won't place you on America's most wanted. You just hang in there, stay cool. Have you called your parents yet?" Troy asks, cornering yours truly.

"I am going to call them after I talk to you," I admit voluntarily.

Troy and I end our conversation, but I'm still not ready to call home, hear that damn music. I can hear it now; they are going to say they knew something like this was going to happen. Eventually I find the courage to dial my mother's number and get it over with.

The phone rings two times before it is answered. We say our hellos, and then the questions start. I tell my mom the details of what occurred last night. "So you are hiding you from the police?" my mother asks straightforwardly.

"Yes and no, ma'am," I reply, justified. "I just spoke to my friend Troy a few minutes ago. He spoke with the district attorney, and since the guy didn't die, no one knows what I am going to be charged with."

"Where was Troy your friend when all this happened?" Mom asks directly, upset.

"He went and played at the wedding, but he was too tired to make the wedding reception," I reply.

"Have you called your father yet?" she asks subjectively.

"No, I was hoping you were going to do that," I say, being hopeful.

"I will call him and let him know, but what I want you to do is let me know what's going on. Keep me posted, do you understand me?" my mother commands.

"Yes, Mother. Love you, talk to you later," I say carefully, then hurriedly hang up the phone. I know they are going to want me to move back home, but I am not moving back. I am a citizen United States of America, and I served my country honorably. And I should be able to live anywhere in the USA, especially in my home state. I relocated to Seaside Oregon to work, live in peace, along with prosper and enjoy the fruits of my labor.

Trying hard not to think about smoking a cigarette since I'm out, the door unlocks and the doorknob rotates. The door quietly opens as Sherri comes in with two large grocery bags, which I assist her with. I quickly shut the door and grab one of the bags off the ground hallway, then out of Sherri's hands as she walks towards the round brown dining table, setting the rest of the groceries on the counter. "Hi, baby, I stopped by the trailer and got us some clean clothes, went to the store, bought some food as well, and I got you some cigarettes and a surprise," Sherri says, smiling.

"How did the trailer look?" I ask curiously.

"It was fine, honey," she says. And then she tells me that our neighbor Arthur saw that a gang of those bikers at the trailer last night, making all kinds of noise, chanting, "Come outside nigger, we are going to kill you."

I spent my New Year day drinking beer watching football games, the next few days isolated with my Sherri in the condominium by the sea until it got real dark, and then we strolled on the moonlit sandy coastline, gazing up periodically at the twinkling stars. We continued to stay low-key and out of sight until I called Troy a few days later, and I learn that I have now been formally charged with first degree assault. I let him know that I would turn myself in tomorrow.

Friday afternoon comes and Sherri's dad picks us up and drives us to the Seaside police station. "Sherri, honey, please don't cry. This is the right thing to do, honey. Okay? I love you," I say, while holding her tight. Then I let her go and walk up to the front door of the Seaside Police station. All of the Seaside police that had been harassing me last year in Seaside, Oregon are lined up in two columns in police uniform, facing each other. As I walk slowly past, the smiling officers start applauding loudly, as if I had won the multimillion dollar lottery and was going to share it all of them.

I never imagined first class-treatment as a prisoner.

"Eddie, the Astoria police are running late, so why don't you just hang out and use the phone out on the wall over there if you like, okay?" Sergeant Barnett happily says to me.

Two hours later, while I'm sitting in a chair, watching television, the Astoria police come to transport me up to Astoria because there is no courthouse in Seaside. They handcuff me and put me in the back of the Astoria patrol car. Once in Astoria, I'm processed in the Clatsop county jail system. They escort me into general population with numerous white males. There is no way in hell I am going to sleep tonight. Word is going to spread like fire, and it's only logical that they may jump me, along with kill me.

Soon after, on that night, a correction officer comes in the dorm with his flashlight, checking the inmate bunks, and flashes the light in my face. "Why are you sitting up on your bunk?" he asks bluntly but quietly.

"Well, officer, if you look up why I am in here I'm pretty sure that will explain why I cannot sleep in here," I respond wisely. He leaves the spacious, cemetery-quiet dorm.

Minutes later, he comes back in. "Mr. Williams, roll up. Roll up. Come with me," he orders suddenly. I immediately eject myself out of the prison bunk, very relieved. I grab my linen and follow the guard down the hallway. "You were right to sit up. They were going to lynch you as soon as you went to sleep," the officer says.

"Thank you very much," I say, relieved as we walk up to a smaller cell that has only two bunks, with a Latino man sleeping on the top bunk. I get on the bunk and immediately go into a deep sleep.

In the morning they the officers bring breakfast, and that's when I meet Hector. Hector is from Guatemala and is in jail for drunk and disorderly conduct. He eats his breakfast and goes back to sleep for the most of the day. The correction officer comes to the cell to let me know I have visitors. He opens the cell and walks me to a visiting room with a bunch of phones with little windows and chairs positioned at each booth. Sitting on the other side of the booth is my mother and father. It's always nice to see your parents together sometimes; they have been divorced for a long while now.

I sit down in the booth and pick the receiver off of the base, and my father does the same on this side. "Hey, son, how is you doing?" my father asks, as my mother put her fingers up to the side of her face. "How are they treating you?"

"They are treating me really good, Dad. They took me out of general population. Now I am in a cell with a Hispanic guy named Hector." I am trying my best to ease their minds.

"Now, son, would you please explain to me what happened?" my dad asks. I proceed to recount to my dad exactly what happened. "In my experience as a correction officer that is most likely to be self-defense," my father says. "We just wanted to come up here and make sure you are in one piece." He then hands the phone to my mother.

"How is my son?" she says.

"Mother, I am okay, under the circumstances."

"Well, it's just hard to see your child locked up for defending himself," my mother says solemnly.

After a few moments of making sure I'm in decent shape, they leave, but my mom makes it clear she wants me to call her immediately after I see the judge concerning my arraignment. The accommodating correction officer returns and escorts my anatomy back to the two-man cell with Hector, where he talks my head off in broken English all night until we both fall asleep.

The next morning comes quickly, and I am expecting a correction officer to come and get me for my arraignment, but instead it's my probation officer, ready to terrorize me with her privileged power that be. "Mr. Williams, you have quite a few charges pending on you. Five, to be exact. A DUI, two counts of disorderly conduct, one count of interfering with justice, and now first degree assault," she says with her hands on her hips.

"Yes. Isn't that something? I haven't even lived here practically a whole year yet and a half dozen times someone has attempted to kill me," I mention, then I continue cause I'm tired of her elaborate bullshit. "None of this would have anything to do with racism?" I ask my brainwashed bamboozled and hoodwinked probation officer.

"Mr. Williams, as long as you don't get convicted, you don't have to worry about me, but by the time you get through all these charges you will be convicted with violating your probation," she says proudly, prejudging outcomes, and walks away. Announcing my fate, as if I'm was born guilty. Then a head-on straight correction officer comes to the cell and handcuffs my hands behind me so I can be escorted inside the courtroom.

Inside the high-ceilinged courtroom I meet Nicholas Zafiratos, my attorney, on the opposite side of the dark-suited DA. The judge reads the charges as he sits on the bench; I am charged with first degree assault, which carries a sentence of twenty years. "How do you plead?" the judge asks.

"Not guilty, your honor," my attorney states.

"Mr. Williams, where exactly do you work?" the judge instantly asks me.

"I work at the Shilo Inn in Seaside, your honor."

"What do you do at the Shilo Inn Mr. Williams?" the judge asks me.

"I am the kitchen steward, sir."

"What is that?"

"I supervise, hire, and fire the janitors and dishwashers in the kitchen of a restaurant."

The judge then turns and asks the district attorney if he has any problems releasing me to close street supervision.

"No, I see no problem releasing Mr. Williams, your honor. Mr. Williams turned himself in to authorities when he said he was going to, and he never left township and stayed in contact with the courts," the DA says spectacularly.

I can't believe he just said that, I tell myself.

"Mr. Williams, I am releasing you to close street supervision, which is you are to go from the Shilo Inn and then home without delay. Stay in your trailer park," the judge orders seriously. "Due to the gravity of this situation, I am ordering that a Seaside police officer escort you to work and from work to your Pine Cove trailer park until this ordeal is resolved. Stay out of downtown Seaside, Mr. Williams. Understood?"

"Yes, sir, your honor," I say with the ultimate quickness.

"The grand jury hearing is set for January 10 at ten o'clock a.m. The defendant may now be released. Court is adjourned." The judge picks up his gavel and hits the wooden circular block hard. Immediately the correction officer who brought me into the courtroom takes the handcuffs off my wrists, letting me know I am free to go. Sherri appears out of nowhere in a gray cotton sweat suit and hugs me like she hasn't seen me in years.

"Let's get out of here," I say swiftly, surprised. I grab Sherri's hand, leading her out of the courthouse. We get in Sherri's mother's car, parked outside. "Hello, Donna. How are you doing?" I say, freely amused.

"They let you out, Eddie?" Donna asks, not hiding her surprise. "What happened in there?"

"I answered three questions and the judge and district attorney set me free, plus I will be having the Seaside police escort me to work every day till the grand jury hearing. By the way, I devoured some roadkill while incarcerated. Elk chili and elk burger, and some elk stew," I say.

As soon as we arrive home in the Pine Cove trailer park, we are greeted by our neighbors Arthur and Sandy. "Hey, I haven't seen you good people since last year," I broadcast loudly. We hug ecstatically and say our hellos. Then I am informed that Bubba's racist, dysfunctional acquaintances are going around town, spreading rumors—lying that I battered Bubba in the back of the head. Also that I wasn't even invited to the wedding reception. The radical lies make me furious.

"We know that's not what happened, silly," Sandy says, dropping her cigarette butt on the ground and stepping on it with her tennis shoe. "Eddie, you are the good kind of crazy. Not the ignorant kind, like those punks that tried to kill you," Sandy continues, folding her arms.

"You are a hero at the Seaside Shilo Inn, Eddie. However, on the streets—you excuse my French—they are just calling you a crazy ass nigger that hit Bubba blindly from behind," Arthur admits.

Another friend, Mike, Justin's dad, is in on the conversation by this time. And out of nowhere he makes the point that at least no one else will mistake me for the other black guy named Joe. We all laugh at the thought.

"Call your mother, honey, and let her know you are out of jail and that you are all right, please," Sherri says with her hands on her hips. I say goodbye to my friends and go into the house to call her. My mother thanks me for calling, but she does not want to talk about it while she's at work, she is very private. Then I pull out my lawyer's card and call him, and we have a very short conversation. He tells me if everything is the way he understands it, with all my friends from the wedding reception, the grand jury will believe it was in self-defense.

The next morning, I get up at seven thirty, since my police escort is here in thirty minutes. I walk into the bathroom and turn on shower so it will warm up before I get in. I notice it's partially cloudy outside, but the sun is shining into the bathroom window. I jump in the shower frantically because the trailer is freezer cold, and it is time to get going.

It's my first day back at the job since the hammer incident. I have to get back into the swing of things. After I shower and shave, I put my clothes on, and finish with putting my wallet in my back pocket of my black denim jeans. I put my pack of cigarettes in my shirt pocket, grab my black jacket, and give Sherri a kiss goodbye as she lies in bed in her white gown. Then a police officer drives up to our trailer and parks directly in front of it. I really don't believe that this is really happening to me. I wonder if I get to sit in the front seat.

The officer looks similar to one of my favorite actors, Jack Nicholson. "Good morning Mr. Williams," the officer says, smiling. "How are you doing today?"

"Under the circumstances, I feel blessed to be alive," I reply sociably, cautious. I walk up to the passenger side of the patrol car, placing my right hand on the handle, opening the front passenger door of the patrol car then getting in. *It definitely feels different up here in the front seat,* I say to myself.

"My name is Sergeant Steve Barnett," mustached, clean-shaven officer says.

"Well, good morning, Steve," I say, strangely relaxed. I feel like a human being, I'm not under arrest, and there are no handcuffs. I am truly overwhelmed and will never forget this moment. "What is the date today?" I ask the kind sergeant, viewing the interior of the police patrol car.

"Today is the January 8, 1991," Steve says.

"January 8, 1991. I have to tell this to my grandkids about this," I state, fascinated, sitting next to a twelve gauge shot gun. "Yes I must let them know their grandfather was escorted in the front seat of a patrol car, without handcuffs without harassment, just respect," I proclaim, looking all over at everything.

"You have a great sense of humor, Mr. Williams," the cheerful officer of the law says.

"Please call me Eddie, Steve," I say politely. "Yeah, but some people don't like my humor or the color of my skin, you know what I mean?"

"Yes, Eddie, that is definitely true. There are a few idiots around here, and unfortunately some of them want you to see you dead," Steve reminds me.

"Yes, about that. Would you like to hear what happened?" I volunteer.

"Sure, I'd love to hear it, but you don't have to tell me."

"You have shown nothing but respect, I have to trust somebody. My intuition says you are a good man, so, therefore, I am going to tell you exactly what happened." By the time the story is over, the police car pulls up to the Shilo Inn main entrance.

"Well, Eddie, I have a good feeling about you, so do me a favor. Don't get all worried, everything will work out," Steve says, patting me on the shoulder before I exit the clean patrol vehicle.

I walk through the automatic doors, then down the hallway that leads to the employee door of the kitchen. I stroll in and find my timecard and punch in. I spot some of my coworkers.

"What's up, you guys? I haven't seen you since last year," I say, ecstatically loud.

"You saved my life, dude," Spin says as he gives me a big bear hug. "I owe you, man. Big time. If you need me to testify, man, I am there, man."

"You are very welcome, my friend," I reply, ecstatic.

"What is going on, my brother?" Jim asks as he shakes my hand and hugs me. "Man I should have been there, that was some cold ass shit," Jim adds, consoling me.

"No, man, it's not your fault. That's just the way. Some ignorant people have no respect for nothing," I say in his defense.

"Brother Ed. Bam, you can't touch this," John says as he hugs then shakes my hand. "When do we all have to go to court?"

"It is Thursday tenth at ten o'clock in Astoria," I say swiftly. "Let me go and check in with the boss man." I walk into Dennis's office and he's ready to discuss some things with me.

"Eddie, first things first. How are you doing?" Dennis asks caringly.

"I am mentally stable, if that what you are asking, under the circumstances," I say.

"You have an extreme charge against you. I will help you in any way I can, just kill all conversations on the property concerning the incident for me. Would do that for me, Eddie?" Dennis warns. I assure him all talk at work about the incident is finished. "Well, good luck on Thursday with your hearing, and have somebody cover your shift for you that day," Dennis says as he stands up, steps from behind his desk, and shakes my hand.

"I don't need luck as long as I have all of good friends on my side to show up and tell the truth," I say calmly, before leaving his office.

I emerge from the smelly elevator to go downstairs to Troy's office. Inside, Troy is sitting, reading the newspaper. "Hey, little brother. How are you doing?" Troy asks as he stands up to give me a hug and handshake.

"Good to be free, that's how I am doing," I answer, uplifted, smiling profoundly.

"Have you talked to your lawyer?" Troy asks.

"Yes he says if everybody that was involved attends the grand jury hearing and testifies on Thursday, I should get found not guilty based on self-defense," I say.

"Now you are talking," Troy says, clapping his hands together. "Let Lady Justice take her running course." Nevertheless, Troy knows I have to be sensationally careful, since half of the town is on my side and the other half assumes that I thumped Bubba in the back of his head and would like to see me get twenty years in prison, or even worse—attempt to murder me.

I stride into the main kitchen from downstairs, headed to the break room to make the necessary changes on the schedule, when Melinda Duke—bold-legged waitress, uniformed in white blouse and blue jean skirt—the New Year's Eve bride—comes around the corner. "I am so sorry, Eddie. Is you okay?" Melinda asks, embracing me tightly for a moment.

"Melinda, they were not your friends, were they?" I ask while holding her hand.

"No, sweetheart, of course not," Melinda replies. "Are you mad at Dave?"

"I don't know, Melinda. You saved my life. Stop that, it was just a huge mistake," I say firmly.

"That's why I am saying sorry for everything," replies Melinda, rubbing her temple with her fingers.

"All I need you to do is help make sure everyone shows up Thursday to testify before the grand jury in Astoria at ten o'clock."

"Okay, sweetheart. You got it. Anything," Melinda announces. She and I hug, and she heads back to work. Then Lori approaches me in the break room, smiling, hugging me, saying thank you for everything, Eddie.

"How is Rayann doing, Lori?" I ask, very concerned about her mental health.

"She's doing okay, considering what happened. However, Eddie, Rayann says a chocolate superman saved her father's life," Lori utters beautifully.

"You're quite welcome. How is Joe doing?" I ask curiously, reaching for a cigarette out of my shirt pocket, sitting down.

Marty then comes looking for me with some crazy-ass news. "Hey, Eddie, that dude you been getting mistaken for is outside right now on the handicap ramp with Troy," he says. I have wanted to meet this dude Joe, for a long damn time. I head upstairs to find a man who is similar to me in height, with a darker chocolate complexion, chatting with a slight southern accent to Troy. Standing in the bright, unusual sunlight in January, he doesn't look like me at all, yet some people assume we all look alike.

"Hey, Eddie, here is your twin," Troy says as he introduces us.

"What's up, Joe?" I say, smiling, finally meeting this chocolate human being.

"What's up, Eddie?" Joe says, leaning on the light-blue handicap rail as we courteously shake hands.

"It's about time I met you, man. Do you know how many times I have been called Joe in the last eleven months?" I ask, seriously amazed.

"No, but do you realize how many times that I have been called Eddie?" Joe says as he puts out his cigarette in the mental box ashtray. "Hell the night you hit that racist asshole in the head with that hammer, the police came to my job at the El Tu Can Lounge, calling me Eddie. They must be crazy inadequate, wanting to arrest me," Joe announces to Troy. "I mean, Bob Senior, the owner of El Tu Can, had to cosign, informing the police that I was not Eddie. Then they started asking me all kinds of investigative questions about you and if I was hiding you somewhere."

"What really gets me is you guys look nothing alike," Troy states, standing, looking at us. "And yet they assume they are so superior but can't tell the difference between you guys," Troy says, laughing, glancing at the both of us.

"Then I heard that you slapped some white young woman down to the ground on in one of the clubs on Broadway Street," Joe Alexander interjects, motioning with his hands.

"Now, there was another tall brother, Eddie, just before you got here in Seaside, by the name of Joe from Chicago, Illinois. A pimp of sorts," Troy points out, putting a hand on my shoulder.

"That makes sense about this bamboozled circle of we all look alike misunderstandings," I suggest rationally. "But on a serious note, are you who I should talk to about working as a dishwasher or janitor?"

"Yes, that would be me," I reply proudly.

"I would officially like to apply for a job," Joe says politely.

Then the exit door swings open, and it is Jim, my friend, in his cook's uniform. He strolls up to us chocolate humans, proclaiming,

"Is this one of those NACCP meetings or something? Should I come back?" Jim blindly says rubbing his palms together, as we all start laughing harder than ever. I introduce my old friend Jim Dunkin to my new friend Joe Alexander from St. Louis, Missouri.

"Well, Joe," I say, "I would like you to fill out an application first, then we can sit down and have a discussion about what the job entails and give you a grand tour of the property."

"What are you doing after work, brother man?" Jim asks me, smiling heavily.

"Stay in my trailer park like the judge ordered me to," I answer swiftly, logically. "Why? You coming over, bro?" I ask Jim, hinting him to come over my dwelling, which incidentally works every time.

I maintain a low profile, staying in my trailer park as ordered, and then my day in court finally arrives. I am very nervous, even though everyone from the wedding reception is here: the bride Melinda and the groom David Duke, his honorable grandmother who made sure all my witnesses were going to be present, the best man Joe Nicolazzi, the maid of honor Lori, Sherri, Janelle, and Sherri's parents, Marty, John Trent, and Kenny or Spin, David Duke and his grandmother and wife Melinda Duke along with my mother and father from Portland, Oregon, Troy Hunt, his gorgeous wife Carmen, and Officer Sergeant Barnett. I also see Bubba's associates: four men and two women dressed in black leather plus jeans. They would be like to see me in a graveyard, dead. I will never ever forget their faces as long as I exist.

All of a sudden, this huge mocha-brown African American brother—six foot five, stocky, wide, 320 pounds of muscle dressed in a white T-shirt under blue overall jeans, black boots, trimmed beard, low afro—climbs up the two dozen stairs, looking upward at the bikers in the opposite corner like they had done something to him. He reaches the top stairs, breathing hard, and walks directly up to me. "Excuse me, sir," he says with a southern twang, "but are you the brother in the Astorian newspaper that was attacked at a wedding reception on New Year's Eve?"

"Yes, that would be me," I say easily, answering the mocha-chocolate individual, wondering who this massive gentleman is.

"Well, my name is George, and I live way far out in the sticks, but something told me to come up here and make sure you are okay," he confesses, shaking my hand.

"Well, that was very nice of you," my mother says, smiling.

"I have been reading about you in the paper every day for almost two weeks now," George says, hands on his hips, sweating. "Is that them over there?" George asks, glaring at the gloomy gang.

"Yes, that would be them," I respond swiftly, not bothering myself with looking at the dysfunctional racist thugs.

Outside the courtroom for the grand jury, my lawyer informs me things look good. The six so-called bikers are summoned one at a time into the hearing room until they all have testified, then dismissed from the premises due to safety precautions. Then it is time for the witnesses on my behalf to testify one by one, while I nervously stay outside, holding Sherri's hand for comfort, watching them go in one by one and then leaving downstairs as instructed by the court. After everybody testifies, I am all alone, sitting on the bench in my black dress shirt, gray slacks, black dress shoes, and Guess black jacket. I lean over gently, close my eyes, and say a heartfelt prayer. Finally, my name is called, and I enter the grand jury deliberation room halfway crazy and very prayerful. I'm checking the facial expressions of almost a dozen human beings, as they sit in these individual chairs in a half circle. No expressions. None of the jurors will directly look at me; there is an empty chair, with my anatomy written all over it.

"Mr. Williams, raise your right hand and repeat after me. Do you swear to the whole truth and nothing but the truth so help you God?" the bailiff says respectfully.

"I do," I reply, feeling a cold draft.

"Please be seated. Mr. Williams, tell us where you live and where you work, please?" a random dark-haired man in a seat in front of me asks me, making direct eye contact. I tell him that I live at the Pine Cove 2481, Highway 101, Seaside Oregon, and I work at the Shilo Inn as a kitchen steward.

"On the evening of December 31—would you mind explaining the events to us, Mr. Williams?" he asks. I inform the grand jury the whole, entire story of what exactly happened that outrageous night, and it was exactly the same story I have been repeating all week long. Then the well-mannered bailiff thanks me and asks me to please wait outside in the lobby. Everybody else in my group is downstairs. I appreciate the silence on the hard, cold wooden bench. Before my rear could get the long bench warmed up, the dark, average-sized, suited bailiff comes out, shakes my hand aggressively, and tells me that all the charges have been dropped and I am very free to go.

"Now all charges were dropped due to?" I asked for my own knowledge of the law.

"You were acquitted, found not guilty due to self-defense due to racism, okay, Mr. Williams? So take care." He walks back in the grand jury courtroom as I sit for a moment of silence and thank the almighty for blessing me once more again. Now it's time to spread the news to Sherri, my parents, and my friends. I walk slowly downstairs, where I see all the people that care about me and I thank god for all of them as well.

"Well, what did they say?" my mother asks desperately.

"Oh, they said thank you for coming in. You can go home. All charges have been dropped," I say joyously. Everybody immediately starts cheering like we're at a super bowl football game. So the whole joyful gang vacates the Clatsop County court house and head to the Pig 'N Pancake a couple of blocks down the street for a bite to eat.

We are all seated after management places together some tables for our large group. We eat joyously, everybody getting to know one another. Then my apprehensive mother erupts with the downbeat. "Now that you have made it through this ordeal, you should give some thought to moving back to Portland," my mom says strategically, as Sherri writes *I love you* with her index finger in the palm of my hand, as I return the sweet gesture.

"Eddie, obviously these are your friends. However, you don't want to put them in danger," my father chimes out loud, insignificantly.

"Sir, with all due respect, we are already in deep shit just by testifying and being here," Marty says sincerely.

"You have a very good, valid point, young man," my father replies candidly.

"I am going to have to chill for a while. Let things calm down, Mother. I can't leave. I just have to be more careful from now on that's all," I say, reassuring my mother.

"Well, son, we are going to go back to Portland. So you give it some consideration, okay?" my mother says openly, standing up. "Nice meeting everybody, and you guys take care." I get up to hug both of my parents goodbye.

"Goodbye, Eddie's mother. We will take care of him," John says eagerly, comfortable in T-shirt and jeans, as my parents are exiting Pig 'N Pancake's swing double doors. After watching my good-looking parents, who I love so very much, walk away, I picture my mother's midnight-blue 1988 two-door Thunderbird drive off, headed towards Highway 30.

15

. . . .

Pink Ribbon Hero

It's cloudy on the Pacific Northwest Coast as I'm punching out my time card, destination Pine Cove Trailer Park, when Troy, who seems to be on a mission, practically jumps out of the lemon-smelling kitchen elevator before I can even exit the Shilo Inn.

"Hey, little bro, excellent timing! Please come and have a beer with me? We haven't had one this year. So let's celebrate, shall we?" he says persuasively, smiling, hugging me very firmly with one arm, then removing the nametag from his gray V-neck sweater.

Without hesitation, I grin an earnest nonverbal yes and take my nametag off my sweaty, white cotton short-sleeved shirt. I'm game to oblige, so out in the parking lot I hoist my lightweight bike into the rear of Troy's mustard-colored Chevy truck, then we head out for a drink.

"Yeah, for the past week-and-a-half, we haven't been able to kick it," Troy says as he pulls into the wide gravel parking lot of the Beach Club.

"I know, and I would like to play a round of golf," I suggest as I step down out of the truck.

"Sure we can. Need to go to the driving range first, though," Troy mentions. We both walk into the bar where we are happily greeted, this being my first time back in the Beach Club since the nerve-wracking New Year's Eve debacle. Then a vaguely weird, strangely comedic silence engulfs the entire tavern; I am sitting at the bar on the third stool from the end, drinking with Troy, discussing the outcome of my recent foray into the criminal/justice system with some fellow local friends, when an intimidating enormous man lumbers through the open doorway of the Beach Club. He's a six-foot-five, 335-pound, wide, full-bearded, curly black-haired, big-ass Caucasian man wearing jean overalls over a white T-shirt and monster-sized steel-toed boots. He's huge enough to whip a bear with a switch. He tromps up to me aggressively as I'm sitting on the black, leather-covered stool in front of the bar. "Are you Eddie?" the giant asks me loudly, looking down at me, not smiling at all. I am so terrified, I can't come up with an immediate answer, and could easily lose control of my bladder and urinate on myself. However, as I am visually probing—eyes shifting left and right in all directions of the tavern—my dozen friends are showing no concern whatsoever as to why this hairy giant of a man wants to know who the hell I am and if this will have a happy ending.

"Yes," I gasp hesitantly, eyes bouncing around at everybody in the tavern, not able to imagine what's going to happen next.

"I'm Joe Nicolazzi's little brother, Bear. You saved my brother's life, dude," the gentle giant announces loudly, placing his enormous hand on my shoulder. "If anybody ever messes with you again, call on Bear! And I will be more than happy to take care of them for you, my friend!" Bear shouts loudly in my face, shaking my hand vigorously. Well, this is certainly a guy on whose good side I am happy to be. And I am so very tremendously relieved. He reaches in his pocket and fishes out a floppy, worn ten-dollar bill, slams it on the bar, and informs Rob, the bartender that he's paying for the next pitcher of beer for yours truly. Then he abruptly leaves as suddenly as he appeared. As soon as he vacates the club, everybody starts laughing loudly at yours truly, like I just took a dump on myself, not knowing whether Bear was friend or foe.

"He petrified the shit out of me! Did you see how big that man was?" I blurt out, comically relieved, facing the entire establishment. "Can you imagine the stretchmarks he gave his mama?" I say loudly as my trusted friends continue to laugh at me. "All right, all right, wait a minute! Why didn't anyone tell me Joe Nicolazzi had a younger, colossal, giant-ass Brother?" I ask insanely. "I thought you guys had my back?"

"Let's go have a real drink," Troy says, standing up, chuckling happily at my expense, along with the rest of my friends. Realizing I've been set up, I down the rest of the beer my new friend Bear bought me, and we journey over to Griddles, which used to be called El Tu Can, the next bar over from Pudgy's Bar and Grill on Broadway, the main drag of downtown Seaside, Oregon.

It's lively inside tonight, with a few people scattered in the lounge area adjacent to the restaurant. We stroll into the lounge, take a seat at a circular table, and order a couple of stiff drinks from the bartender friend of ours, Dusty, a fair-skinned Native American. A live five-piece rock band called The Patriots is up on stage playing, and the bassist announces that the next song is for Eddie.

"Congrats, Eddie, on your legal decision! Eddie, my good friend, we are all behind you!" John says from his stool, and he raises his black, bass guitar in salute. "One-two-three-four," as the drummer clicks his sticks setting up the next song.

Can't touch this, can't touch this, and can't touch this hammer time!

And with that, the music stops dead because the band is laughing so damn hard. All I can do is shake my head from side to side in utter nervousness. Troy is sitting across from me, looking like he's in pain from laughing so hard. "Everyone has a hammer joke," I sigh to myself, slightly amused. And then a slender, five-foot-six man in a black Stetson hat, gray suit, and black shoes comes out of nowhere, walks up to our small table carrying one of the nightclub's lit red candle holders, plants himself in front of me, and asks me stylishly if I am the hero.

"No. I am not," I protest instantaneously, picking up my shot of Yukon Jack and swallowing a sip smoothly.

"Yes! He is the hero! He's just being modest!" Troy announces, smiling from ear to ear.

"Here's a hundred dollars for knocking the shit out of that punk, Bubba," the dark leisure-suited man says as he hands me a bill.

"I don't understand. Why do you want to give this to me?" I ask, genuinely surprised.

"Because that son of a bitch Bubba molested my niece. He's just an all-around asshole, a monstrous, insane bully," the modest, bony man confesses graphically.

"Well, in that case, at least sit down and have a drink with me?" I offer respectfully.

"Thanks, but no, I can't stay. I just wanted to say thank you. Take care, and may God bless you, Eddie," the gentleman says, shaking my hand with both of his, tipping his hat, then striding away abruptly, going about his merry way.

"I guess this means that drinks are on me tonight," I say humbly, looking side to side, being somewhat overly cautious.

"You seem to be on a roll, man!" Troy says, grinning as he lights up a cigarette.

"I know one damn thing is for sure: I've got to watch my back,", I whisper, then take a second swallow of my snakebite medicine.

"You got that right," Troy says, agreeing with me, exhaling smoke into the atmosphere. "That's why I don't ever want to see you downtown by yourself. Promise me," Troy requests emotionally.

"Okay, I promise," I tell him, continuing to scan the club.

"Another request for our beloved friend, Eddie!" Charlie Raw, the lead guitarist and singer announces. He's six feet, stout, long-haired and blonde, blue-eyed, in a light-blue jean suit, and smiling at me while his voice carries over the club through the house speakers. "Eddie, this is just for you!" Then he counts off, one-two-three-four. The band then launches into its rendition of "Sledgehammer" by Peter Gabriel. Unfortunately, I initially feel embarrassed and paranoid, and I begin scanning the area again to see who isn't too pleased regarding the musical hammer jokes.

"Are you all right, man?" Troy asks, looking over at me like he's wondering just what the hell gives.

"Just checking out the people around here. Just watching my damn back, that's all," I tell him, my eyes constantly shifting.

"Well, as long as I am around, you have nothing to worry about," Troy says, immensely confident, setting his glass down on the table, "Eddie, why don't you get up there on stage and sing a song?" he asks, leaning toward me.

"Not tonight. I just want to chill, you know? But why don't you sing?" I respond tactfully.

"Eddie, if you are ready, I'll take you home now," Troy says as he butts his cigarette out in the glass ashtray with an air of finality. I stand awkwardly to my feet, finish my drink, tip the establishment, then wave to the band as we exit Griddles Restaurant.

"Take care, Troy! Take care of yourself, Eddie! We are all behind you!" John announces loudly into the microphone, which causes me to feel fairly good about all the support I have down here. We stroll casually back over to the Beach Club parking lot and Troy's truck.

"You are pretty quiet tonight, man. What's going on in your head?" Troy asks, detecting the fact that I'm currently not the normal Eddie.

"I heard from quite a few different sources over in the Beach Club that a biker gang out of Portland is coming here to execute me," I say, staring up at the Beach Club's neon sign in front of me as I step into the passenger side of Troy's truck.

"I heard that also, but I don't want you to get all paranoid and stressed out about it," Troy admits caringly.

"Well, I can't afford not to watch my back," I say straightforwardly as Troy starts the truck.

The following partially sunny morning on my day off from work, I'm sitting on the picnic bench in my diminutive yard, smoking a cigarette, when the Seaside Police patrol vehicle parks in front of my fortress of a trailer. The officer in the driver's seat accompanying Sergeant Barnett, who I am very fond of, rolls down the window and says to me, "Mr. Williams, we, the law enforcement officers of the Seaside Police Department feel that since you have rid Clatsop County and our nice city of Seaside, Oregon of the number one riffraff piece of white trash, we would like to show our appreciation for what you did." He hands me the very same hammer I had to use on New Year's Eve. They had tied a bow on the pink ribbon-wrapped handle just under the head of the claw hammer, like it was the key to the city of Seaside.

"Are you guys really serious?" I ask, shocked, as I accept the life-saving tool, holding it for the second time in my right hand.

"He is, or was, the first place and foremost criminal bully in Clatsop County. Please believe us when we say you did us all a big favor. Thank you very much," the driver announces somewhat sternly, though very sincerely. "Also, he can't say the word *nigger* anymore, and he's presently—and hopefully permanently—a vegetable for the rest of his natural life," the informative officer mentions from his seat behind the wheel, as I try to mentally block reliving that horrible night, which is threatening to snatch me out of my present state of mind. The police also inform me that they, too, are aware of the rumored threat on my life linked to a biker gang from Portland named the Gypsy Jokers, who're coming to avenge Bubba.

"Just make sure you call us first before you do anything. Unless, of course, you have no other choice but to defend yourself. Okay, Eddie?" the officer says seriously, needlessly reminding me of my lawful right to act in self-defense. "Bubba's wannabe biker gang has been informed that they have to stay a minimum of twenty-five feet away from you, Eddie, and are prohibited from being in the same public place as you," the officer continues, filling me in on all the consequential legal ramifications of the current situation. The shockingly courteous and knowledgeable Seaside Police Officers wish me a good day and cruise away out of the trailer park.

This region of the greater Pacific Northwest, particularly Seaside, Oregon, has got to be populated with the craziest people in the world, I say to myself. "Oh my goodness! Snooky Nooky! Come out here, please?" I yell to Sherri, who was observing the entire exchange from the diminutive front kitchen window of our unattractive trailer.

"What did the police want with you, baby?" Sherri asks as she carefully walks down the steps barefooted, tying her hair up with a black scrunchie behind her head with both hands.

"This is the same claw hammer I hit that racist ignorant bully with, the one who attempted to destroy me that night at Melinda's? Furthermore, the police just handed it back to me, gift-wrapped, complete with a pink ribbon in a bow! Honey, what the hell was really going on just now was them saying, 'Thanks for getting rid of the riff raff!'" I tell her in a rush of words, then take a drag off my cigarette and exhale the delicious smoke in a deep sigh of relief, blowing it out into the open air.

Consequentially, not everyone is a happy camper gearing up for the Eddie Dee Williams Saves the Day Parade, however. If you are a racist, thinking that there was a shred of heroism involved in any part of this infraction is ignorantly unlawful. While working my early morning shift the following week at the Shilo, everything is going along fine, until Sherri approaches me sadly with her apron in hand in the kitchen hallway just outside of the break room. She tells me she was terminated by Andrew, the restaurant manager, for tardiness after being five minutes late for work. I struggle to comfort her and let her know that everything is going to be okay, but we both know that Andrew has a substantially brainwashed issue with our *Jungle Fever* interracial relationship, anyway.

A few days later, Sherri drives me to Astoria for my scheduled court date regarding my DUI, which ends with a hung jury, resulting in a sensational decision. However, it may come back up if the DA has anything to say about it. Meanwhile, the Seaside Police, and anyone else who cares, are constantly reminding me of the ongoing rumor regarding the biker gang located in Portland that's coming to Seaside to slaughter my thirty-two-year old life. After finally getting some work hours of community service in, I say goodbye to the manager as I leave the gray-painted food bank, when an average-sized man dressed in brown slacks, a white dress shirt, a boring tie, with a long, tan raincoat over the entire ensemble approaches me reverently on Holiday Street as clouds of steam float up from the recently drenched sidewalk now baking away in the sun. "You are him, aren't you? The one trapped in the corner with the bride, whose only line of defense was a claw hammer?" he asks, speaking gently, standing motionless, both hands buried in his pockets. It seems to me like I'm outside of my body, watching both of us, as if I am having a superficial vision of the encounter, and I'm obviously staring at his pair of human hands stationed in his coat pockets. Only after what I experience as a horridly ominous eternity of dread does he quickly remove his hands from his pockets, finally realizing he was presenting an unnerving threat to my anatomy. Then he peacefully extends his open-palmed hand to shake mine, giving me instant relief, signaling that he is not the enemy of the human righteousness of self-defense. "I would have done exactly the same thing if I was surrounded by five evil-hearted men," this awkward, black-haired, clean-shaven stranger states, looking me straightforwardly in the eye, which doesn't make the situation any better. It's all I can do to respectfully pronounce a low-uttered "Thank you"while shaking his hand, which closes the door on our conversation, allowing me to escape from this individual abruptly, and down the sidewalk to ponder any additional, unwarranted dramatic altercations which lie ahead.

"Well, you have a nice day," I declare anxiously as I stride down the street, headed to the Beach Club to meet Jim Dunkin. As I arrive at the tavern, the owner—six-foot-two, healthy build, dark-haired Dale Ballou—is bartending with his sidekick, a five-year-old, seventy-five-pound, black-and-brown German Shepherd named BC, who will remove your empty bottle or can of beer, bring you another one, all the while accepting tips in his trained mouth.

Dale is standing behind the bar, relaxed in a burgundy T-shirt and jeans, and immediately shakes my hand for my heroism, then places a pitcher of beer in front of me "On the house!" Dale proclaims. "We got your back, Eddie! Congratulations!"

"Thank you," I reply with heartfelt sincerity.

Then I spot Joe Nicolazzi to my left among the large number of local customers scattered around standing, looking down at his mug of beer. We haven't seen each other since the grand jury hearing convened as a result of the dysfunctional melee gone awry. His involuntarily camouflaged face, replete with two, grayish-black eyes and a slight concussion, catches me in his peripheral vision. He marches over and gives me a big thank-you hug and a handshake. "Let me buy you a beer!" he says, the strong aroma of his already beer-saturated breath wafting into my face. "Thank you for saving my life," he utters in a monotone, though genuinely grateful. I knew that took a lot for Joe to say, and I appreciated every word of it.

"You are more than welcome. I do think you forgot to inform me that you have a huge-ass baby brother,", I mention casually, reaching in my black Guess jacket for my cigarettes.

"Oh yeah, I heard about that," he says, chuckling, then toasting our glasses and taking a long pull of cold, thirst-quenching beer.

"How is your daughter doing?" I ask, failing miserably in my attempt to avoid looking at his nearly lethal facial lacerations.

"Thanks for asking. Rayann is doing better," he says, setting his now-empty glass down on the bar.

"I am very glad to hear it," I reply. Then Jim Dunkin, dressed in civilian clothes, merrily enters through the wide-open front door. He is followed by my good friend, Joe Wingenbach—an olive-skinned, my height and weight, long black-haired, mildly thick-mustachioed Caucasian guy—along with his lady: slender, five-foot-six, blonde-haired, green-eyed Theresa. She walks up and gives me a congratulatory hug, then as I go to shake Joe Wingenbach's hand, he fakes being assaulted like I knocked him down, hitting the carpeted floor with a *WHAM!* Harder and louder than a pro wrestler, faking unconsciousness, laid out on the barroom floor, causing everybody who does not know us to be vigilantly alarmed. Jim and I immediately start laughing at Joe's acting ability as he lays motionless on the carpet. Then, Theresa wittily informs Joe that he has to get up before all the tourists present who witnessed Joe's antics initiate some kind of unnecessary emergency action, since the scene has attracted no small amount of concerned attention, which was probably what Joe wanted to accomplish in the first place. Finally, Joe gets up from the worn, maroon carpet to his feet, then hugs me vigorously as usual, followed by a heartfelt high-five.

"Did you see those people's frantic faces, Eddie? As if you really knocked him out!" Jim Dunkin proclaims with his addictive laugh.

"You crazy-ass human being, you are so cock-a-doodle crazy! And I like it a lot!" I announce, ginning contentedly, embracing Joe's crazy, dramatic ass as well. After, I pour Joe and Theresa some beer into some pounder glasses from the large pitcher as Joe puts his arm around me. We all toast in celebration of my grand jury self-defense dismissal due to racism, then Joe quickly leans over and whispers in my right ear about the big-time rumor spreading like a virus all over Seaside about the ill-advised death threat on my life. While he's reassuring me he's one thousand percent on my side, out of my peripheral vision, I notice

Steve wearing a dark T-shirt, left hand in his jeans pocket, mug of beer in his right, who had mistaken me for Chocolate Joe. Unbelievably, Chocolate Joe Alexander actually waltzes in through the door wearing a black-and-white sweat suit, a black cap on his head, saying hello to everyone!

Now, since we are both in the Beach Club together for the first time ever, long-haired pal Joe W., standing directly between Chocolate Joe and me, pointing the index fingers of both hands at each of us respectfully, announces loudly that he's a dermatological instructor and, "Ladies and dumbass gentleman! *That*, is Joe Alexander! And *this*, is Eddie Dee Williams, of Seaside, Oregon! They do *not*, I repeat, do *not* look anything alike!"

Finally, Spin strides through the doorway in jeans, sweater, and Beach Club ball cap, as Dale leans over the bar and says, "Eddie, you guys really do look nothing alike," as he's sanitizing the bar with a towel.

"Yeah, how could anybody mistake Joe Alexander for Eddie when brother Ed has those big, luscious chocolate lips?" Spin says, easing into the conversation and sexually motivating it. "Can you imagine the suction of those perfectly chocolate, big lips on my hog?" Spin announces, laughing jokingly, causing the Beach Club to roar into utter hilarity. "Hey, Ed, you saved my life! That's just another damn good reason you should consider sucking my hog!" Spin says laughing, holding on to me very firmly. "I love you, man," Spin says sincerely as he orders a pitcher of beer.

"I love you too, bro," I reply, grinning affectionate human sentiment. "Say, Chocolate Joe? Look there. Is that dude right there the one that called me you? Right over there!" I say, pointing in the direction of the guy called Steve, bringing him to Chocolate Joe's attention.

"I don't owe that man shit over there. As a matter of fact, I don't even know that man, Eddie. C'mon, let's go straighten him out as well too!" Joe exclaims as we calmly walk over to Steve, and I introduce him to Joe Alexander.

"I don't know this man, Eddie. There must be another Black Joe around here, a little taller than you guys," Steve replies, then chugs some beer. We finally realize to perfection that Bullshit-Brown Joe Green of

Chicago is accountable for all of this misconnected ethnic mayhem, which I mention to Chocolate Joe as we walk away from Steve and back to the circle of our well-regarded associates. Jim, Chocolate Joe, Spin, Theresa, Joe W., and I grab a table large enough for all of us and play a series of games of darts, then a couple games of pool. When the evening finally winds down, we get an escorted ride home with Jim, Tiffany, and Darlene.

When business at work starts to taper off for the turtle-slow end of winter, I hire Chocolate Joe Alexander as a part-time janitor at the inn. There's just no way I can give him forty hours a week because things are way too slow along the wintry Pacific Northwest Coast.

One day after, I finally get the skirting at the base of the trailer, Sherri smooches me and takes off with her mother to a few garage sales, leaving Jeremy with Dinah next door, to play with Rob and Katie. I laze around the trailer, taking a nap, flopping on the built-in queen-sized bed since I have to work a split-shift today and close up the kitchen at the Shilo Inn tonight, only to be awakened thirty minutes later by next-door neighbor Dinah's blonde, five-year-old daughter Katie, alerting me that the trailer is filled with smoke and on fire. Still fully clothed, I jump up, dash outside and around to open the trailer's back door, grab Katie and Jeremy, and set them outside, away from the trailer. Then, leaving the back door open for ventilation, I instinctively sprint in through the front door where smoke has already filled the constricted living space of the trailer. I quickly discover the source of the fire in Jeremy's miniature stained-gray plywood bedroom; the bottom mattress of the built-in bunk beds is in flames, trying very hard to reach the mattress above. Continuing to hold my breath as there's way too much smoke, I hurriedly snatch up the twin-sized mattress and toss it out the front door into the fire pit, turn on the water, and hose the flames down until they're utterly extinguished. Katie is now my hero who saved my life. What goes around comes around.

The very next week, my youngest brother, Keith shows up right after my mother calls and states that if I see him, to take away the keys to the truck and drive it back to Portland. Of course, I'm not going to do any such a thing. Mother is just simply releasing maternal anxiety steam. Keith is six feet, 225 pounds. He has a Hershey chocolate complexion, perfectly pearl-white teeth, and bears an uncanny resemblance to my dad. My baby brother is somewhat bigger than I am and shows up in my stepfather's white '99 Ford Ranger up here from the state capital, Salem, Oregon, with a new girlfriend in tow. They pull up and park next to the Blue Chevy I recently purchased from Bob next door.

They both emerge from the truck and Keith says, "This is my older brother, Eddie, and Eddie, this Crystal."

"Nice to meet you, Crystal," I say to her, smiling.

"Nice to have finally met you, Eddie," Crystal replies. Keith is dressed in a white T-shirt, jeans, and black-and-white Nikes. Crystal is five-seven, mocha chocolate, with braided hair and brown eyes. Then Sherri, dressed casually and barefooted, steps out of the trailer with a single, thick ponytail going down her back, and in support of some strange motivation, does exactly the supreme opposite of how I would handle the current situation.

"Mom says you are supposed to give the keys to Eddie so he can take the truck back," Sherri declares, standing hands-on-hips next to the white truck on the passenger side in the gravel, being superciliously disrespectful to Keith.

Looking obviously violated, Keith erupts into a cross-eyed mode of verbal dictation in response to Sherri. "This is *my* stepfather's truck. Who is not *your* stepfather. He permitted me, Keith, to drive it up here to the beach. So, would you please mind your own damn fucking business, please?" Keith announces across the hood of the truck, visibly distressed. Sherri glares at me, searching for support as I remain silent, standing there smoking a cigarette. Then, mega-bothered Sherri jams it into high reverse back inside the trailer subsequent to our trivial wordless conversation.

"Man, let's go somewhere, shoot some pool, and have a beer, Eddie! I am not trying to be around Sherri, my brother!" Keith states, eyes piercing, very self-controlled, with his hand on top of the cab of the truck.

"Okay, let's go to the Beach Club. That is the safest club around here. For me, anyway," I suggest. I go to tell Sherri that I will be back soon since she was somewhat upset I did not take her side. When I tell her I'm going to the Beach Club with my brother, she stays quiet, and I just turn around and exit the cat litter-smelling trailer and into the cab of my stepfather's short-bed truck. Keith, Crystal, and I take off in the pearly white new truck with Keith driving.

We cruise down to the Beach Club and as we're parking in the gravel lot, Keith says, "Bro, your woman needs to mind her own damn business!" Keith exits the rig, still harping on what Sherri said to him.

"Keith, just forget it! Damn! It's over!" Crystal says logically, refereeing the circumstances. "We came down here to have a nice time with your brother," she adds.

"Every now and then, you can ignore people's actions," I say in defense of Sherri, as I get out of the truck.

"Well, you need to teach your pink-ass girlfriend to mind her own damn business,", Keith throws out one time. I ignore my brother's comments since I am really very glad to see him. We enter the Beach Club where a lot of my friends have already gathered in the bar, conversing, having a good time. Without delay, we seize a vacant pool table, I put a quarter in the slot, push in and pull out, and rack up the balls. After that, I introduce Keith and Crystal to everyone and stroll casually over to the bar.

"Hey Eddie, how's it going, brother?" Rob, the bartender, asks.

"Rob, my friend, how are you doing, man?" I ask.

"Hanging in there. What can I get you?" Rob asks.

"A pitcher of Miller and three glasses, please," I request, handing him a worn ten-dollar bill.

"Eddie, your turn," Keith says, after racking up the balls and replacing the rack.

"Go ahead, Ed, I'll bring the pitcher over to you," Rob says kindly. I walk over to the rack full of cue sticks, pick out a sixteen, and roll it on the table checking to see if it's straight or somewhat crooked. Rob brings the pitcher and three chilled drinking glasses over, sets them on the wooden table, and hands me my change. I in turn give him a two-dollar tip and introduce him to Keith and Crystal. Rob thanks me for the tip and heads back to the bar.

"Crystal, now don't get too upset, but I have to teach my younger brother a lesson in pool," I mention to Crystal, smiling. Then I stroke my break shot and make two stripes. I focus as I take another shot and make it, when through the front door of the tavern walks in a blast from the recent past: one of Bubba's boys, Ronald Greg. He has on black leather biker attire, the same steel-toed boots he wore that radical New Year's Eve night, and he positions himself at a small table by the large window. However, he is not to be in the vicinity of me, especially in a bar. The presence of anybody who has tried to kill me just has a definite way of instantly energizing the adrenalin in my anatomy. In this case, it exploded into lock-and-load mode, focusing on him intensely and firmly until he notices me, standing there with a new two-tone brown wooden pool cue in my hand.

"What is wrong with you?" Keith whispers, noticing my face and stance.

"One of my enemies from the hammer incident is right over there," I hiss to my brother. "That's one of the bikers who wanted to kill me. He is not supposed to be around me. At all!" I mention purposely loud, holding onto the pool cue tightly.

"What do you want me to do?" Keith asks me carefully, caringly.

"Tell Rob that punk has got to vacate the premises!" I announce as my defensive adrenalin comes to a rapid boil.

Rob has already walked the short distance to the table, leans his partially bald head over as he's holding a bar rag while he whispers, "Eddie, is you alright?"

"Hell to the no," I reply stonily. "The Seaside Police, in addition to the judge in Astoria, ruled that those bikers who attempted to murder me were legally prohibited from being in the same place where I am. Moreover, I was here first," I tell Rob.

"If he makes you uncomfortable, Eddie, I will have him leave," Rob says to me, shaking my hand vigorously.

"That would be just fine, Rob. I don't want any problems," I modestly request of Rob. "I'd rather be safe than sorry. This situation just won't work." Then, Rob goes and tells Ronald that he has to leave. Without so much as a word of disagreement, Ronald finishes his beer and exits the bar in peace. The minute the door closes behind Ronald Greg, the twenty local customers in the Beach Club Tavern initiate cheering and applause so loud, you'd think they were at the Super Bowl.

"Damn! I guess you are not the only one in this town that has a problem with them bully-ass bikers," Keith states over the noise, amazed at the outcry of support in my behalf, then swallowing down his beer.

"I guess so!" Crystal says, sitting back down at the table. We happily play a few more games of pool before Keith takes me home to the trailer park, then heads back to Portland.

My days are pretty much the same, even now that I have had my Oregon State driver's license reinstated. I'm still riding my bike. John Trent comes by the trailer early one clear, crispy, sunny winter morning when the wind is blowing so hard, I put car tires on the metal roof of the maroon trailer hoping the weight will keep it attached. We walk the coastline, smoking cigarettes, watching the wind-torn coast as a black cat strolls up to us, only to be caught up in the high, vacuum-sucking air, screaming out of our sight into the outer limits, traveling backward through the air, screeching in terror.

"Dude! Did you see that shit, Brother Ed? Please tell me you just saw that," John says, laughing like it hurts as the black cat disappears way up into the gray, gloomy sky, as if headed for outer space.

Later on, John, Marty, and I hoof it into downtown Seaside so I can get in some community service hours. Marty and John start out on a quest for female miniskirts on the beach after I peel off for work at the foodbank. It's a gray shack of an antique-looking building to do my community service hours on 101, just across the highway from David and Melinda Duke's house. But they turn me away suddenly, with only thirty-two hours left to do. They say I am a good worker, however, they need to allot hours to other people, who I've never seen.

I am at work a few days later preparing for spring to come around the corner, when I am called to the chef's office. I knock on the office door and Dennis says, "Come in and have a seat," and he takes his seat behind the desk. As I am sitting down, Dennis says, "I don't want to upset you, Eddie, you are doing a fine job. But it has been brought to my attention that you might be discriminating against white people."

Grinning broadly I look over the walls covered with health and safety posters, get tickled, and start laughing very hard. "So, I don't have to tell you what you need to do?" Dennis asks, smiling, leaning back in his chair.

"Not a problem. I didn't know that it could be a problem when I hired the only African-American I have ever hired in a calendar year," I reply, positively ingenuously. "So, I will make sure I even things out with the Caucasians, as soon as I find some Caucasians who don't mind having a Chocolate supervisor," I say truthfully.

"Thanks, Eddie, that's all I wanted," Dennis says, as I rise out of the stained, wooden chair and head back to my preparation labor.

Fed up with being escorted around town, arguing and getting nowhere with no-housekeeping Sherri, I solo robustly down to the Beach Club, where I come across a man I've seen around town who got my attention. He's about my size, wearing jeans and a short-sleeved shirt, a cat lover named Duane, so I take the stool next to him at the bar. Rob, the bartender, in T-shirt and jeans as usual, sets a pitcher of beer in front of me. By way of starting a conversation, Duane leads off with saying he's contemplating blowing his head off; life is not worth living anymore.

"Look, my friend, don't talk like that," I reply, turning my stool to face him. Forgetting about my own screwed-up situation, we talk about his problems until closing time, when he promises he is all right before we go our separate ways.

The next day, the news spreads like wildfire through Clatsop County that Duane has indeed blown his brains out. When the Seaside Police arrived at the dreadful crime scene, his cats were ingesting his brains out in his front yard, just like the drunkard freakishly predicted the night before to my face, in front of Rob Spivey.

Consequently, I hire Bob Redding, along with Bill Tumwater, who both had recently been respectfully hassling me for employment. They don't mind working for work for me. Bill Tumwater is a stout, clean-shaven six-footer and owns the Tumwater Motel on Roosevelt Drive. He needs extra work to make his mortgage payment before losing his property, just temporarily until business picks up in the coming spring.

"Bitchin'" Bob Redding has been my neighbor for quite some time since moving in with Dinah, next door. Now, it is time for a fire pit and barbeque get-together. I have only one little, itty-bitty problem with them: they turn up their ghetto blaster music real loud, any time they get good and ready. Every time Dinah gets a fifth of Black Velvet and some Southern Comfort, she turns up her stereo to listen to her favorite song, "Funky Cold Ma Dinah," by Tone Loc, which quickly turned into a springtime ritual.

Arthur moves his small trailer out of the park, and my other social contact, Mike, purchases a small brown trailer just big enough for him and his son, Justin, and moves into that space directly across from Sherri and me.

Now the Pine Cove Trailer Park has gotten unmistakably, appealingly fresh. With the expansion of the horseshoe pit area of the park, Christy, Gene and Darryl, Merle and Tammie, and Robin and Lamar come over to the pit fires, bringing their kids, drinking beer, being neighborly, and having a good old time. Our trailer was not a virgin to terror; we are now enjoying the privilege of the unwanted company of a black-and-white striped skunk, who strategically sprays the undercarriage of our narrow-skirted trailer, which blends in nicely with the stench from the litter box. Our life is not a many-splendored thing. Upon the skunk's arrival, we were abruptly awakened by the foulness of its deposit, which crept up into our entire world for two to three weeks. We avoided cooking or eating in the stench-filled trailer and would sleep and eat next door at Bob and Dinah's, across the highway at the Pizza Palace, and at Sherri's folk's house. Being evicted from your own place by a skunk is horrible.

Death threats continue to filter into my life, plaguing the tourism town of Seaside, Oregon, as well as unfounded and legitimate recent sightings of out-of-town biker gangs, cruising around town suspiciously. I'm still being advised constantly by the Seaside Police that I should not be caught alone, which could be dangerously fatal. My six feet tall, 240 pounds of muscle, mocha complexioned cousin Gordy and his magnificently buxom, blonde-haired, blue-eyed, pretty-smiling Caucasian fiancée Sherri with the excellent personality, would come down at least every other month to check on me. But nothing ever happened when they were here, just good, happy times.

The very first time Gordy and Sherrie visited, we accidently got stuck in quicksand in their brown Ford station wagon on Del Ray beach. We had to have somebody who just happened to be on the beach with a truck at four o'clock in the morning pull us out. All because Gordy wanted to park the station wagon on the sandy beach at night.

Driving to work in my blue bomber Chevy only takes five minutes with no Seaside Police harassing me. As a matter of fact, Sergeant Barnett once pulled me over on my way to work just to tell me a humorous Michael Jackson joke. I am jamming to the sounds, "Don't Worry, Be Happy" playing on the radio, parking my blue bomber in the Shilo Inn lower level parking lot, entering the employee door where John approaches me.

"Hey, Eddie, what do you call Rodney King in Spanish?" he asks me as I walk in the break room at work, laughing before he can tell me the punch line.

"I don't have the slightest, my friend," I say, clueless, grabbing my cigarettes.

"A piñata!" he says, laughing hard at his joke-telling, turning a shade of Bach mauve from laughter.

Spring break is here, surprising my son and daughter, by picking them up and taking them to the beautiful Pacific Northwest Coast. Crabbing in the Nehalem river, corn dogs, cotton candy, caramel popcorn, salt water taffy, arcade bumper cars, swings and seashell hunting on the beach, along with a couple of pizza parties at the Pizza Palace Restaurant across Highway 101 from the Pine Cove Trailer Park. The time zips by and I'm already driving my children back to Portland.

My cousin, Ray, would also come up to the Shilo Inn from Portland out of the clear blue to check on me after my brutal, racial altercation. I get off work early one day and we decide to venture out to the Beach Club. Ray, who looks like a butterscotch hulk, gets all the attention from the moment we enter the establishment. Boozed up and ballsy, this toothless, short, heavy-set, sandy-blonde Caucasian lady immediately hits on Ray, so we order up a pitcher of beer and start a game of pool, giving her no cosmic chance in hell of pouncing on Ray's muscular anatomy with his biceps oozing out of his white, short-sleeve polo shirt.

My second day off in a row is nice and sunny, and with a last-minute warning, my cousin Donny shows up in the passenger seat of a nice, '59 Ford truck with alloy wheels in mint condition. They pull into the space next to the blue bomber, park, and I exit the trailer to greet my close cousin. Donny and the driver exit the beautiful truck.

Donny, six months younger than me, mocha chocolate with braided hair, is sporting a leg cast, wearing sweat pants, a sweatshirt, and a brand new baseball cap with the Trailblazers logo. He's come down with his Hispanic partner, Joe—five-eight, stocky, mustached, and loves to eat.

Donny introduces us. "Joe, this is my Cousin Eddie."

We shake hands, saying one to another at the time, "Nice to meet you, man."

"See, those were some good directions," I say to Mexican Joe, still shaking his hand firmly.

"Well, I can see that you guys made it," Chocolate Joe replies, as he walks up to Donny and gives him a handshake, then a hug. "Well, let's go somewhere and shoot some pool!", Chocolate Joe suggests immediately.

Chocolate Joe and I leap in the flatbed of this beautiful truck, and he tells Alice he will return, while Donny and Mexican Joe get into the cab. We head out of Pine Cove, merging off Highway 101 onto Holiday Street, headed for downtown Seaside, when the Seaside Police pull us over. The officer emerges from his patrol car, smiling, and it's none other than Sergeant Steve Barnett. "Now, you know, Eddie and Joe, if I see three soul brothers *and* a Mexican in a very beautiful antique truck, you just know I got to pull it over," Steve says jokingly cheery, and we all start laughing. "Racial profiling will be strictly enforced!" he continues, laughing. "Okay, you guys, have a nice evening!" Steve says, waving and walking back to his patrol car.

After Sergeant Barnett gets into his patrol car and drives away waving, Mexican Joe and Donny are still sitting in the cab of the pickup, shocked but relieved. "That is one cool-ass police officer!" Donny says, completely surprised, smiling.

"Yeah. You know, none of the police have pulled me over in a car, or bike, or even walking down the street since the hammer incident," I add, thinking to myself, *Welcome to Seaside!*

"Yo! Mr. Hero! This be a tavern right here?" Donny asks me, eyeballing the Bridge Tender Tavern.

"Yes, but this isn't the place I usually patronize," I say with serious apprehension.

"Well, we are right here. Why don't we have one beer, then go somewhere else?" Donny says, limping out of the passenger side of the truck.

"Yeah! That sounds like a plan," Chocolate Joe says, agreeing with Donny. We walk up to the entrance of the Bridge Tender Tavern, a huge cabin built overlooking the Necanicum River on Broadway, just as you enter downtown Seaside, its door wide open. We walk in casually, looking like tourists, and take up some of the chairs close to the pool tables so we can play some pool. We order a couple of pitchers of beer and are just getting settled around the table when this ignorant Caucasian asshole-of-a-person—five foot ten, slender-build, and blonde hair—who lives in Seaside and who has an uncannily raunchy disposition that we try to pay no mind and tolerate just the same—walks over to our table. Chocolate Joe is sitting there, telling a joke, when all of a sudden this drunken person we are trying to ignore whips Donny's hat right off his head, grinds the brand new red, black, and white Trailblazers hat into the groin area of his trousers, throws the hat on the table, then forcefully bangs his elbow down on the table, as if to arm-wrestle my cousin, almost knocking over our pitchers of beer. Mexican Joe grabs the crazy Caucasian, takes him out the front door, ands proceeds to whip this drunken asshole's ass. Joe has him knocked out in a flash, laid out horizontally on the sidewalk, right in front of the Bridge Tender Tavern.

"C'mon, Joe! Let's get the hell out of here," I shout, respectfully, to Joe, as I try to convince him to get into the driver's seat. "You don't want to go to jail down here!" I say, with a dead-serious face. Mexican

Joe, hotfoots it into the truck, Donny limping quickly into the rig's passenger side, while Chocolate Joe and I hop in the bed just as Mexican Joe drives off down Broadway.

They drop us off at my trailer in Pine Cove, then head back to Portland, only to get pulled over by a Clatsop County Sheriff just outside of Seaside, but are luckily released without incident.

Preceded by various citations for late-night loud music, excessive partying, disorderly conduct, and freaky female babysitters, Dinah and Bob are finally evicted from the Pine Cove Trailer Park and move their trailer to Nappa, Oregon, which gives us back our large lot. I light the fire pit early, and out of habit, extinguish it by 9:30 p.m., even though the police have stopped harassing me entirely. On the back road behind the park, our silver Siamese cat has been hit by a car, which made Jeremy very sad. A new era is in motion as situations change; there's a high turnover of people living at the coast, Chocolate Joe relocates to St. Louis, Missouri soon after I had to terminate him for not showing up to work three days in a row. Fortunately, there are no hard feelings between us; I just had to do my job.

I keep watching my back, trying not to become the next Rodney King, in any sense of the word, constantly calculating each step I take. I get so good at it I even do it in my sleep, until it becomes second nature, since the periodic sightings of the Gypsy Jokers continue to filter back to me from my closest friends in this coastal tourist town. The trailer is now painted white, with a bright mauve trim, which I can personally say has transformed it into something other than a ghetto eyesore. Sherri still not working is somewhat of a hardship, most especially where housekeeping is concerned. We keep quarreling, debating racism, and Sherri wants to meet her maternal, racist grandfather, who is in town visiting. I give in, knowing what this entails, as Sherri, Jeremy, and I drive over to her parents' abode, where they are all sitting on the deck in upright, multicolored lawn chairs, enjoying the mightily brilliant sun.

As we approach, I see Sherri's Grandfather all dressed in white; T-shirt, shorts, *and* flip flops. She says to him, "I'd like you to meet Eddie." He sits there in his lawn chair next to his wife, purposely ignoring his granddaughter, even looking the other way, as if I didn't meet the criteria of respect for a human being. No longer needing to prove my point, I simply head back to the driver's seat of the blue Bomber and light up a cigarette, ready to leave Sherri if need be. Unlike the last time Sherri tried to introduce us and we instantly left the premises, this time Sherri decides to stay at her folk's house and visit with her judgmental family for a while. On the return trip, I am becoming numb as hell, the waves of resentment breaking steadily over me as I drive back to the trailer. Before we get there, I stop at the store and grab a case of beer to subdue the pain. Once we arrive home, Sherri attempts to validate why she conducted herself in that manner, which was grossly different from the last time we were there. Needless to say, I'm not having any of it.

A short while back, I had acquired some Spalding golf clubs, so Troy and I would frequent the driving range in his unmistakable mustard Jimmy truck to release the stress brought on by the surrounding racial ignorance, which still plagues me from time to time. We also play a couple of music gigs in Astoria together at the Labor Temple and Annie's Uptown Tavern. Troy sings and plays the piano, then he introduces me onto the stage, and I sing in absolute, first-rate times of pure elation. I'm hanging out in Astoria a lot after work just for a change of pace. I drive the blue Bomber bar-hopping as Spin and I make the off-white Hong Kong Restaurant located on Marine Drive with the yellow neon sign above the main entrance. Happy, plus high off cannabis, Spin and I enter the establishment, breeze into the nice-sized lounge, and order a couple of happy hour drinks. The bartender and manager, who resembles Ken Jeong, the actor from the movie *The Hangover*, is smiling and always in a good mood, dressed in a white, short-sleeved shirt and black denim slacks, hands me a couple dollars' worth of quarters to play pool.

"You want to break?" Spin asks me, racking up the balls, then removing his thin, tan jacket, tossing it across the top of the built-in booth in front of one of the two picture windows. Drinking Zombie cocktails in chimney glasses, we begin to play pool when our host brings out a large, silver bowl of fried chicken, setting it on the table for the happy hour customers, which I assume are all-you-can-eat appetizer miniature drumsticks. As Spin orders another round of drinks, I accidentally make all of the excellent fried drumsticks disappear from the bowl within a matter of ten of fifteen minutes. After being tipped heavily and laughing with the other locals who are also quenching their thirst, the host takes the empty silver bowl back out into the kitchen and returns with it replenished with more fried chicken. As I sink the eight ball in the wrong pocket, losing my game, I re-embark on eating all of the chicken once again, just like an addict, without giving it a second thought!

As Spin continues to win pool games, without even thinking about it, I stomach another entire bowl of fried chicken. This time, the host realizes what has transpired and gets very upset. "You did it! You did this! You go! You get out!" the oriental brother announces loudly, setting the empty silver bowl down on the table, glaring at me as I devour the last drumstick. "You get out! You eat all chicken, you get out!" all the while being very dramatic, yet very comical, and everybody chuckles while Spin is helplessly laughing his ass off, and the Asian Brother of another mother points his small, erect finger in the direction of the exit to his warm, picturesque establishment. I kindly apologize to him, attempting to be serious. However, his initial reaction was too funny. I'm grinning in his face and he does not want to hear it. "Just get out! You eat all fried chicken, you get out!" We slam our drinks down on the table in high hilarity and leave the lounge nonchalantly, laughing our asses off.

"Dude! I have never seen anybody get eighty-sixed out of a bar for eating all the happy hour fried chicken, dude! That's got to be an all-time new!" Spin says as we hop into the prehistoric blue Chevy Bomber, high, laughing, and laughing high.

16

. . . .

Summer Fun?

Able-bodied and blessed that it's summertime sunny, I make good on my promise to my kids, drive down in the blue bomber, scoop them up from Portland, and motor back up to Seaside where we have a blast in the downtown arcade after we arrive. Then it's happy play time at the beach as Sherri, Shamelah, Jeremy, Deon, and I embark on a camping trip that very same weekend to visit Sherri's father's side of the family, who're very down-to-earth people camping in Central Oregon on the Deschutes River, specifically Maupin, Oregon, where it's ninety-plus degrees in the shade.

We're all looking forward to some fishing, white water rafting, and accelerating our fun quotient. Shamelah is dreadfully afraid of the water and says she does not want to go white water rafting at all, period, so she stays with Sherri's Aunt on the desert-dry land while the rest of us head out in blue rafts down the natural amusement park provided by the sparkling, swiftly moving river. We float downstream at a fair rate of speed, having a blast with my son, Deon, wearing a pink-red-and-blue life jacket. Ron, Sherri, and her other aunt and uncle are in one raft, while the rest of the clan is in the other, enjoying the warm, sunny weather, comfortably riding along in their sky-blue-and-red raft. Ron's sisters are so cool and solid people, it's difficult to grasp them having a brother with a racist agenda.

After a couple of hours of floating downstream in the early afternoon, everyone is sipping on hydrating liquids that have been chilling silently in the cooler, when we accidentally manage to float across some rocks and get stuck. Ron, sitting next to Deon, says to me, "Eddie, grab the rope and pull us out of here!"

"Okay! Not a problem!" I answer, standing and stepping up onto the side of the multicolored raft. I grab the rope and step off the side of the motionless raft with the aim of pulling from the rock once I'm standing on it, but I misjudge my footing, missing the rock entirely, and I'm suddenly in the liquid quicksand of an undetectable, whirlpool undertow, which in a blink snatches the deck shoes off my feet. I'm instantly vacuum-suctioned down thirty-five feet into the vast, swirling, pitch-black Deschutes River's underwater world, down to this ghoulish hole in the river bottom. My water-logged black-and-white-patterned tank top and shorts outfit suddenly feels like it weighs a ton. Fortunately, my surrounding guardian angels are watching over me and quickly tranquilize my purpose-thwarting-panic. Still holding my breath with my lungs half-full of oxygen, I fall back on what I was taught at the YMCA; I close my eyes, fold my arms across my blue-and-red life jacket and grab the outside corners at the shoulder, cross my legs, and twist my entire anatomy to break the undertow's strong suction that's holding me down.

Suddenly disengaged from the eddy, I open my eyes and am free to float out into the far-flung ebony darkness, where I instinctively slowly blow bubbles to let me know which way is up, which logically, and life-or-death wise, is exactly the direction I start swimming forthwith. Follow those bubbles! Up, up I kick and stroke, until the murky water world above starts slowly revealing a barely discernible, pale luminosity, then it begins to brighten more quickly, and I know I'm heading in the right direction. My lungs are close to running out of air when I'm finally able to recognize the blue skies above me. Before I know it, I'm back above sea level, gulping in air faster than a newborn baby who's just been smacked on the ass.

Once I'm able to slow my breathing down a little, I hear my kids screaming downstream on the beach, crying in the belief that their father has tragically drowned in the murky waters. I soberly recall my cousin Tracy drowning in the Sandy River, not being able to survive the brutal, unpredictable undertows of that particular dark, wet underworld. I slither out of the water onto the riverbank, panting violently, still inhaling all the oxygen I can suck into my lungs, sitting on the bank, arms wrapped around my knees pressed to my chest, my clothes soaking the sand a darker shade of beige. I'm a little shaken, but thankful for the Almighty and my past swimming instructors who taught me how to actually survive in the event of the very near disaster I just encountered. I take a few more moments to calm down considerably, and slowly make my way down the shore to within about fifteen yards of where the rafts are beached, and call out, "Anybody have a beer?" much to the great surprise of our little family band.

After heartfelt hugs and more tears, this time of relief, and everyone relating how scared they were that I was dead and gone, we finish off the day rafting for a few more hours, followed by a campfire that night, before heading back to Seaside the next morning.

Overall, the kids had a nice time during their summer stay. They really enjoyed the arcade in Seaside, the bumper cars, and eating the tasty elephant ears made directly across the street. They got to play on the beach, watched the sandcastle contest and the volleyball tournament, as well as explore some of the caves along Cannon Beach.

Before I know it, it's time to take my beautiful son and daughter back to Portland; time to go back to school. They had so much fun and I am very proud of how they're growing up. I love them very much.

In the fall, on a not-so-sunny day while I'm home alone, since Sherri's gone with her homemaker mother to a few garage sales, there is a loud knock at the trailer door. I throw on my thin, funky black robe to camouflage my nudity, thinking the only somebody it could be is a relative popping up from Portland. I walk to the front door and with no hesitation, turn the knob and open it, and it's none other than my probation officer, dressed in official attire, complete with bulletproof vest and accompanied by the Clatsop County sheriff. She strides quickly up the steps to the door with a sort of combative air about her, as if I am about to shut the door in her face.

"May we come in, Mr. Williams?" she asks repugnantly, already easing herself inside the doorway. I back up barefooted as she forces herself into my untidy, cat letterbox-smelling abode, which is courtesy of the new replacement Siamese cat's bowel-and-bladder habits. "Mr.

Williams, you are under arrest for violation of probation," the PO utters, while the slender, uniformed, six-foot-two Clatsop County sheriff guards the front door.

I back up a couple more steps, keeping my robe closed with one hand to maintain decorum, as well as my modesty, replying, "I understood you to say you would not violate me since I have not been convicted of any of the charges brought against me?" I remind her of the statement she made to me in the Clatsop County Jail, just before I went to arraignment.

"I did say that, yes," she admits, hands on the hips of the trousers of her Department of Corrections uniform, analyzing the present attire I have over my anatomy. "Nevertheless, you have not completed your community service. Have you, Mr. Williams?" she says, rubbing her hands together as the sheriff, feet spread shoulder width apart, folds his arms, blocking the door.

"No, I have not. The Food Bank won't give me any more hours toward community service, and that's the only place in town that does community service around here," I answer truthfully, somewhat annoyed.

"Well, you still have thirty-six hours to complete. So I am going to send you back to Multnomah County. I consider it doing them a favor," my probation officer says boastfully, savoring the moment so intensely, it looks like she may start drooling any second. I immediately turn around, place my hands behind my back, and my untied robe separates, revealing my earth-toned anatomy. "Are you trying to be a smartass, Mr. Williams?" she says disapprovingly, at an earsplitting volume.

"No. Why would I do that?" I ask calmly over my shoulder, looking sternly into her grim face. "I am only cooperating with you, lady," I abruptly reply, staring straight into this individual's seriously piqued eyes.

"Well, go and put some clothes on! And furthermore, don't try to run, Mr. Williams!", the power-tripping probation officer threatens.

"I've had worse charges brought against me than the ones here in Clatsop County. Did I run then, ma'am? Or did I turn myself in?" I answer, looking at both of them on their mega-privileged power trip.

"Mr. Williams, I am violating you because you have not been violated the whole five years of your probation. So, whether you like it or not, go and get changed into some clothes," she orders commandingly. Irritated, I walk casually down the hallway to my bedroom, take the robe off, put on some fresh clothes, and grab my tennis shoes.

As I walk out of the bedroom I ask the drunk-with-power lady PO, "Is it okay if I brush my teeth and wash my face before we go?" I drop my shoes on the floor in the hallway outside the minuscule lavatory.

"Yes. Just leave the door open," she commands, looking directly down the narrow hallway, standing there with the light bouncing off the silvery, shimmering handcuffs she's holding in her hands. I rinse my mouth after brushing my teeth, dry my face, step out into the hallway and slip my feet into my tennis shoes one by one, and tie the laces on each shoe.

As I walk down the hall toward my unexpected company, I grab my black Guess jacket off of the couch, put it on, and then place my hands behind my back so she can put the handcuffs on me. Once the handcuffs are secured tightly around my wrists, all three of us exit the trailer with my PO slamming the door shut. The sheriff opens up his patrol car and unlocks the right rear door so the PO can open it and slide me into the rear seat and shut the door. They both take their seats up front, and the sheriff drives us to Astoria, where I am transferred into the rear of a police vehicle, in which I ride another ninety miles straight to the downtown Multnomah County Courthouse in Portland, where I am taken to Judge Abraham's chambers.

The judge enters from another door a few moments later and asks the district attorney, "What's this is all about?" He takes a seat in his desk chair behind this fancy, huge desk.

"Your Honor, Mr. Williams is here for violating his probation because he has not completed thirty-six hours of community service. And his probation terminates tomorrow," the district attorney says, reading from some documents he's holding in his hand.

"Where was he apprehended?" the judge asks, glaring at me for a forever-second.

"Seaside, Oregon, Your Honor," the DA says, quickly answering the judge.

"What are you doing in Seaside, Mr. Williams?" the bearded judge asks me very harshly.

"Changing my life for the better, Your Honor," I answer quickly.

"Are you employed down on the coast, Mr. Williams?" he asks me in a condescending tone.

"Yes, sir. I have worked at the Shilo Inn as the kitchen steward for almost two years now," I reply politely, trying not to look out the window.

"What is a kitchen steward?" he asks me curiously, actually sounding highly interested.

"I supervise, hire, and fire the janitors and dishwashers. I also own a single-wide mobile home in Seaside, Your Honor," I add quickly.

"Your Honor, since he has not completed the terms of his probation, we should extend his probation, and add some jail time," the DA suggests.

"Are you serious, Mr. District Attorney?" the Judge blares, furiously loud. "This man took twenty-eight years to get into trouble this one time! He's no criminal! Why are you wasting my time with this…this…case?" the judge says, obviously perturbed as he sits back in his lavishly upholstered chair. "The man is obviously working. Plus, he has established himself as an upstanding citizen in his community who's gainfully employed. He is not a criminal," he bluntly shouts out. "I sentence Mr. Williams to thirty-six hours in jail. At the end of that time, he is released from his probation," Judge Abraham declares stridently from behind his impressive desk. "Now get him out of here and quit wasting my time," he finishes to the DA, very irritated. "Mr. Williams, you stay out of trouble. Understood?" Judge Abraham says to me sternly as he looks me straight in the eye, yet it comes off in a profoundly sympathetic, positive manner.

"Yes, Your Honor," I reply eagerly, ready to get this ordeal over with; I've got to be in Seaside for work at six o'clock Sunday evening.

The Corrections Officer escorts me upstairs to an eighth-floor cell, where I call Sherri collect on the cellblock phone to let her know exactly what's going on and where I am. So I wind up staying in jail for thirty-six hours, being released on Sunday afternoon, and I'm finally off probation and one step closer to going back in the army.

I have to catch Mike, the mail truck driver, as he's headed back to Seaside from the rear of the Main Post Office in Portland in less than thirty minutes. I sprint full-speed out of the courthouse, up to Sixth Avenue, catch the number nine Broadway bus, which takes me to the Greyhound Station bus stop just across the street from the Main Post Office, which is the last stop before crossing the Willamette River by way of the Broadway Bridge. I dash across the street and around to the rear of the central building, which is a good quarter of a mile. I finally make it to the rear dock area of the post office and there sits Mike, warming up his rig, ready to depart for the Pacific Coast. I wave my arms insanely to get his attention, and he, in turn, taps his air horn lightly, acknowledging that he's seen me, and waits for me as I cover the last few yards to the five-ton commercial truck.

"Thank you, Mike," I say, breathing hard, sweat streaming off me as I open the door and step up into the truck. I make it back in time to be only a half an hour late to work. Chef Dennis informs me that Andrew, the Shilo Restaurant manager, is out to get me terminated, which means I should anticipate some sort of foul play, so I reply, "I am ready to upgrade to the position of cook."

I'm still a little exhausted after having to function like a roadrunner, as Buddy stands there, more or less chatting with the chef. "I've paid my dues," I tell Dennis. His crafty response to my statement is, "We will see."

Out of the blue on Christmas day, I receive a phone call at work from my mother, who tells me that my Great-Aunt Renal passed away today in Beverly Hills, California, leaving me in an emotionally fragile state. Which does nothing to mitigate the fact that it's nearing the one year anniversary of the Night of the Hammer, and I'm still dealing with all kinds of imagined threats, rumored biker sightings, and the like since I got back to Seaside.

Troy and Jim Dunkin, but mainly Sherri, are all being especially vigilant concerning my whereabouts during the holiday season. Next year arrives before I know it, and I am thankful to the Almighty One for letting me see and enjoy the day.

I drive the blue bomber, this time legally, to the courthouse in Astoria, and Sherri and I arrive for me to once again face more absurdly bogus charges stemming from the night I was inadvertently maced while at a traffic stop because Sherri assumed she was privileged enough to run a stop sign on Lewis and Clark Road in the middle of the night.

As Sherri and I enter the foyer to the courtroom, there in front of us I see the lady officer who stood up for me twice that night, which is probably the only reason that her idiot racist male sheriff coworker did not kill me. A fluffy, nicely dressed man about my height emerges from the courtroom and walks toward me asking, "Mr. Williams, I presume?"

"Yes, that would be me," I answer.

"My name is Shawn, and I'm your public defender," the average-sized, black-haired man in the two-piece gray suit and black loafers says, shaking my hand. I introduce him to Sherri, who's in a patterned jean dress and white flats today.

"Can we sit over there on the bench for a minute, Mr. Williams, please?" the cordial lawyer asks politely, as he gestures with the manila folder he's holding in his hand.

"Sure, no problem," I reply, and we walk over to the long, cold wooden bench. After we all take a seat, he starts to explain what's going to happen.

"If the female sheriff does what I believe she is going to, I have no doubt the hearing will probably go rather quickly," he says charismatically, looking flamboyantly relaxed. "So, I will see you inside," the lawyer says, smiling to reassure me, then gets up and returns to the courtroom.

The lady sheriff is called into the courtroom first and testifies. Five minutes later, she emerges from the courtroom, smiling, then winks at me as she walks past in her full uniform, then exits the building. The next witness called is the other male sheriff—around five-foot-nine, medium build—who did absolutely nothing to me that night. He disappears into the courtroom for a few, short minutes, then comes back out and he leaves the building.

Finally, the redheaded, racist sheriff who unlawfully harassed, falsely arrested, and falsely imprisoned me is called into the courtroom to give his testimony about the events of that evening. In another very few minutes, he too emerges from the courtroom, only he's looking abused, disgusted, and like a puppy who just got a butt-switching for crapping on the new carpet, forcefully pushing the door wide open and leaving in a hurry. Then my public defender comes out and announces, "That's it, Mr. Williams. You are free to go. All charges have been dropped."

"What exactly happened in there?" I ask, sincerely wanting to expand my limited knowledge of the judicial system.

"Well, it is all relatively simple. The female sheriff understood very well that you had done nothing unlawful on the scene, and testified thereto, and this was pretty much corroborated by the other male sheriff's account of the encounter. Which made the arresting sheriff look really and truly stupid when he said you did this, and you did that. Of course, the judge knew he was lying the minute he opened up his mouth and immediately dismissed the charges against you. Um." He looks like he's trying to stop himself from wetting his pants from holding back his laughter as he relates, "His Honor appeared (hic), to relish the opportunity of (snort), chastising the officer for his thoroughly unprofessional conduct, Mr. Williams!" He's suppressing his snickering so hard he's trembling with the effort as he shakes my hand.

"So, how do I file a complaint or lawsuit?" I ask seriously.

He quickly regains his composure upon hearing my question and tells me, "I believe you have to initiate that process in Portland."

"I was locked up three days for nothing, just because they can! Just because of the shade of my skin! I committed no crime, but selective harassment by law enforcement *should* be a crime," I announce.

"I'm so sorry you had to go through all that, Mr. Williams," the nice public defender says to me, solemnly apologetic.

"Thank you for saying that. You take care now," I tell him, still somewhat aggravated.

"Well, honey, you did it again," Sherri says as she stands up, ready to go home. Sadly, as soon as we make the drive back to Seaside and park in front of the trailer, the blue bomber gives out a chassis-shuddering death-clunk, and before I can even turn the ignition off, her engine finally fails and dies, never to take off again, leaving us sitting together in the quiet darkness.

A month later, as I ride my bike home from the Shilo Inn after working an eight-hour, cloudy, molasses-slow day, it feels like there's something different is in the air. Ah, I know what it is: it's the 21st of January, my mother and father's wedding anniversary. They would have been married thirty-four years today. I always wondered what it would be like if they were still together.

Sherri comes into the bedroom where I am sitting on the bed, getting ready to change out of my work clothes, and says, "Honey, I have some bad news for you. The policeman at the door says your brother Keith called the stationhouse and said your grandfather passed away today. I'm sorry, Honey." She hugs me tightly as I sit on the bed in shocked bewilderment. I immediately remember that the last time I saw him, which was the day when I went to pick up my kids; how he took my son, Deon, to get some ice cream. I continue to sit there numbly as a brief surge of grief washes over me. I wipe away the tears, drifting in my memory's reflection, now more than ever concerned about my mother.

The last time I talked to my grandfather was about six months ago, just before our phone was disconnected. He was my last grandparent to pass on, and they all went in a matter of just six short years. Can't say Grandma, no more Grandpa, Big Dad, or Big Mama no more. All of them departed to the other side of eternity. Of all the days that Grandpa could have passed away, it would have to be exactly on my mother and father's wedding anniversary.

The next day on the job, I make out a new weekly work schedule for the dishwashers and janitors so I can take some time to be with my family in Portland. I don't stay at work too long as I'm still somewhat upset and sort of numb; I just make sure everything is in order before I leave. Sherri and I take the coastal bus up to Portland and stay at my mother's house, sleeping in the guest room.

While we are mourning our loss, Tamara, my first cousin on my father's side, calls and asks me to bring Lisa, my monstrous, legally separated wife, over to Tammy's house that evening. Following up on Cousin Tamara's request, I borrow Pops's truck, kiss Sherri good-bye, and inform her that I am going to get to the bottom of this paternity ordeal once and for all so I can reenlist in the army.

I pick up Lisa and we drive over to Tamara's and knock on the front door. Tamara lets us in. Tamara is five foot eight, thick-bodied, with a caramel complexion just like her mother, Anna, who was one of my favorite aunts until she passed away in 1986. Tamara, quietly polite, shuts and locks the solid wood door, commands us to have a seat on the tan couch, pours us both humongous brandies in double shot glasses, and kicks off her slippers. She then demands, "Lisa, tell the truth about who Little Eddie's father is, or I'm going to kick your ass all over this house," very calmly, balling up her fists, ready to do some serious damage if need be.

I quickly remember that this had been one of my Aunt Anna's requests before she passed away. I sit there saying nothing, waiting patiently for the truth to set me free. After an eternity of deafening silence, Lisa finally breaks it. "His name is Randy Patterson," Lisa utters for the first time, very obviously looking away from me. I've been in the dark since 1976, and my ears are finally getting to hear the undisputed truth.

I take Lisa home without saying one word to her. Had she said this years ago, I most likely would have been stationed in Hawaii, or possibly the Philippines by now. This is so disturbing to me, I cannot even bring myself to sing a solo at my own grandfather's funeral. I am crushingly humiliated. It weighs so heavily upon my spirit, the day before my multitalented bully of an uncle, Harry, along with my family, buried grandpa without me and my brother Keith; I am just not there at all. His death, family, plus this recently uncovered fraudulent paternity rips through my soul, leaving an open wound of false accusations, that's keeping company with a bitterly stinging overdose of stupidity.

After the lengthy funeral, which was packed solid mostly with relatives, some friends, and dignitaries from our House of Worship, we broke bread at Maranatha Church in Northeast Portland, consoling one another in our time of loss, grief, and sorrow. Realizing I am not Little Eddie's biological father leaves me so overwhelmed and numbed, my sensitivity is no greater than that of a gnat. I am suddenly overcome by an insane fixation to see the Pacific Ocean, so we quickly return to Seaside. Even though I am one step closer to reenlisting in the army, I need to get a divorce, like yesterday.

My first week of cooking goes quite well after finally being promoted. Just the same, there is a new couple who just got hired as cooks at the Shilo Inn, and they've been sleeping in their car since they moved down here from Portland. Tom is five foot seven, slender, olive-skinned, with black hair and a moustache. He approaches me in the break room with a golden smile on his face. "Eddie, my man," he says, leaning across the table, lighting a cigarette. "I have a sweet deal for you, my friend. You need something. And I need something." He takes a drag off his filtered cigarette. "If my lady, Rachel and I could stay with you for a couple of weeks, until the next pay period that is, you can have my car," Tom says.

"Well, if you are serious, my friend, let me call Sherri and make sure it's okay," I reply.

"But there's one little request with this deal. And that is to drive me to Portland next week to get our checks for our last employer," Tom says, inhaling smoothly on his cigarette.

"Let me call Sherri right now," I answer, dialing the phone, since ours has been turned back on. Sherri answers on the second ring and I tell her, "Hi, honey. We have a proposition to think about. You know Tom and Rachel, who just started working here and came over to the house last week? Well, they need a place to stay for two weeks, and in exchange, they'll give me their yellow '76 four-door Maverick with the funky dark-green top. What do you think?" I ask excitedly. "There's nothing wrong with the car. I checked it out and it's in immaculate condition, interior, as well as exterior," I add ingenuously. "Okay, baby, I will see you in a little while, sweetheart. Bye," I say, then hang up the phone. "Well, Tom, its looks like you have got yourself a deal," I tell him.

"Thank you, brother," he says, shaking my hand.

"You're welcome, Tom. Helping one another, that's what it's all about," I say stylishly.

The two weeks fly by like birds heading south for the winter. And Tom and Rachel actually turned out to be pretty good roommates, especially being clean cooks. They were such excellent guests. If I'd had more room, I'd have asked them to stay longer.

Unlike yesterday's snowy conditions, today is particularly rainy and it's time to drive Tom to Portland so he can pick up his and Rachel's final checks from their last place of employment. We reach

Portland and notice the snow has not quite been melted away from the still-falling rain. Tom's former employer gives him something of a runaround for a little over a half hour, then finally comes across with both paychecks.

"Eddie, can we stop at a store and pick up some cigarettes before we hit the freeway?" Tom asks, lighting up his last cigarette, crushing the empty pack, and rolling the window down slightly.

"Not a problem," I reply, making a right on MLK from Killingsworth.

I pull my new-to-me yellow Maverick into a space in the Safeway parking lot and both of us head for the store. As we walk inside through the automatic doors, we're just in time to hear this roughly five-foot-nine Caucasian dude call an African American lady *nigger*. Damn, just when you think it is safe, racism suddenly rears up its ugly, ignorant face. He must have thought she was by herself and he could get away with it. Then, that lady's man starts whipping that Caucasian man's ass up, down, and all around aisle number two. Tom and I back out of the way of the flying fists and feet, and head over to the check stand to get Tom's cigarettes.

"We didn't really just see that, did we?" Tom asks, standing in front of the cashier.

"Yes, we did," I reply, still observing the dustup at hand.

"Carton of Camels, hard box, please?" Tom asks the cashier, pulls out a bankroll of money, hands her a twenty, and she gives him his change. We are walking out through the automatic door as the police arrive, who take the African American man and woman into custody, usher them outside, while the Caucasian guy involved follows them, telling the officer he did not say the N-word, yet Tom and I both heard him call her a nigger.

"Officer, excuse me, that's not true. He did call her nigger," I politely say to the officer.

"Hey, boy. You just back up fifteen feet," the officer says to me. I immediately back up about sixteen feet, while the Caucasian man repeats that he did not call that woman a nigger.

"That is not true," I say again. Then, the officer quickly walks over to me, pulls out his baton and holding it chest-high, shoves me down onto the snow-slushy pavement. The five-foot-eleven officer stands over me, enforcing his own brand of official oppression. "I said move back fifteen feet!"

From out of nowhere, a lady screams, "Somebody do something!" Suddenly, a six-foot-seven African American man in a long tan winter dress coat, gray slacks, and a Stetson hat exits the store, holding a brown paper bag in his arm. He walks straight up to the police officer, looks down into his face, reads his badge number and name tag, and says loudly, looking down at him fiercely, "Why don't you do to me what you just did to that young man for doing nothing?" I slowly get up off my cold, soaked backside, pissed and upset that once again I had to interrupt a so-called white lie in progress and spotlight the privileged trust code in its most extreme effect.

Tom apologizes sincerely for what happened, even though it wasn't his fault. All I can do to curb my frustration is get in the car and drive, stop for some gas, get on I-5 South, put the pedal to the metal to Highway 26 West, get the hell out of Portland and head back to Seaside.

Just a few weeks later, our neighbor, Sandy, with her right arm in a sling from dislocating her shoulder at work, saunters down to our trailer to retrieve her cigarettes she left behind from a previous visit. "What the hell is up with your ignorant-ass next-door neighbors with the shit green van, and a KKK cross on their roof?" she asks as she walks up to our front door.

"Just ignore them, Sandy. They aren't worth it," I reply, getting up off the couch.

"I forgot my cigarettes," Sandy says to herself, and she turns around and walks back toward her trailer. As she gets a few feet from my front steps, I suddenly overhear this back and forth between two women, yelling loudly. I step outside the trailer to see what's going on and at that moment, the racist neighbor lady comes off her porch, running, lopes up to Sandy, grabs her by the top of her curly hair, and slams her into a mud puddle in front of my trailer like she was Tanya Harding taking out Nancy Kerrigan. I jog over and attempt to break them up, when the racist neighbor's husband blindsides me, jumps on my back, and holds me down on the grass. While this has been going on, someone on the opposite side of the trailer park has already called the cops. A don't-know-shit Seaside Police rookie, who I have never seen before, rushes over to our happy little party and directs my racist neighbor to keep me pinned to the ground. I raise my head out of the dirt and grass, and my peripheral vision picks up the presence of another officer attending to something else in the trailer park.

That looks like Sergeant Barnett, the officer who escorted me to and from work in the front of the police car during the Hammer Incident, I say to myself. "Is that Steve Barnett?" I ask the rookie officer loudly.

"Yes, it is," he replies, very shocked. I quickly elbow my neighbor hard in the face so I can maneuver myself out of his clutches, flip him over onto his back, give him a sharp elbow in the ribs, stand up, and inform the rookie cop, "Big mistake, officer." I stride over to Sergeant Steve Barnett. "Steve! What is wrong with this crazy-ass officer?" I ask, bending over at the waist, panting from the scuffle, one hand on my hip, pointing at the officer. "All I did was try to stop a fight right in front of my trailer, and the next thing I know, my racist next-door neighbor sucker punches me and jumps on my back! Plus, this officer ordered him to hold me down!" I say, once again pointing my finger in frustration.

"Listen, man! This is Hammer—I mean, Eddie. He is a very good person! Don't ever treat him that way again!" Steve announces, critically chastising the nitwit rookie.

After Steve and the toy officer exit the trailer park, I come up with a solution to circumvent the current problem. I inform my family in Portland that I am having problems with my racist next-door neighbors. The very next week, Mojo, my six-foot-four, 260 pounds of muscle, premed dew, camel-brown complexioned cousin hears about my next-door problem. He comes down on the Greyhound, catches a cab to the trailer park, gets out, pays the driver, walks over to me and, very concerned, asks, "Which trailer the punk stay in?"

I point out the trailer with the cross on the top of it. Mojo says, "Grab my suitcase. I will be right back," and starts for my neighbors' trailer. He walks up the steps of the trailer and knocks on door. The man who blindsided me opens the door, Mojo instantly grabs him, and throws him bodily over the railing off his own porch. He steps down from the porch, stalks over to the bully, and says real low and slow, "Don't you ever touch my cousin again, you Jehovah's Witness-ass son of a bitch." He is in a boxing stance, standing there big-fisted, just itching to finish what he started. Then, my racist neighbor, whose instinct for survival has kicked in really good, quick-like-a-bunny jumps up off the ground, jackrabbits it up the steps into his trailer, and slams the door behind him. Mojo assumes his role of vigilante one more day for good measure before he has to return to Portland.

Another blessed day and I am cruising at work on a break, eating a tuna melt in the break room when Frank, the bartender, comes in looking for me. "Hey, big guy. The sheriff is here to see you. Plus, it's a good thing," Frank assures me, smiling and using positive hand gestures. "There is nothing wrong, Eddie. You are not in any kind of trouble," he assures me.

So I walk out to the lounge and this six-foot-two sheriff in a starched uniform says to me, "Mr. Williams?"

"Yes, that would be me, sir," I respond.

"Well, Mr. Williams, I have some good news for you. You are now a free man. Here is your divorce decree," he says, smiling, then shakes my hand. I quickly open it like it's a birthday card with money in it. It lists Deon Lee Williams as my son, with no mention of Little Eddie D. It is finally official in black and white: Eddie D. is not my biological son. The truth shall set you free, but in my heart, he is still my son and I love him. After all, this is not any of his fault. I need to talk to an army recruiter, now that I have the official, certified documents. I am divorced with only two biological children. I can't wait to submit this to the army recruiter in Portland.

I am so excited, I have to go for a walk on the beach to calm myself down, because the excitement is also mixed up with the realization that I was hoodwinked for so long, plus there is the added factor that I don't know how it's going to affect those boys. After all, they are blood brothers. I contact the recruiter who says once my DUI charge is complete, I can reenlist in the Armed Forces.

It's Sunday brunch once again, and, thanks to the numerous positive compliment cards from the guests concerning yours truly,

Dennis posts me, dressed for success in my white starched cook's outfit from head to black-leather industrial shoes, out on the brunch line to carve the roast beef and prime rib for the customers. However, a peculiar-looking, obscurely-pale, black-haired Caucasian gentleman around my size, but not muscular, in a thin, beige coat is sitting at the bar having a drink, and he keeps glancing over at me. We have a very large crowd today because the Portland Trailblazers and the Chicago Bulls are in the finals. The lounge is crowded to capacity, complete with lots of die-hard Portland fans. The brunch goes very well, and, as usual, I make about sixty dollars in tips, which impresses Dennis. However, Andrew does not quite see it that way, but what that's what happens when a so-called colorless person in a management position claiming to be a Christian is, in actuality, an outright, light-skinned, supremacist hypocrite.

So, after we break down once brunch is over, put all the food away, and I punch out feeling really good, we head for the bar to have an after-work shot of Yukon Jack, with the added bonus of getting to watch the game for a few minutes. The restaurant and lounge are still somewhat packed with Portland fans and I take a vacant seat at the bar until Frank finally notices me and says, "One second, Eddie," as he finishes ringing up a customer. "What can I get you, big guy?" he asks.

"Let me have the usual, Frank, please," I tell him.

"Coming right up, buddy," he says, picking up a glass, then the bottle of Yukon Jack. He brings me my drink and I smile gladly, then thank him.

The customer who had been glancing at me weirdly gets off his bar stool, walks over to me and asks, "You work here don't you?" in a non-threatening way.

"Yes, I work here," I answer, wondering where this is going.

Then he walks back to his seat and sits there for about three minutes. "Hey, Eddie? What's that all about?" Frank asks me, concerned.

"I don't know, Frank. Maybe he thinks I am Joe?" I reply, not giving it too much thought.

Then, the guy stands up and walks towards me again. He stops two feet in front of me and asks, kind of forcefully, "You live here, don't you?"

"Yes, I do," I answer, finishing my drink and more than ready to get out of there.

Then the pugnacious, crazy man stretches his arms out so wide and yells loudly enough that the whole restaurant and lounge can see and hear him, "You are the black son of a bitch who is bringing the dope into this town!"

"Hey, man? You can't talk to him like that! You're out of here! Now beat it!" Frank announces forcefully.

"But, he's a black nigger!" Mr. Crazy yells and points at me. "He's been bringing the dope to Seaside! That nigger right there is a dope-dealing nigger, disguised as a cook! Somebody should make a citizen's arrest! Arrest that nigger!" Mr. Crazy Racist continues, having definitely gotten everyone's attention. As security comes and escorts the man swiftly down the hallway and out of the crowded lounge, Andrew, the restaurant manager—who unfortunately looks like Jon Stewart—makes his way over to investigate what just happened, and tells me, "Maybe it would be better if you don't have an after-shift drink at the bar still wearing your cook's uniform?"

I knew at that moment that the racial bias syndrome was tightening the noose's knot around my neck, and that I was not long for the Seaside Beachfront Shilo Inn Hotel & Restaurant.

Since losing her job, Sherri has transformed into a disreputable anti-socializing prude who neglects housework yet always manages to find something else to do, rather than look for work. My new friend and neighbor, Norman, lives in a very wide, white, burgundy-trimmed trailer with a gorgeous lady named Chasanet, along with four young stepsons.

My mother, stepfather, Aunt Marie, Uncle Walt, and his son and his wife travel to Seaside to check on me. However, Sherri, who refuses to clean up, panics instantly, freaks out, and puts a pile of clean—or dirty? —clothes in the middle of the living room floor. At least the trailer no longer reeks of used cat litter since the replacement Siamese was hit by a truck the previous week on the same logging road where the first one bought it.

I put my mother off as long as I could so she wouldn't find out that Sherri has devolved into a lethargic, garage sale-hopping individual who sits in the tub soaking for hours, reading, and neglecting our home's level of cleanliness. My family visits for a very short while, realizing I am embarrassed to the nth degree of mortification.

By this time, I'm pretty much worn out from the stress of my new position at work, my grandfather's death, and the truth about my number-one son. The death threats around downtown Seaside seem to be mounting up, making me totally paranoid and hyper vigilant to people glaring at me, when it didn't even used to bother me. These death threats eating away at me are like a morbidly addictive game of Pac-Man. I begin supplementary drinking, plus calling in sick extra often. On top of everything else, after Sherri and I return from a much-needed, relaxing eight-day vacation in Las Vegas, I receive the news that my cousin, Darryl Glass, was killed last week in Portland trying to break up a fight between two rival gangs. I handed Andrew the ammunition he needed to terminate my employment at the Shilo Inn after working there almost three years. I then started flirting eagerly with a major case of rejection/oppression/depression, drinking heavily to mitigate being paranoid, wondering when, where, and how the biker gang was going to come and exterminate me. Somehow, not long after I was fired from the Shilo Inn, I dredged up the wherewithal to pick myself up and dust myself off like my grandfather taught me. Consequently, I landed a job at the opening of a brand new Ocean View Hotel a few blocks down the promenade from the Shilo Inn.

Today is orientation day at the Ocean View for all new employees and brunette-haired James is the chef at Ocean View who worked with me as a sous chef at the Shilo Inn for a short while. After giving his orientation speech and introducing everyone to each other, he caps it off in front of forty-five people by announcing, "Eddie, you don't have to steal the watermelon. It's free!" as all eyes in the room were on me. The majority of them let out some minor giggles. Some didn't laugh at all, and looked at me like they assumed immediately I just might be some kind of thief. Unfortunately, it's amazing how quickly supposedly intelligent people willingly hop on the bandwagon of ignorant stereotypes. Not a one of them knew, or cared to find out, that I am allergic to any and all melons. Since somebody reported

James's behavior toward me that day; he figured it best to fire me before I took some kind of legal action. Yeah, right.

Then one day, Sherri's father comes over and takes a seat on the couch in the living room. "Honey? Dad's here and he wants to talk to you," Sherri says as she walks into the bedroom where I am laying down on the bed, contemplating my next move. I get up and walk down the hallway to the living room to see what's up.

"Hey, Eddie. I would like to talk to you for a moment," Ron says, sliding his hands under each of his legs as he sits in the chair, like he's trying to restrain himself. "It appears that you have given up," Ron mentions quickly.

"What do you mean by that?" I ask, remaining standing.

"I mean you have given up on looking for a job," he unnervingly says boldly.

I have never in my life seen or heard of a man going into another man's home and tell him that he should get a job, especially when that man cannot hire him at his own damn business because of the color of his skin, because of his racist-ass clientele. I tell him, "Either you are part of the problem, or you are part of the solution. Don't talk to me about the solution when you are letting the problem live rent-free in your own house, Ron. Now, you understand me. Don't you ever talk to me like that again. Don't come into my house with your two-faces showing and tell me you need to hire an employee, but just because of the color of my skin you have the right to tell me to get a damn job in the same breath? That's institutional slavery," I reply, hurt, as well as flabbergasted with anger at this representation of ignorant, bowlegged racism. "I'm not playing with you. I don't know who raised you up to think that this is okay, so I'll let you know right now: that's ignorant, Ron. So we are done!" I walk back to the bedroom, getting away from this so-called man who is funded by the terrorist association of (H-A-T-E): Having a Traumatic Error.

I am so ready to go back into the service, but the reenlistment sergeant in Portland informs me that all of my court cases need to be resolved before I can return to the army. I can't wait to get the hell up out of here, though there are times I want to stay forever plus a day. Then, all of a sudden, it's verified that Sherri is pregnant. I desperately desire to be sworn in before the baby's born. Sherri and I drive up to Portland to my mother's house, where my brother Keith happens to be. We go inside, announcing the good news about the baby, when Keith asks Sherri without delay, up close and personal, "Hey Sherri, how does it feel knowing you are going to have a nigger honky baby?" Sherri turns all shades of reddish colors, not knowing what to say.

We visit for a good long while, making sure my mother is okay, then we head back to the coast, but Sherri's not speaking to me. The car starts having serious problems, and Sherri thinks it is time to pay her dad back for helping us out with the expenses of putting the trailer together. "The Maverick would clear the bill with him," Sherri alleges skillfully. So I go ahead and pay my debt by advancing the car, only to find out later that the "major" problem with the car was simply a disconnected alternator wire.

I'm sitting on the couch with Jeremy in the living room, watching *Bill and Ted's Excellent Adventure*, when there's a knock at the door of the trailer. It's the manager of the food bank: a very tall, slender man with gray hair who's dressed casually. "Hello, Eddie. I was just wondering if you were available to do some yard work for me at my house in Ghearhart?" he says, very businesslike.

"Sure, when would you like me to start?" I ask eagerly.

"Tomorrow? I will come and pick you up, Eddie, at...let's say 7:00 a.m.? See you then," he says.

The very next morning, I go to work for the manager and complete the huge job in one day.

"Wow! I can't believe you did all of this work in one day! You know, you coloreds get a bad rap. It's really the Indians who are the lazy ones," he says, confidently assured of himself. "I hope that one day, which I probably won't be around for, that you see a colored president, Eddie. I hope you do," he says sincerely.

What is this fascination with a colored president? Jesse Jackson literally got them spooked!

I'm laying content on the living room couch, watching my cousin on TV, Sway Calloway hosting, MTV Raps. There's an unexpected knock at the door. I shout come in, and John Trent enters, with two beers in tow. "Brother Ed, looks like you could use a cold one, my brother." John hands me the beer, grinning somewhat suspiciously. "Drink up, buttercup, have an excellent day," John says, laughing again as he takes a seat on the raggedy gray recliner. As time goes on, I start feeling uneased, dizzy, and quite paranoid. "You all right, Brother E?" John asks, with this stupid idiot grin on his face, spitting chewing tobacco in a Styrofoam cup. All of a sudden, I begin to hallucinate, all the walls in the trailer are slowly melting. My heart starts beating faster. As I nervously slide down into the couch, I'm sweating like a pig in heat. John begins to laugh as I contemplate, I've been spiked with some kind of drug or I am losing my damn mind. My vision is somewhat blurred, toes tingling. I try to sit up, but it's not happening. I'm tripping badly, like I'm falling and can't get up. "John. I don't see what is so damn funny. Did you spike my beer with acid?" I ask, holding my head up off of the couch.

"Sorry, Eddie Dee, I didn't think you were going to have a bad trip," John says, smirking.

"You should always think before you act," I shout, high as the sky. Trailer door wide open, everything outside is bright as hell. Sherri enters the trailer, immediately assuming that I am drunk.

"Hey, John," Sherri says sarcastically. "What's wrong with you?" Sherri asks as I attempt to sit up again.

"I spiked Eddie Dee's beer with acid, Sherri. Sorry about that," John says, as he stands up to leave.

"Wow! I can't believe he did that to you, honey," Sherri mentions as she approaches me, on the couch. "How can I help you, baby?" Sherri asks, concerned.

"Just hold me, and don't let me sink into the couch. I'm higher than Mt. Hood."

I continue working odd jobs here and there when Sherri coincidentally drops the bomb on me. Translation: she is leaving me. "The doctor says I need to be in a non-stressful situation, so it's best I move out. Unless you are?" she asks, little gears in her head scheming.

"Why would you want to get pregnant by somebody you don't want to be with?" I ask seriously, loving the way she lies.

"Well, this way, I will always have a part of you," she says, gazing blankly out into the distance.

17

• • • • • • • • • • • • • • • • • •

JL2K

John Trent, along with his cousin Marty, drops by from time to time; however, Jim is not speaking to me, since last year since he knocked out Steve the line cook. Then, after another barbecue, walking home Jim also knocking out Spin for upsetting John Trent, somebody ignorantly starting a rumor saying I wanted to fight Jim, which if you know me that be painstaking outer space incorrect. I said Jim is too damn close of a friend to fight, I love the guy. However, secondhand dung gets turned upside down hearsay shit.

Sherri moves into a fifth wheel across the Highway 101 in front of her sister's house, just before Christmas. I know Sherri thinks I was sexing April, the fun, charismatic redhead prep cook who worked at the Shilo Inn. She had a thin waist and a voluptuously blessed in the chest; a redhead Carmen Electra of sorts. But she and I were just good friends, that's all.

April, John, and I drink a sizeable full-sized cup of mushroom tea, psychotically tripping all night long, cruising through the small coastal town on foot, having an excellent moment in time once upon an instant when the town was completely tourist dead last winter, nothing but locals pleading with us to share our party favors as we laughed at a whole lot, pure gut-busting comedy setting us off.

If I have had my choice it would have been sugary gorgeous brunette Susan—perfect body, charming aura, breakfast and lunch waitress—or dazzling Melinda Duke, who is already spoken for. Furthermore, I'm not a very good cheater.

Sherri is working part time at the bowling alley in Gearhart across the highway from her father's business slash residence. Then on Valentine's Day she surprises me by spending the night in our fabulous trailer, accompanied with lobster along with steak dinner as we always commit to on this day, which would be our very last time—probably merely pity sex. I'm wondering, *What's Sherri Lynn really up to?*

Springtime, waking up constantly alone, emotionally flattened like a first-class fool, I disrupt the zany strategically landing employment at the Seaside Hospital, positioned on snob elitist hill as a cook/dietician, ten minutes away on my faithful ten-speed bicycle. However, after working for just one month, on a somewhat nice spring day, I was down in the dumps, dejected drinking, drowning my pain heavily, with my neighbors Mike and Norman and his brother Danny, Mexican fair-skinned Carlos.

Working swing shift at the Seaside Hospital, I was so awfully hungover, pickled while running the cashier register, taking a customer's order dressed in all white cook's uniform, I suddenly got lightheaded. I got dizzy, then started hyperventilating, causing myself to have an alcoholic seizure, flopping like a fish out of water, collapsing, lying on the floor. No second chance: I was terminated because my supervisor thought that I might be drunk. However, I didn't appear under the influence. You do the math. More likely grossly hungover.

Brokenhearted comedian-mouth neighbor Norman—stout, blue-eyed blonde hair, five foot ten, like me, scorched; his woman also left him. So Norman, Carlos the dishwasher, plus yours truly are getting drunk after the firewood has already burned out outside. We transfer the party to Norman's house, sitting at his wood-stained table and drink all the beer we can drink. Then the three of us, determined to stay liberated, decide to play cribbage for Nyquil shots at three o'clock in the damn morning till six o'clock in the morning, when the Seaside Police approach, knocking on the door, informing me that my father has had a severe, major heart attack.

After the officer exits, Carlos insists that we go to Portland pronto and check on my father's condition. Now, earlier the day before, I had purchased an old school black two-door celebrity, which had seen better days, from my distinguished, excellent neighbor Darryl, for two hundred dollars, since Sherri had helped me get a job as a cook at the Whaler restaurant in Cannon Beach Oregon, which total turnaround mileage fifteen miles.

"Come on, man. I will go with my brother, but we have to see about your father," Carlos constantly hammers home. Carlos, is you sure we haven't stayed up two long?" I ask, standing up, numb, ready to drive the black piece of car to Portland. So as the sun begins to rise, Carlos and I drive up Highway 26, east towards Portland.

I vaguely recall seeing Saddle Mountain. At that moment, the strangest miracle occurs: I'm awakened by my guardian angel, after regaining conscience from an overdose of Nyquil, to find us upside down in the car, windshield smashed out entirely. The top of the car is crinkled, also this black banged-up Celebrity is leaning halfway over a thousand foot cliff on Saddle Mountain, unmoving, frozen on the side of the highway. I can see death over the dashboard, however the car is very still. Carlos is regaining conscience from Nyquil plus beer, looking at me, saying, "What happened?" Before I can answer, Carlos suggests we get the hell out of this damn car before it tips over the cliff. Glass shatters all over us everywhere. Carefully, I exit the car through the window since it's shattered also.

Carlos is getting out of the vehicle when a state police officer drives by, noticing the wreck. At the same time an eighteen wheeler is headed west up the hill. Carlos informs me that he has a warrant, and would it be all right if he just took off to avoid an arrest, to which I say, why of course, go for it.

Carlos takes off across the street, flags down the driver of an eighteen-wheel truck, then unlocks the passenger door, steps up into the cab, before the Oregon state police could turn around. When the state trooper arrives, he immediately assumes that Carlos was driving, in addition to that's why he left the scene. Which I just go along with, since the officer has the circumstances all figured out. The six-foot-tall officer calls a tow truck on his patrol radio. Shaken, I sign off on the piece of demolished car over to the tow truck driver. I cannot help but rewind to when my cousin Ronnie went off a cliff in Kansas, which he did not survive.

The Oregon state police officer is nice enough to give me a ride in the backseat of the patrol car to my trailer park, where I manage to catch Mike the mailman and hitch a ride to Good Samaritan Hospital, downtown Portland. After spending quality time with my father and aunts plus my immediate family for a few days as he heals from a quadruple heart bypass surgery.

Unfortunately, I have to start work, at the Whaler in Cannon Beach as a line cook. but before I even dare to head back on the bus to Seaside, my stepfather Rob assists me in obtaining a 1985 four-banger gray Sprint automobile, in excellent condition, on an automotive high-end lot in North Portland on Lombard street.

Returning to Seaside, after a few weeks, Sherri and I are working together again, except I am the line cook. I'm getting the hang of the job when one night, Sherri's night off at the Whaler Restaurant, I am closing up, my white cook's uniform, still clean, when the daughter of the owners comes in with her beautiful children, a boy and a girl, asking if it was too late to get a kid's fish and chip meal. I say, "No problem at all. I just turned the deep fryer off, so it is still somewhat hot." So I turn it back on quickly and make them a nice seafood kid's meal. Then the owner's daughter wanders into the kitchen with the behaved kids to thank me for the fabulous meal. I reply graciously by saying, "You are welcome." Then the owner's daughter says for the most part outrageously revolting racist comment to her son and daughter, youthful susceptible offspring, reassuring subtle racism. She quickly informs her kids, unflinchingly malicious, "Let's go home and take a bath so you won't grow up and look dirty like that black man right there who just fixed your meal." What the fuck is the owner's daughter proverb, these statements not more than two feet away from me like I was some unmanly domicile house slave. Nevertheless, what's worse, analyze precisely what she is teaching her children: the wrong definition of earth-tone citizens, brainwashing her offspring's early education of obvious racism.

Not quite a week later, my employment is terminated by the owner's son for no real reason, talking to me like I have a tail, decisive, informing me to get my finger out of my black ass, which I wasn't going to tolerate him talking to me like I'm his pet four-legged dog. So I asked him to come outside and say that to my face; he logically turned down my offer.

A few days later, after I qualify for unemployment insurance, out of the blue my ex-mother-in-law calls me on the phone, since I had the phone turned back on once Sherri had voluntarily evicted herself. "Eddie," she says. "How are you doing?"

"I'm doing just fine, ma'am," I reply, curious about why she is calling me.

"Lisa has your thirteen-year-old Deon out there in those streets, on Alberta Street, Eddie, on a bicycle selling crack for his mother, along with gang bangers," Mrs. Bowles says to me, critically apprehensive. "Furthermore I wish you would leave, plus get him right now, Eddie,"

"Where is Eddie Dee?" I ask Mrs. Bowles inquisitively.

"He is doing fine in San Diego in the company of his cousin David," she replies softly. "Eddie, please help. Lisa has gang bangers running her entire house," Mrs. Bowles speaks to me sincerely.

"Not a problem. I am on my way to get my son right now," I say to my ex-mother-in-law, hanging up the phone. My plan of attack is to gas up the Sprint, then drive up to Portland Oregon, arriving just before darkness overcomes the light. I drive up to my ex-wife's house on North Alberta, just off of interstate five, notice that there is a gang banger dressed in all flaming red hat and shoes, sagging red-stitched jeans, talking to my son who is sitting on a used ten-speed red colored bike. I park my silver five-speed Sprint, feverously adrenalin overwhelms me. I quickly emerge from my vehicle, right hand inside my grey sweatshirt, calling my son Deon, dark T-shirt red shorts posted on the corner, obviously appearing to approach to me right now. Without hesitation, he rides the bike up to where I am standing. "Hello, son, you are coming to live with me now. Please go and put the bike up, then get all of your clothes together," I calmly command my son.

We both scale the huge wooden stairs up to the porch. Deon opens the door of the large dark green house with white trim, and we go in. Door wide open. Once in the ominous house, there's a trivial cannabis smell, along with residue crack cocaine smoke hovering throughout the hideous shadowy abode. To the immediate right in the spacious, white high-ceilinged living room, Lisa is sitting on a Bach-pattered reclining chair I had never seen before, with a glass pipe along with lighter in her right hand. Two gang bangers are posted convalescing on the couch then one other young banger, lounging on the love seat, all of them look at me like I'm crazy, while placing their hands, close on their concealed weapons under their various red shirts, sagging jeans. Strangely low-esteem Blood gang bangers, one of them with his feet on the coffee table I purchased overseas. Gang banger staring, nursing a 40z of Ole English, smoking a cigarette, sitting up, alarmed by my trespassing on their safe haven.

"That's my ex-husband, Eddie Dee," Lisa announces to all of the bangers in the living room.

"Excuse me, partner, but could you please excuse your feet off of the table? I purchased it in Europe," I say, making my presence known.

"Oh, my bad, OG," the gang banger replied, staring, rolling his bloodshot eyes into my stern face.

"I am taking Deon with me to the coast, Lisa," I say, not waiting for any authorization.

"That is fine, Eddie Dee. Do what you have to do, baby," Lisa says, smoking a cigarette.

Deon comes down from the upstairs with a large plastic bag of clothes. "Go hug your mother and tell her goodbye. We will be back soon so you can visit your younger brother Darryl and your mother," I say to Deon as I pick up the bag of clothes and we both exit the dwelling. We get in the car, drive back on interstate five, then Highway 26 west, driving directly nonstop to Seaside.

First thing I did as a single parent was take Deon out to dinner, plus play arcade games at the Pizza Palace across the highway from the trailer park till closing.

A few weeks later in June, Sherri and I are in relationship tranquil synthetic limbo. Because of the boys, we are in somewhat constant contact. Sherri is very fond of Deon, wants to take Deon along with Jeremy in her sister Kelly's Station Wagon to Portland for the day.

A day of freedom, Thursday, early, partially sunny afternoon I exit the beach club, parking the Chevy Sprint parked in the gravel parking lot, as Carlos and I stroll somewhat uninterested, both desiring a shot of hard alcohol. Bob Sr., the owner of this establishment, is nowhere to be found; too early for the band to play. Dusty is the bartender, who also bartends at the Beach Club, just brought our drinks to our table, which is in the lounge, just me and Carlos, along with two other fellows, facing the front of the restaurant, toasting our drinks, having a good time, with our backs against the wall.

All of a sudden six big biker dudes, approximately weighing 250 pounds apiece, walk into the restaurant, quickly taking a seat without bringing attention to themselves at a table directly in front of us. They have on denim biker jackets, jeans, and big black steel-toed biker boots. I have no idea what was going on until I pick up my drink, and all of a sudden Carlos says, "Eddie, I think they found you."

"Who, Carlos?" I ask, looking at Carlos, curious to what he was talking about.

"Them right there," he says, nodding to the bikers. When I look back over at the bikers, right away I make eye contact with the largest one—all of them damn near the size of my friend Bear—who takes his fat index finger, motions it across his neck, relaying to me that he's going to cut my head off. He points at me then says, "Nigger you a dead man!"

Well, shut the front door. Once again, I have been death trapped, threatened again simply because of the complexion of my skin. Furthermore, the privileged so-called white man must have their racial revenge. So there are a lot of punks that want to kill me. Finally, we meet. I understood, staring nervously at them as adrenalin kicks in and my anatomy starts to quake.

"What am I going to do?" I ask Carlos, not taking my eyes off of them, getting charged up.

"Here take this pistol under the table. You take it, Eddie. They want to kill you, not me, amigo," Carlos says anxiously. "Good luck,"

Carlos says as he stands up and tries to leave. But the biker motions, shaking his head: nobody leaves.

The biker is promising to take my head off. "He going to kill you, nigger," the biker states, and I quickly, with nerves of steel, get up to my feet, not waiting for him to make his move, for death is not freaking river dancing in my life at this moment in time! I walk up speedily, my adrenalin ignited, until I'm in really close range. I aim the snub-nosed .32 caliber brown-handled pistol, pulling back the hammer with my thumb, military instincts kicking in. I've got my right arm straight, gun pointed at the biker's forehead less than fifteen feet away. I say in a thunderous voice, "Move, punk motherfucker! I dare your ass to flinch today! Bitch-made motherfucker! This is a good day, for you and your punk-ass friends are going to greet death today! Move, motherfucker, I dare you. Get up! Flinch! You want to kill the nigger? Well, get up, then! Because, bitch, it going to be the last time your punk ass gets up in this lifetime! Get up, I dare you, you sorry motherfucker! Come on, kill the nigger! Come on! Get up! Punk bitch, move!"

Dusty the bartender shouts, "Eddie, don't do it! Let me call the police." Dusty is seriously pleading with me, while the restaurant customers have become silent, still as a cemetery as I kept the pistol aimed at the biker's forehead.

"Yeah, Dusty, that's a good idea," I reply, not blinking an eye. "I still want him to get up and kill the nigger," I state harshly. "You've been talking all that shit for years now, threatening to kill me. Well, get the hell up and just do it, shit, right now," I add deafeningly.

Minutes later, the Seaside police enter the restaurant, guns drawn. "Eddie, it is okay. We are here now. Drop the gun, please," the officer commands.

"Not a problem, officer," I reply, very compliant now that they have finally arrived. I quickly bend down at warp speed, setting the black-and-brown, fully loaded .32 caliber pistol on the floor. I quickly toddle backwards, headed to the table where my drink is resting, and sit down to drink. I'm shaking, guzzling the contents of my glass quickly to calm my nerves down. I'm uneasy, sitting hyped up in the cushioned seat I originally was sitting in before this all had taken place.

So as I finish my drink, the officers pick up the gun that Carlos had handed to me off the floor. "Eddie, we are very sorry, but you are under arrest for felon in possession of a firearm. Please stand up and put your hands behind your back, Eddie," the officer agreeably asks. I gasp, standing up damn quickly, and turn around, placing my now sweaty hands behind my back, for the sixth time arrested here in three and a half years in the good old Pacific Northwest coast. The other police officer plus backup escorts all the enormous bully racist bikers out of town and advises them to not come back. I am standing, getting handcuffs put on me, in front of a room full of tourist people, when the officer starts comfortably talking to me. "Eddie, you did good thing today," the arresting officer says proudly, barely touching my shoulder, guiding me out of the restaurant. "You didn't stoop down to their level, and we are glad you called, like you're supposed to do, so I will tell you this. I will come and testify on your behalf, that your life has been death threats on your life since the hammer incident in 1990, when you were just defending yourself yet again," the officer states magnificently.

"I will testify also," said the other police officer on my right side.

"And I will too, Eddie," Dusty whispers, walking towards me and the police. "I will also testify on your behalf," he adds, patting me on the back. Dusty kindly holds the front door open. The police escort me to their patrol car—sidewalk full of tourists—and open the rear door and properly put me in the car as effortlessly as feasible, like I was some close relative of the police officers that had been arrested. It is quite weird: they take me to jail and transferred me to Astoria for my arraignment.

Hot, fun summer comes to an end. Missing his family and friends, Deon decides he wants to live with our cousins Gordy and Sherrie in Portland for the school year until I relocate back to the City of Roses once all of my business down here is complete. Upon my return to Seaside the following weekend, the day arose that was hypothetically supposed to be a proud day, but it turned upside down into an insult to injury audacity of human beings.

Carlos and I venture up to Cullaby Lake to do some fishing for a couple hours. My cousin Mojo, visiting once again, is hunkered at the trailer with his lady acquaintance. We fish for just a little while, perhaps because Sherri could go into labor at any given time. I decide to cut our outing somewhat short and return to the trailer park, even though I am fully aware that Sherri's family is having her sister Kelly's youngest child Tyler's first birthday party, which they were having at their parents' house in Ghearhart.

When Carlos and I return to the trailer park, I notice Darryl, my neighbor, is walking away from my trailer, when Mojo opens the door—no shirt just jeans on—and yells out of the trailer, mentioning Sherri has just gone into labor, you should go up there right now.

"So she just now called?" I ask Mojo while Carlos quickly emerges from the car, closing the door.

"I don't know, Eddie," Mojo replies, standing barefooted on the steps of the trailer.

"Eddie, get out of here," Carlos says, shutting the car door respectfully. So I immediately drive that Chevy Sprint as fast as I can without getting a speeding ticket to Astoria on Highway 101 north to the Columbia Memorial Hospital and Park.

I enter the unfamiliar hospital and walk up to the desk. "Hello, ma'am. Yes, could you direct me the maternity section, please?" I request politely in my gray sweat suit.

"Is it a friend of yours having a baby?" the white-uniformed receptionist asks curiously, concerned since I'm earth-tone brown.

"My ex-girlfriend is in labor, having our baby," I whisper peacefully.

"What is her name?" she asks, suspicious.

"Sherri Nyberg," I reply quickly.

"Well, she delivered way over an hour ago, sir," she says, rubbing salt in my wound. "Let me escort you to where she is at," the nurse mentions to me.

"Excuse me, they just called me half an hour ago, claiming she was going into labor."

"Well, I don't know what to tell you, sir," the nurse says, walking ahead of me, and then stopping. Then she directs me where exactly to go.

I walk into this spacious, clean, cool hospital room which Sherri and my son have all to their own. The two of them are very quiet, lying down on the bed, Sherri's head elevated, holding with our newborn son in her arms, softly kissing him, a beautiful sight as I walk up, looking at the both of them.

"Hello, Lynn. How is you?" I ask politely, calling her by her middle name, staring at my son.

"I am doing just fine," she says defensively quickly.

"Why are you doing this to me?" I ask, goaded. "You called me way after he was already born?" I ask, trying not to be overly enraged.

"Well, we all were having a birthday party over at mom's for Tyler's first birthday party when I went into labor. I just completely forgot to call you," Sherri claims, lying their minus makeup, pale with a selfish, privileged attitude.

"Who was all here?" I ask, getting slightly irritated.

"My entire family," she replies proudly.

"You didn't have no problem calling me in that damn trailer to have sex just so you could have a biracial handsome son by me, now you're going to put enmity between me and my son? May I please hold my son?" I ask as the demon of uncertainty begins to take its toll on me.

"Yes, you can hold your son," Sherri says, handing him gently over to me. I am holding my precious newborn son. He has beautiful black, wavy hair. He is light-skinned and will turn fair-skinned, judging by his dark, tiny ears. I walk the floor of the room very carefully, smiling at how handsome he is and how much he's going to look like me. Not even ten minutes later, Sherri says she's worn-out with everybody being up there for the delivery, and now she wants to get some sleep. So I kiss my son goodbye, handing him back to Sherri, and I leave the room instantly, since I know things are going to drastically change now that Sherri has been brainwashed in opposition to me. In turn, Sherri will brainwash my son against me. It's the lynch theory: divide and conquer father against the son, and there isn't anything I can do about it. My stomach turns into sharp, nauseated knots. I leave the mystic hospital very uneasy. I have a son, however, neither the mother or her parents want me to have anything to do with my seed.

The very next day, waking up on the repulsive green couch, I get up early, brush my teeth, shower, and get dressed without waking up Mojo and his girl, asleep in the spare room. I drive my car to the Columbia

Memorial Hospital in Astoria, Oregon to see my handsome newborn son. I enter the hospital room where Sherri and our handsome son are staying. I say hello, walking up to the bed, with no real response. There is a lady—about five foot six, slender, very pale, with a not-so-friendly disposition—standing next to the bed on Sherri's right hand side, holding a clipboard in her hand and a pen in the other. This lady, looking down at the clipboard in her hand, impolitely says, without making eye contact, "You are the father, correct?" The shrewd lady then rolls her eyes at me, waiting for an answer as if somehow she used to own me.

"Yes I am," I reply, preparing myself for whatever is next.

"You need to sign these papers right here, right now, so we can get everything processed as quickly as possible," the lady commands me as she hands me the clipboard. I start to read my son's last name listed as Nyberg, not Williams, taking on Sherri's father's last name. Nevertheless, he's my son. That makes no sense.

"Why are you doing this to me, Sherri?" I ask, staring at Sherri being vindictively unruffled.

"We—all of us—notion it would be best if we all have the same last name," Sherri mentions selfishly.

"Who all thought it was best for my son?" I ask as serenely as my mental strain would allow me.

"Above and beyond, Mom figured, since Kelly's kids are all Ames and my brother Steve has no boys, we felt the baby should have Dad's last name," Sherri says.

"So I have no say in my son's last name?" I ask, looking directly in Sherri's eyes.

"Yes, that is correct, Mr. Williams. There is nothing you can do about it, so just sign the papers," the rude, repulsive woman insists, speaking to me like I am an underclass metropolis dweller.

"I was not talking to you, lady. I was talking to Sherri," I say abruptly, shooting a glaze of disapproval towards the evil lady. I glare back at Sherri, now realizing I am nothing except a sperm contributor, a first class fool. Obviously she wants to raise this son of mine without me, however accumulate child support money at the damn same time.

"What is this form for?" I ask nobody in particular.

"This is for child support so the process can start immediately," the evil lady mentions with authority. I never ever run from my responsibilities when it comes to all my children, so I sign the papers for my son's sake, also pretty much let it go, about going back retiring in the United States Army. I would hope that they one day the VA will heal my right foot and I will be somewhat good as new.

Sherri names our son Trevor Shane Nyberg, whether I like it or not, and that's just the way it is. When it comes time for Sherri to sign, she looks at the form to register Trevor's name. Sherri has a complaint, wrongfully out of this world. "Why under race my son's nationality is African American?" Sherri says boldly noisy, akin to somebody making a gigantic, appalling racial mistake.

"Because your son is African American," the unpleasant lady promptly informs Sherri.

"Now, you listen. This is my son. I am white, therefore my son is white. He is not a damn African American!" Sherri says, sitting up uncertainly in the hospital bed, peeved noisily towards the evil xenophobic lady.

"I understand your dilemma, Sherri. However, the bylaw says if you have a baby by a black man, the baby automatically becomes African American," the evil lady states, truthfully reciting law, holding her clipboard to her side. "Sorry about that, but that is the law, and there is nothing you can do about it," the evil lady says, showing no sympathy for Sherri. "Look at the bright side of it," the evil lady tells Sherri. "The good thing, in these kinds of situations, is at least he will be called, African American, therefore not being exposed to the downward stigma labels such as black or colored or negro, which they all of them, possess on their birth certificates," the privileged, hideous, racist, evil lady says, reassuring privileged Sherri. "Your son won't have that same stigma that they have on their birth certificate," referring to me and my race, the evil ass lady alleged proudly.

I'm trying not to get upset about the evil lady's embellishing the truth. Sherri, less unaware of the fact, hands me my son, finally, while they debate. His beautiful hazel eyes open and stare at me quietly. Sadly. I think to myself, I best enjoy these infrequent moments. Just good enough to conceive and pay child support, but not good enough to be a father for my son. So I ignore the obvious false equivalency by softly singing "You Are My Sunshine" to Trevor, walking slowly back and forth, minding my business until they are finished discussing why Trevor is African American. I whisper a solemn prayer over my son, knowing it will be eighteen years later before we are allowed to get father-and-son close.

Sherri, almost dressed once it is time to check out, tells me that I have the privilege to give my son and Sherri a ride home to her parents' abode.

Weeks pass quickly. On a September day, I visit my son Deon in Portland, Oregon. My father is in full recovery, very thankful to the Almighty, as I visit a few relatives—not in a hurry to return to the coast—single, free, earth-tone male American.

I stop by a club that night on MLK and run into the LaGrone brothers, who I grew up with in North Portland. Since my birthday is four days away, we three party all night, attending an after-hours just off of MLK and Russell until the dawn, George and Ronald finally allowing me to drive to the coast. A few hours later, my mother calls me in Seaside, saying George LaGrone was murdered about an hour ago. I am devastated, thinking maybe I am next, since death is so close to me, my good friend gone just like that.

I drive up to Astoria, Oregon, to my DUI court date. Yet every time I go to court, it is a hung jury. which has happened twice now. The third time I have been tried for this particular infraction, which the jury wrote not guilty down on the paper, then illegally the DA erased it after I testified and the jury found me not guilty. Pissed off, the bogus, dark-suits DA asked me to step outside to the hallway of the court room. Then the DA harshly shuts the door, and all at once he starts shouting at the jury when he thinks no one can hear. However, I then tiptoe up to the door, kneeling down so they can't see my silhouette through the door window, so I can listen through the gap in the doorway. The DA shouts this message to the Clatsop County all-Caucasian appointed jury: "This black man has come down here and has been found not guilty on all of his charges, so before you people think about going home, you are going to change that verdict too guilty immediately. Now take another damn vote, people, and convict this man so we all can go home," the district attorney announces, not concerned if I can hear him. I quickly dash back to my seat on the long wooden bench without anybody knowing, that I was eavesdropping. The DA calls me back in and says the jury found me guilty. Now that is what's I call straight-up, good old fashioned, privileged, bullying racism. Now if anybody in Clatsop County records were to look at that file today, they would see that the not guilty verdict was clearly erased by the district attorney himself. So much for fair, equal justice. How many hung juries, does it take to get a guilty verdict? Answer: any means necessary. What does justice truly have to do with it?

Waking up alone, sobering up from the libation the previous night on the unbearable raggedy green couch, still not used to being alone in this trailer for over a year now, ready to sell the memories that linger in my history. Thanking the Almighty for another day, quietly praying for the positive outcome of my court trial in Gerhardt, Oregon. I've never been to court at this particular courthouse, as many times I been requested to appear in court. I will never, ever forget, for the rest of my life, today—Monday, April 11, 1994, charged in the county of Clatsop County. Felon in possession of a firearm. I arise quickly from my uncouth slumber, not knowing exactly what time it is. I believe courts starts at 1:00 p.m. Nobody's been over; the door is very much unlocked. Carlos promised he would be there to testify on my behalf on the events which took place on June 17, 1993 at Griddles Restaurant. At this extreme moment, I'm feeling quite destitute as the sun beams through the side window, thinking about when Sherri and I made our first payment for this dump of a trailer exactly four years ago today.

Dusty the bartender, a Native American and a good friend who called the police on the racist empire, promised he would be there to testify. I truly believe he will be present. I'm going to court once again, feeling somewhat like a ping-pong ball since I've moved down to the Pacific Northwest Coast. However, if the outcome is a positive one after this court proceeding, not bowing down to racism, I'm just going to vacate my residence in Seaside Oregon. I must see about my son Deon in Portland; he needs me just as much as I need him, even though I don't know if I can change my son after compellingly taught to be a dope dealer. This murks my soul tightly to no end, difficult to think about, hard to accept what my ex-wife has done to my sons. Whether biological or not, I love them both. I'm glad Edward is in San Diego, California, doing much better with his first cousin that serves in the military, away from that gang activity crap.

The sun is shining bright. A nice, clear day in April the Almighty has made. I am so damn nervous my natural low blood pressure is now elevated to visual high blood pressure, heart thumping out of my chest. I can't even kid myself: it makes no sense to lie when it happens to be written all over my face. My mother, stepfather, and his best friend Bub are definitely driving down from Portland to the courthouse for moral support, along with Sherri and her sister Kelly, with my son Trevor. The Seaside Police are going to testify, telling my true story. Moreover, Dusty mentioned he would testify as well. My friend Carlos is nowhere to be found; this is a red flag in my defense.

I pull up to the one-level, newly built upscale courthouse in my little gray silver Chevrolet Sprint, parking curbside, adjacent to the courtroom main entry double doors, and turn the ignition off. I sit in my car because I am as nervous as a cow in a slaughter house. I light a cigarette with the car lighter, allowing myself to be exposed to an overdose of paranoia threatening racism which attempted to snatch my life a minimum of a dozen times. I suppose not being aware of the outcome of my destiny may have something to do with it. I expect my lawyer to repeat to me it's still a fifty-fifty chance that nothing has changed since our office visit in Cannon Beach. My lawyer, Mr. Orr, informed me that he is going to give it his best shot with the self-defense angle, since the gun was handed to me. Not to mention, just a few months ago, Sergeant Barnett plus five officers arrived at the Beach Club, surrounding me because of a verbal threat on my life in the friendly tavern. Also, prelude to that, a similar occurred incident occurred at the new Beach and Brew bar. I was with Norman's brother Danny and our friend Bob. The Seaside police were called again, surrounding me because of brutal death threats from some discontented, ignorant, inebriated racist locals.

I speed walk through court house double doors. I see Mr. Orr—dark suit, clean shaven, with a nice briefcase—is already seated and preparing to go to work. "Good afternoon, Mr. Orr," I say.

"Mr. Williams, hello, How are you doing?" He asks, while shaking my hand.

"I am a bit nervous," I say, smelling of nicotine in the gray slacks and black shirt I wore on New Year's Eve.

"That's to be expected, but I'm going to need you to relax so you will do great on the witness stand. Okay, Mr. Williams?" Mr. Orr asks, effortlessly opening his briefcase.

"I will be fine when the time comes," I respond, slightly hungover. In the courtroom, everyone rises to their feet as the judge walks out and is introduced by the bailiff. I notice the jury seems very concerned after hearing the district attorney's opening statements. There would not be a lot of witnesses to speak on my behalf; Carlos was nowhere to be found, and I still don't see Dusty, the bartender. I recollect what that racist Aryan advised me in the bar: there will never be a black president. God created us all equal, but that doesn't mean you have to treat them that way.

The vigorous, amped district attorney cross examines the arresting Seaside police officers. Both testified eloquently that I am the person who pulled out a gun only in self-defense. My lawyer cross examines individually both Seaside police officers, revealing a murder plot on my life ever since I was attacked at the wedding reception, and have since receiving constant death threats from Portland all the way to Pacific Northwest coast. Then the district attorney, not giving up, cross examines me and attempts to deceive me with trickery.

"Mr. Williams, did you walk into Griddles with the gun on your person?"

Realizing he is attempting to trick me using deception tactics, I astutely answer, "No, Carlos handed it to me under the table only after the biker threatened to kill me by cutting my nigger head off." I am sitting in the witness stand and my eyes shift from one side of the room over to the other side, where Sherri, Trevor, and Kelly are sitting. Then both attorneys verbalize their closing arguments, and then the jury receives their instructions from the judge.

The jury deliberates for what seems like an eternity. After holding Trevor, waiting patiently with my parents plus my best friend's father, finally the bailiff calls the court to order so we can rise to our feet for the tall, slender judge to enter.

"Has the jury come to a verdict?" the judge asks.

"Yes, we have, your honor," the foreman says aloud. "We, the jury, find the defendant not guilty due to self-defense, due to racism."

"We thank you, jury, for your time and your decision. The defendant is free to go," the judge says as he picks up the gravel and hits the strike block. Court is dismissed. I sit there in my chair in disbelief, not that I was found not guilty but because of all the bigotry that I have encountered. Mr. Orr attempts to shake my hand, then pauses, rubbing his head, then with both hands rubbing them together, as if there is more to this equation. He gives his contemplation some more reflection. Then he says, a look of sheer disbelief on his face, "Mr. Williams, let me be the first to congratulate you." He stands, shaking my hand, looking me straight in both of my dark brown eyes. "In the state of Oregon, you now have a license to kill a white man!" he says straightforwardly, dead serious.

"What did you just say?" I ask, as if I were going crazy as a carrot cake. I stand up quickly, waving, signaling my parents, and then I sit back down, overwhelmed at hearing this newsflash.

"You have a license to kill a white man," Mr. Orr states for the second time to me again.

"I don't want to kill anybody. Besides, there is no such thing as a white person," I whisper, alarmed that erupted out of his light-skinned mouth.

"I know that, Mr. Williams, but if they ever try to kill you again and you kill them, you won't go to prison."

"I don't understand. I am somewhat confused, I explain to Mr. Orr"

"Okay, Eddie, let me explain the law, so you will understand," my lawyer replies. "Since you were found not guilty by the grand jury—of first degree assault—by reason of self-defense, due to racism—and now a jury trial, found not guilty, possession of a firearm, self-defense due to racism. By double jeopardy statutes you now have a license to kill a white man in the state of Oregon," my attorney says seriously.

But Mr. Orr knows that I am going to have troubles if I stay here. He advises me of the obvious. "Eddie, time to move back to Portland." After packing up his attaché case, he shakes my hand once again, then he exits the court room. My parents hear exactly what the trial lawyer says, deciding to stop by the liquor store, leaving town as soon as possible. I can tell they are somewhat relieved.

"Mother, I am going to move back to Portland," I whisper genuinely, realizing the Almighty God once again sent those angels concealed as police officers. He definitely had my back in court this afternoon. I look up to the ceiling, whispering, "Thank You, Lord Jesus."

Then Sherri approaches, exhausted, standoffish, with Trevor awkwardly asleep in the collapsible stroller. "Why are you still sitting here?" Sherri asks, standing over me, blankly.

"I strongly believe I've overshot my limit. I have had entirely enough of this coastal life. I am going home," I say seriously, sighing, kissing my son on the cheek.

"Well, I just came for moral support," Sherri says, making it crystal clear about our relationship.

"Thank you for coming," I say halfheartedly, but sincere. Sherri and I say our goodbyes as I kiss Trevor farewell; I know I won't see much of him. I've sold the trailer to a Mexican couple, paid all my outstanding bills, including necessities for my son. I love my children; they mean everything to me. Their guardians know that as well.

That night, Jim Dunkin and I head to the Beach Club for a farewell celebration of sorts in my honor. It's the last time we are hanging out before I relocate back into metropolitan Portland, Oregon. We both head out, exiting the Beach Club to toddle to Mars to have a stiff send-off drink, when this six foot, harmless long blonde-haired skinny hippie punk of a rocker, staggering, inebriated, walks up to me and nonchalantly says, waving his skinny finger excitedly, "Dude, I just came from the nigger's grave, dude!"

"Hey, don't talk to him like that!" Jim says, balling his fist up.

"Dude, seriously, I just came from the nigger's grave, dude!" the rocker says again, staggering.

"Man, stop saying that word. That's offensive, dude," Jim says loudly to the dude, not backing down.

"Jim, don't hit him. Let's celebrate!" I cheer, then I look toward Broadway, and I see something that made my spirit smack to the damn floor. I discover out of my peripheral, like some kind of malicious dream, a waxed, shining, canary yellow Chevy Nova with the very same wheels parked across the street from where Jim and I are standing.

I am shocked, blinking, not taking my eyes off of this parked canary yellow vehicle which was very close to assaulting and otherwise murdering me when I first arrived in the city of Seaside. However, I have not seen this vehicle since 1990, which bewilders me somewhat, still in some form of a shock stemming from everything I've been through for the very last time hope to never ever to see that vicious supped up car again. I instantly inform Jim that the yellow Nova across the street is the vehicle that they tried to kill me with over six times in one year, yelling, "Nigger better go home!" Jim looks at me with the craziest, obscure stare on his face, as if I am special-ed challenged, or I just plain straight out don't quite get it. Before Jim can respond, someone exits the shiny yellow vehicle used to lynch me, a thin man with round glasses on his face.

"Eddie, that's the car you are talking about that tried to run you over, that yellow Nova?" Jim states, putting his hands on his hips, staring at me like I'm crazy. "That's Bubba's car, Eddie. The nutcase you assaulted with the hammer. You've already got your man. That's Bubba's brother over there. Let him go, he's suffered enough," Jim says to me, patting me on the back then hugging me, getting me to calm down after I yell at Bubba's brother as he heads towards the Bridge Tender Tavern.

Regaining my logical senses, exhaling good oxygen, I allow these ignorant circumstances to go, concentrating on the brighter side of my life. Sadly, the very next day I sold my fine three-bedroom, one-bath, 52-foot long, ten-foot wide trailer to a nice young Mexican couple with a child. I promised myself the last time I was evicted from a place, the next place would be in my name and only I can put myself out. Well, the day has finally arrived as I hand over the trailer, receiving the money in cash from the young couple. I settle my bill with Mr. Baske, the slum landlord, pay my miscellaneous utilities, pay Sherri's father the bill for helping us through thick and thin, or so she says, and then I give her a substantial amount of cash for Trevor's wellbeing, giving her back what funds she might have spent on Trevor. That's what you do as his father. I should be more than happy to pay as a good father, even though I am not going to get the opportunity to see my son. He is still my responsibility, and I don't scamper away from responsibilities. Some people for some strange reason get away without paying child support, which I consider wrong, just from the point of view as a child of divorce.

My first cousin, Glenn Jr. comes by to check on me when he works in Astoria, Oregon. I have packed the somewhat clean Chevy Sprint with the clothes I have acquired since I arrived in Seaside, Oregon four years and four months ago on Martin Luther King Jr. holiday weekend. What was I really thinking?

Last night I strolled intoxicated from the trailer over to the middle of the overpass on Highway 101, tossing the hammer with the pink ribbon tied on the neck of the tool into the secluded Necanicum River. Sadness lured, heading back to my baby brother Keith's abode, who lives in Salem, Oregon 140 miles south of Seaside.

While I was there, it was necessary that I made it perfectly crystal clear, explaining to Adrian who lives at the Partridge Lane apartments in Kaiser, Oregon, which is adjacent to Salem, Oregon. I've been seeing Adrian from time to time for a little evening delight of this scrumptious Hershey pigeon toed Nubian sister with blinding pearly white teeth, full chocolate pouty lips, five foot seven, petite, slender physique with long black hair. We seem to get along exceptionally well; however, it appears there is mega dysfunction when it comes to fabricating detrimental games.

I parked the Chevy Sprint in the visitor's space at the Partridge Lane Northeast apartments, locking my car door, realizing I am not in the country. Time to adjust to my whereabouts. As the clouds move away and the sun makes his appearance entering the doorway where Adrian's apartment door is. She unlocks the front door, allowing me in. The apartment is clean: shag carpet as usual, couch and loveseat, not too much furniture, a couple of pictures on the wall of her toddler daughter. "Adrian, I don't think we should see each other because I don't understand why you had to lie about your age like that to me,"

I say, standing in the living room, hands on my hips, being very calm trying to wrap this relationship up.

She replies, "Oh, really? Is that the way it's going to be? Hold on, let me quickly check on my daughter in the room." I stand patiently, ready to exit the apartment and be on my insane way. Momentarily, she returns, mumbles something smart, opening the front door, not having to tell me twice as she slams the door directly right behind me, which I thought was weird. As I took moderate steps towards the four-speed gray Sprint, out of the great mighty damn blue, shut the front door, there has got to be a least fifteen patrol cars with sirens blaring like a crime is being committed, surrounding the parking lot. All of sudden they are pointing their guns in addition to rifles at me, to my surprise telling me to get both my got damn hands in the fuckin' air! "Get your fuckin' hands in the damn air where I can see them, or else I will blow your head off!" the head, medium built officer with a thick, trimmed mustache says loudly, pointing the gun at my head. B-L-A-C-K, meaning Boy Let a Cop Kill! Scaring me close to urinating, I'm raising my hands, looking as if they want to gun me down out of extreme felonious fear!

Then, out of nowhere, Adrian's own mother trotted out of her daughter's apartment, running while yelling at the top of her lungs, saying, "Stop, please, stop! He did not do anything. My daughter is lying! Don't shoot this man, he's innocent, my daughter is lying! Don't shoot!" She blocked the dark blue uniformed Salem police from silencing me for eternity. After Adrian's mother made her plea and after a mini investigation, we found out that Adrian was just crazy mad high, jacking my freedom in the name of falsehood. A sickening, fabricated charge! That frightened the very shit out of me, even after the Salem and Keizer police officers apologized one by one, shaking my hand because I was obviously shaking from fear, like the time in the year 1976. I was accused of robbing the 7-Eleven on North Greeley and Killingworth's because I had on an orange cap. I had just graduated from basic army training just the day before from Lawton, Oklahoma, surrounded by twenty Portland Police weaponry. Very overwhelmed very paranoid, for an instant I had never even held Adrian's daughter, let alone anything else. Sick, twisted, slanderous accusation!

A couple days later, I'm in Portland entering the state building on North Vancouver Avenue jobs program orientation, which included about 40 plus African American people, mostly women, single parents. As I enter the room, this slightly darker shade than me African American—six feet tall, tiny afro, clean shaven in dark grey slacks along with a dress shirt—turns toward me, saying loudly, "Here comes another one, trying to get some free money," the man with the name tag Floyd on his light-blue colored short sleeve shirt. My answer to this obvious Uncle Tom racist statement was nothing less than the truth.

"You don't know me, you have no right to speak to me like that, you brainwashed slave ass of a man, you! I just relocated up here from Seaside, Oregon, just got custody of my son, who wants to live here in Portland instead of Seaside, Oregon, and you think you have the constitutional right to humiliate me in front of all of these ladies, you bitch-made punk you. Shame on you, Uncle Tom, racist ass idiot," I announce loudly so the entire building hears me. Then a lady supervisor quickly enters abruptly through the door, wondering what the shouting is all about. I explain to her the situation at hand, which the female witnesses in the room immediately all agreed with me, excusing me from his orientation. The lady places me in the jobs program, only to acquire a temporary job.

After I prove that my ex-wife was evicted from her home by forwarding the eviction notice to her caseworker, she's living in a tent behind the house, I obtain full legal custody of my son, Deon, finally halting my child support to Eddie with my divorced decreed, as well as Deon. However, my ex is not required to pay any support to me.

A few months later, George Clinton and P Funk All stars are in town. My VIP pass from George C. is my early birthday present. Deon and I have acquired an apartment furnished with my furniture from Europe since I now work full time at Wacker Siltronics in the northwest area. I work twelve-hour graveyard shifts, 7:00 p.m. to 7:00 a.m., plus constant overtime.

Then to my astonishment, even though I was on the straight and narrow, I am evicted from the Kenton apartments because my first cousin David T. Duke cussed out my apartment manager. He slams me a 14-day notice of eviction, and Deon is up to no damn good. I temporarily move to Northeast Portland to my cousin Carmen's house, while Sherri strategically contacts my mother by phone informing her that she, Jeremy, and Trevor, have relocated to Southeast Portland. Sherri swiftly radars me down pathetically only to suggest, "Live with me, baby." I am manipulated repeatedly like a trained bat, falling foolishly for Sherri, eventually bypassing me like a hamster on a wheel. So why in the wonderful world did I say yes? Awkward, surprised, gently rubbing the top of my cranium, I'm definitely positive my lump has raised from the dead, protruding out of my head again, very damn sensitive. How the holy horizon does this happen? Old-fangled century passes away along with my demons, realizing in my many therapy sessions along with rehab that I have a remarkable obsession with selecting the wrong women, not compatible to me in any way.

My father and I extinguish our indifferences after he finally sees me performing, singing, as well as playing various musical instruments for the first time in his life.

On my father's death bed, he whispers the greatest words of wisdom I have always sought after to hear. "Eddie, you are a good son. If I had known you were multitalented, I would have moved the entire family to Los Angeles, California. Eddie, you can do anything," my father announced boastfully, eternally setting me free.

On the good side, I'm a homeowner just about ten years now, relaxing in my hot tub on my deck, attached to my master bedroom. I glance upward through the clear awning attached to my three-bedroom, double garage, ranch-style home to the bright blue sky. I live in Portland, Oregon with my Caucasian lady, Brenda, whose mother resides across the street from my mother, who ironically so happens to be Floyd's ex, the radical Uncle Tom employee at the state building. Thirteen years sober, relaxed, blessed. Father, son, brother, cousin, nephew, uncle, grandfather as well as great-grandfather, I glance up to white pillow clouds, sunny skies. I can't calculate all of my blessings, as my tree hovers, waving their limbs, flocking high above as Chris Matthew's voice blares through soundwaves on a 32-inch flat screen high-definition TV, discussing the first fair-skinned African American, winner of a second presidential term, born in Hawaii, Nobel

Peace Prize recipient, forty-fourth president of the United States of America, Barrack Hussein Obama!

Dark-skinned, fair, and light,
They are precious in his sight.
Jesus loves the little children of the world!

Peace.

ARREST #04 1993/06/17   OR0040300-SEASIDE POLICE DEPARTMENT   FPN/144370B
  NAME USED/WILLIAMS,EDDIE DE NARVAL   OCA/932888
  01 ORS 166.270 FELON IN POSSESSION OF WEAPON
COURT
 *01 1994/04/13 OR0040133-CLATSOP COUNTY CIRCUIT COU   ACQUITTED
    ORS 166.270 FELON IN POSSESSION OF WEAPON-FIREARM/FELONY
    DOCKET #/931281

ARREST #05 1991/01/01   OR0040300-SEASIDE POLICE DEPARTMENT   FPN/12651100
  NAME USED/WILLIAMS,EDDIE DENARVAL   OCA/910811
  01 ORS 163.185 ASSAULT 1ST DEG
COURT
 01 1991/01/10 OR0040133-DIS CRT ASTORIA   DISMISSED
    ORS 163.185 ASSAULT 1ST DEG
    DOCKET #/F91001

ARREST #04 1990/05/12   OR0040090-CLATSOP COUNTY SHERIFF OFF FPN/1221200
  NAME USED/WILLIAMS,EDDIE DENARVAL   LAN/03260002
  01 ORS 166.025 DISORDERLY CONDUCT
COURT
 01 1992/01/17 OR0040133-DIS CRT ASTORIA   DISMISSED
    ORS 162.235 OBSTRUCT GOV/JUDICIAL ADMIN
    DOCKET #/M90141
 02 1992/01/17 OR0040133-DIS CRT ASTORIA   ACQUITTED
    ORS 166.025 DISORDERLY CONDUCT
    DOCKET #/M90141
 03 1992/01/17 OR0040133-DIS CRT ASTORIA   DISMISSED
    ORS 166.025 DISORDERLY CONDUCT
    DOCKET #/M90141

ARREST #03 1990/03/06   OR0040100-ASTORIA POLICE DEPARTMENT   FPN/11693
  NAME USED/WILLIAMS,EDDIE DENARVAL   LAN/A13811   OCA/900188
  01 ORS 813.010 DRIVE UNDER INFLUENCE INTOX
COURT
 01 1994/01/13 OR0040811J-ASTORIA MUNICIPAL COURT   CONVICTED-MISDE
    ORS 813.010 DRIVE UNDER INFLUENCE INTOX
    $750 FINE   2D JAIL   1YR PROB   DOCKET #/900188

CPSIA information can be obtained
at www.ICGtesting.com
Printed in the USA
LVHW090802030820
662069LV00001BA/20